2

,D

LINES OF DEVELOPMENT IN
PRIMARY
MATHEMATICS

LINES OF DEVELOPMENT IN
PRIMARY
MATHEMATICS

Mary Deboys & Eunice Pitt

THE
BLACKSTAFF
PRESS

BELFAST

First published in 1979 by
The Blackstaff Press Limited
3 Galway Park, Dundonald, Belfast BT16 0AN, Northern Ireland
with the assistance of The Queen's University of Belfast Teachers' Centre

2nd edition 1980, reprinted 1984, 1985, 1986, 1987
3rd edition 1988, reprinted 1989, 1990, 1992, 1993, 1995, 1996

© Mary Deboys and Eunice Pitt 1979, 1980, 1988
All rights reserved

Printed by The Guernsey Press Company Limited

ISBN 0-85640-194-3

Foreword

This book is the product of both the distinctive abilities of its authors, Mary Deboys and Eunice Pitt, and the organisational arrangements which have enabled them to develop and demonstrate their abilities on a larger stage than their own school classrooms. The authors have been in recent years assistant organisers in the Queen's University of Belfast Teachers' Centre. As such, while they remained practising teachers, they have been on secondment during part of each week to the Centre where they have worked on curriculum development with the teachers' panel in primary mathematics. They have both in turn stimulated their colleagues and been stimulated by them. They have developed teaching methods and materials which have been tried and tested in a variety of classrooms. The outcome is a work which directly or indirectly has been realised through the co-operative support of other teachers and of various agencies within the educational service. The Management Committee of the Teachers' Centre acknowledges that support and is grateful for it. It particularly wishes to thank the South Eastern Education and Library Board which released Mrs. Deboys and Miss Pitt on partial secondment and also the principals, Mr. A. Porter and Mr. J. A. Magee, and the management committees of Lisnasharragh Primary School and Bloomfield Road Primary School, Bangor, who permitted the arrangement. The Belfast Education and Library Board also helped with a grant towards publication.

In indicating the context within which this work was realised the Management Committee in no way wishes to diminish the creative contribution of Mary Deboys and Eunice Pitt but rather to draw attention to the endorsement which their exercise in curriculum development has already received.

It should be stated that the authors alone are responsible for their work: Eunice Pitt for the section dealing with the teaching of infant classes and Mary Deboys for the remainder of the book.

H. Rex Cathcart,
Professor of Education,
The Queen's University of Belfast and
Chairman of the Management Committee,
Q.U.B. Teachers' Centre.

Introduction

The title *Lines of Development in Primary Mathematics* reflects the changes that have taken place in recent years, not only in the mathematical content of the primary curriculum, but also in the methods used. In the past, much of the teaching of arithmetic was concerned with the development of computational skills. Today, even in a world of electronic and mechanical devices for calculation, it is still essential for children to acquire proficiency in basic arithmetical computation, but it is even more important that they should understand the processes they are using and be able to apply them constructively in unfamiliar situations.

One of our aims in teaching mathematics is to equip children to think for themselves. This may best be achieved by providing opportunities for the exploration of the order, pattern and relationships which form the basis of mathematics. Certain skills in calculation are necessary and these can most profitably be developed through their application to practical solutions, meaningful for children, through problem solving and mathematical investigations.

As it is very difficult to trace the lines of growth in a programme of work in primary mathematics, the problem of choosing a suitable format has been considerable. At times a certain sequence of steps is appropriate, and certain well-defined stages must be reached before children can proceed further. In general, however, we do not regard the development of primary mathematics as following a fixed, linear, hierarchial structure: it is cumulative rather than strictly sequential. For this reason, although the development is presented as a step by step sequence, we envisage teachers using the scheme with some flexibility and adapting it to suit the interests and stages of development of individual children.

For convenience, the book has been compiled in three sections, corresponding approximately to the following age groups: 5 to 7 (Section 1); 7 to 9 (Section 2); 9 to 11 + (Section 3). In each section the development of topics follows a similar pattern and is set out in a framework at the beginning so that the full range of ideas may be presented. In following this framework, teachers are advised to work horizontally as well as vertically to ensure that no topic is developed to the exclusion of any other and to highlight relationships within a broad mathematical curriculum. It cannot be emphasized too strongly that children develop at their own individual rates and it is of paramount importance that they should be given work appropriate to their level of attainment.

Our aims and objectives, which we trust will be apparent to all who use the book, are based on the following premises:—

1. a stage of free exploration is necessary when new or unfamiliar material is being introduced;
2. practical activities precede abstract calculations;
3. understanding is more important than the learning of rules;
4. language development through discussion is necessary at all stages;
5. application and practice help to consolidate concepts.

Acknowledgements

Our sincere thanks are due first of all to the Organisers of the Queen's University Teachers' Centre for their part in the initiation of the project and for their continuing support and encouragement at all stages of its development.

We would like to thank all the staff of the Teachers' Centre for a variety of services so willingly and cheerfully given and in particular Miss M. McKinney for her patient and conscientious work in preparing the final draft for publication.

We acknowledge gratefully the advice given from time to time by members of the Inspectorate, Department of Education, Northern Ireland. The constructive criticism of Mr. A. Wear, formerly Senior Inspector in the above Department, was extremely useful.

The mathematical expertise of Mr. R. McKinney, Principal of Avoniel Primary School, proved invaluable in the assessment of the various sections and to him we owe a great debt of gratitude.

We acknowledge with thanks the professional skill of Mrs W. Dunbar who was responsible for designing and paging the book. Our grateful thanks are also expressed to Mr D. M. Backler for his help in the preparation of some intricate diagrams.

The teachers who met with us regularly in the initial stages and the members of the Primary Mathematics Panel gave valuable help in discussion which led ultimately to the structuring and sequencing of topics. For contributions, many and varied, we wish to thank the following:—

Mrs. K. Delaney	Miss L. Hall	Mr. T. McMillan
Miss M. Dore	Mrs. C. Haycock	Miss N. Moore
Miss N. Finn	Mr. P. Hill	Mrs. M. Nolan
Mr. G. Friel	Mrs. E. Jelly	Mrs. M. O'Neill
Mrs. F. Greer	Mrs M. McCorry	Mrs. E. Orr
		Mrs. G. Stewart

Mary Deboys
Eunice Pitt

November 1979

Contents

Section 1

Section 2

Section 3

Section 1

 r — red

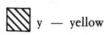 b — blue

 y — yellow

1

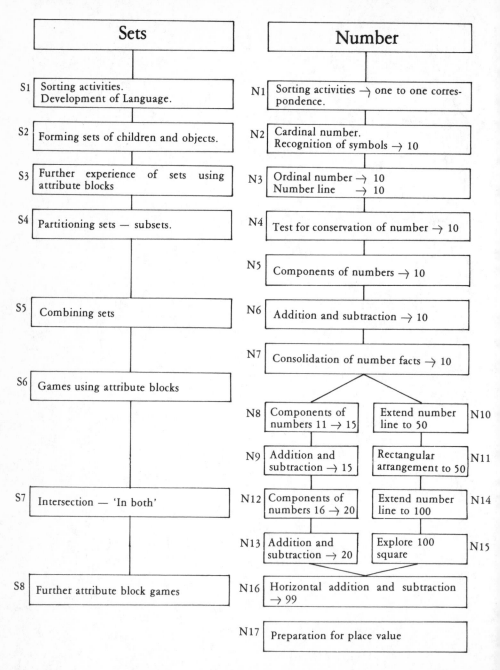

	Sets		Number	
S1	Sorting activities. Development of Language.	N1	Sorting activities → one to one correspondence.	
S2	Forming sets of children and objects.	N2	Cardinal number. Recognition of symbols → 10	
S3	Further experience of sets using attribute blocks	N3	Ordinal number → 10 Number line → 10	
S4	Partitioning sets — subsets.	N4	Test for conservation of number → 10	
		N5	Components of numbers → 10	
S5	Combining sets	N6	Addition and subtraction → 10	
		N7	Consolidation of number facts → 10	
S6	Games using attribute blocks	N8	Components of numbers 11 → 15	Extend number line to 50 — N10
		N9	Addition and subtraction → 15	Rectangular arrangement to 50 — N11
S7	Intersection — 'In both'	N12	Components of numbers 16 → 20	Extend number line to 100 — N14
		N13	Addition and subtraction → 20	Explore 100 square — N15
S8	Further attribute block games	N16	Horizontal addition and subtraction → 99	
		N17	Preparation for place value	

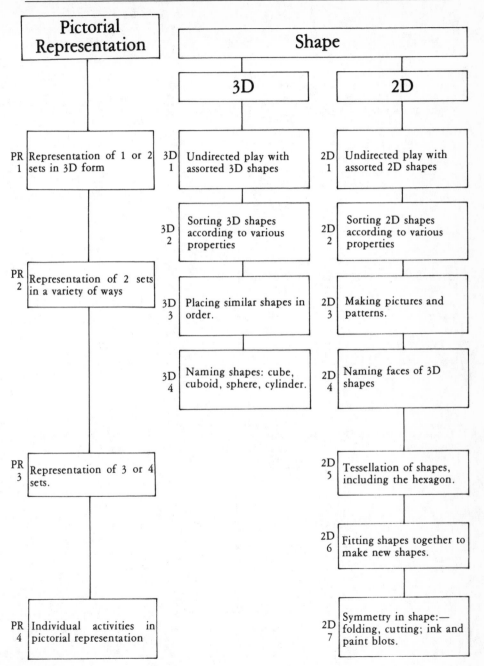

	Pictorial Representation		Shape	
			3D	2D
PR 1	Representation of 1 or 2 sets in 3D form	3D 1	Undirected play with assorted 3D shapes	2D 1	Undirected play with assorted 2D shapes
		3D 2	Sorting 3D shapes according to various properties	2D 2	Sorting 2D shapes according to various properties
PR 2	Representation of 2 sets in a variety of ways	3D 3	Placing similar shapes in order.	2D 3	Making pictures and patterns.
		3D 4	Naming shapes: cube, cuboid, sphere, cylinder.	2D 4	Naming faces of 3D shapes
PR 3	Representation of 3 or 4 sets.			2D 5	Tessellation of shapes, including the hexagon.
				2D 6	Fitting shapes together to make new shapes.
PR 4	Individual activities in pictorial representation			2D 7	Symmetry in shape:— folding, cutting; ink and paint blots.

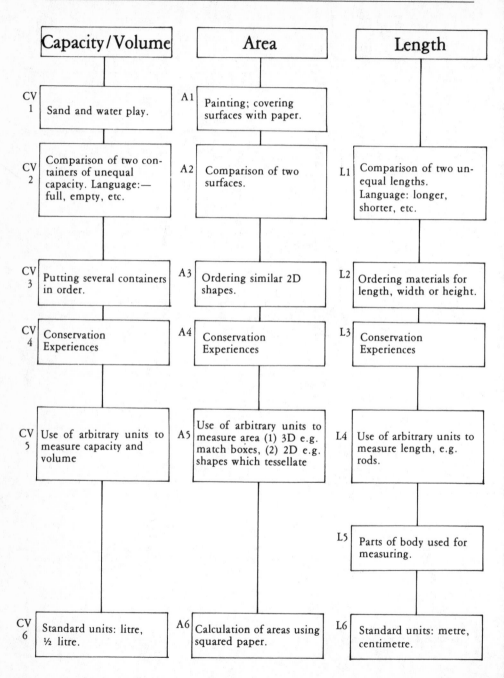

Capacity/Volume	Area	Length
CV 1 Sand and water play.	**A1** Painting; covering surfaces with paper.	
CV 2 Comparison of two containers of unequal capacity. Language:— full, empty, etc.	**A2** Comparison of two surfaces.	**L1** Comparison of two unequal lengths. Language: longer, shorter, etc.
CV 3 Putting several containers in order.	**A3** Ordering similar 2D shapes.	**L2** Ordering materials for length, width or height.
CV 4 Conservation Experiences	**A4** Conservation Experiences	**L3** Conservation Experiences
CV 5 Use of arbitrary units to measure capacity and volume	**A5** Use of arbitrary units to measure area (1) 3D e.g. match boxes, (2) 2D e.g. shapes which tessellate	**L4** Use of arbitrary units to measure length, e.g. rods.
		L5 Parts of body used for measuring.
CV 6 Standard units: litre, ½ litre.	**A6** Calculation of areas using squared paper.	**L6** Standard units: metre, centimetre.

4

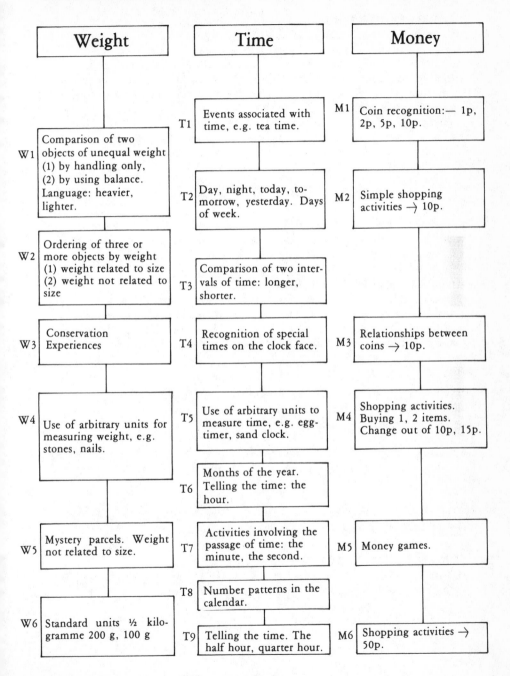

	Weight		Time		Money
		T1	Events associated with time, e.g. tea time.	M1	Coin recognition:— 1p, 2p, 5p, 10p.
W1	Comparison of two objects of unequal weight (1) by handling only, (2) by using balance. Language: heavier, lighter.	T2	Day, night, today, to-morrow, yesterday. Days of week.	M2	Simple shopping activities → 10p.
W2	Ordering of three or more objects by weight (1) weight related to size (2) weight not related to size	T3	Comparison of two inter-vals of time: longer, shorter.		
W3	Conservation Experiences	T4	Recognition of special times on the clock face.	M3	Relationships between coins → 10p.
W4	Use of arbitrary units for measuring weight, e.g. stones, nails.	T5	Use of arbitrary units to measure time, e.g. egg-timer, sand clock.	M4	Shopping activities. Buying 1, 2 items. Change out of 10p, 15p.
		T6	Months of the year. Telling the time: the hour.		
W5	Mystery parcels. Weight not related to size.	T7	Activities involving the passage of time: the minute, the second.	M5	Money games.
		T8	Number patterns in the calendar.		
W6	Standard units ½ kilo-gramme 200 g, 100 g	T9	Telling the time. The half hour, quarter hour.	M6	Shopping activities → 50p.

SETS

S1: SORTING ACTIVITIES. DEVELOPMENT OF LANGUAGE

UNDIRECTED SORTING

Early experiences in sorting and classifying help towards an understanding of number. Sorting boxes should contain as wide a variety of materials as possible including shells, tops, cones, conkers, buttons, spools, beads, pegs, sticks, bricks, plastic toys. Not all these materials, however, will be available at the same time. The child is encouraged to sort the contents of his own box in any way he chooses.

Initially children tend to put like objects together, e.g. all the cones together; all the sticks together. This is an important and necessary stage. Through careful discussion each child is encouraged to explain what he has done and why.

> Why do these objects go together?
> Why does this object not belong?

Having sorted the objects in one way the child is then invited to sort the same objects in a different way. The real value of these early sorting experiences depends on the discussion that results between teacher and child.

COMPARISONS OF PAIRS OF OBJECTS

This is a valuable oral activity planned to develop children's awareness of the possible attributes of the objects being handled. Two objects are displayed and the children are asked to tell in what ways the objects are the same, in what ways they are different. First comparisons should be fairly obvious,

> e.g.   two boxes differing in size,

progressing to comparisons involving more 'imagination'. The greater the range of vocabulary used, the better the foundation for the stage which follows, namely the introduction of sets.

Language: Same, different; big, small; thick, thin; long, short; rough, smooth; hard, soft; roll, slide; round, flat; wooden, plastic; solid, hollow etc.

S2: FORMING SETS OF CHILDREN AND OBJECTS

SOME DEFINITIONS FOR THE TEACHER

A **set** is a well-defined collection of objects. Given any object it is possible to determine whether or not the object belongs to the set.

> e.g.   The set of boys in the class.
> The set of laced shoes.
> The set of toy motor cars.

Counter-example: The 'set' of children with long hair.

There is no standard length by which to distinguish between long hair and short hair. Consequently this is not a satisfactory criterion for forming a set. Ambiguities must be avoided.

The **universal set** is the complete set under consideration for each particular example.

The **complement of the set A** consists of those objects which belong to the universal set but do not belong to A.

To illustrate:— The set of children   (i.e. Universal set for this example.)

Complement of A:—
The set of children not wearing glasses.

A: The set of children wearing glasses.

N.B. It is not necessary for the children to use the terms universal set or complement.

DEVELOPMENT FOR THE CHILDREN

The activities outlined in **S1** should form a good preparation for introducing children to the concept of a SET.

A simple explanation for them might be:—

A set is a 'family of objects' ... they belong together ... there is some way in which they are all the same.

1. SORTING CHILDREN INTO SETS

Some bounded section of floor space is required for children to stand in. An area with carpet would be ideal or alternatively the area could be indicated by a ring of brightly coloured chalk. Various sets may then be formed:—

e.g. The set of children who are five.
The set of children who have crisps for break.
The set of children who walked to school today.

In each case children possessing the required characteristic stand within the boundary. Attention should also be drawn to those children who are **not** in the set because…

> they are **not** five
> they have **not** crisps for break
> they did **not** walk to school today.

2. SORTING OBJECTS INTO SETS

A better understanding of the concept of a set will be gained by sorting one collection of objects in four ways rather than by sorting four collections of objects in only one way. Consequently the selection of objects for sorting must be made with this end in view. 'A well-chosen collection of ten or twelve objects is much more useful than an ill-chosen collection of fifty objects.'

The point is best illustrated by means of an example.

Consider the following collection of objects:—

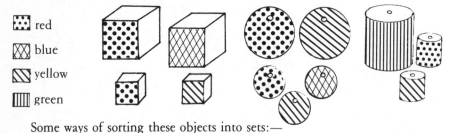

red

blue

yellow

green

Some ways of sorting these objects into sets:—

    (i)   The set of cubes
           The set of round beads
           The set of cylindrical beads.
   (ii)   The set of reds
           The set of blues
           The set of yellows
           The set of greens.
  (iii)   The set of large objects
           The set of small objects.
  (iv)   The set of objects that roll/do not roll.
   (v)   The set of objects that build/do not build.

For each arrangement the child should be asked to describe his sets before re-sorting.

   Clearly a wide variety of collections can be planned along these lines using the full range of materials available in the infant classroom.

3. A SET GAME
Consider the following rectangular arrangement, 3 rows × 3 columns:—

1 red car	1 yellow car	1 green car
1 red van	1 yellow van	1 green van
1 red lorry	1 yellow lorry	1 green lorry

Two attributes are particularly significant here, namely colour and category. A simple game can be played in which one object is removed. Because of the structure of the arrangement children should be able to describe accurately the missing piece. For a more difficult version of the game the objects can be jumbled before one is removed.

The size of the rectangular arrangement can be varied.

e.g. 2 rows × 4 columns
3 rows × 2 columns
4 rows × 3 columns etc.

Comment: These experiences in sets form the foundation for CARDINAL NUMBER which is derived from sets which possess the same number of objects (See **N2**).

S3: SETS USING ATTRIBUTE BLOCKS

1. INTRODUCING ATTRIBUTE BLOCKS
Before children begin to use attribute blocks they should be familiar with the shapes circle, triangle, square and rectangle in a more general context. First experiences of the blocks should be undirected, giving children opportunity to play, explore, make pictures and sort. Informal discussion at this stage will help to develop an awareness of differences and similarities in the blocks.

Introductory games

Teacher makes picture using **blue blocks.**
Child is required to copy using **red blocks.**

Teacher makes picture using red blocks. Child is required to **reverse direction,** using yellow blocks.

Naming the attributes

Children need to become familiar with the four different attributes of each block — size, colour, thickness, shape. Discussion might develop along the following lines:—

Select, for example, **the set of circles.**

Hold up: the **large**, red thin circle
the **small**, red thin circle.

Question: How are these two circles different?

Answer: One is large, one is small.

Are there any other **large** circles?

Put them together. We have **the set of large circles**.

Similarly the **set of small circles** is found.

In this way the 'size' attribute is introduced using the words LARGE, SMALL.

In a similar way children are made aware of the 'colour' attribute and form:—

the set of **red** circles
the set of **yellow** circles
the set of **blue** circles.

Finally the 'thickness' attribute is observed using the words THICK, THIN and the corresponding sets formed.

A simple game can be played to consolidate this activity.

(a) Teacher selects a block.
Child names its four attributes.

(b) Teacher names four attributes.
Child selects the required block.

After these experiences with the set of **circles**, children readily play this game with the other shapes in turn.

For a further game, place all the blocks of **one colour** in a bag. A child selects one block and, keeping block hidden, names the three secret attributes. The block is then removed and the answer checked.

N.B. **In any activities with attribute blocks it is advisable to limit the number of blocks available.**

Smaller systems can be selected by considering the different attributes: —

The set of red blocks
The set of yellow blocks
The set of blue blocks

The set of circles
The set of triangles
The set of squares
The set of rectangles

The set of large blocks
The set of small blocks

The set of thick blocks
The set of thin blocks

2. FORMING SETS WITH ATTRIBUTE BLOCKS

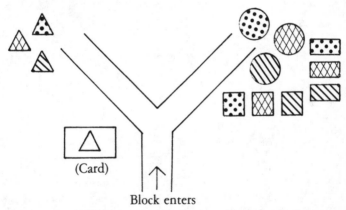

(Card)

Block enters

Select a set of blocks, for example the set of small thin blocks. A card representing one attribute is taken and placed as indicated on the tree diagram. A child chooses a block and at the decision point decides whether to branch left or right. When all the blocks for this particular game have been placed discussion follows:—

Q. What can you say about all these blocks? (Left branch)
Ans. They are all **triangles** — the set of triangles.

Q. What can you say about these blocks? (Right branch)
Ans. They are **not triangles**.

11

This activity can also be represented by means of a Venn Diagram.

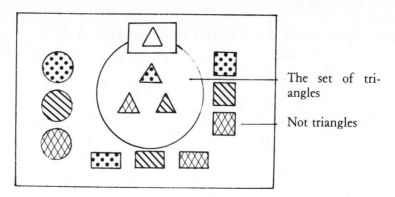

The set of tri-
angles

Not triangles

Cards depicting each attribute:—

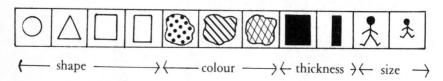

$\longleftarrow$ shape $\longrightarrow$ $\langle$— colour —$\rangle$ $\langle$— thickness —$\rangle$ $\langle$— size —$\rangle$

S4: PARTITIONING SETS — SUBSETS

To introduce the concept of a subset, form, for example, a set of girls. Within this group select the girls who are wearing white socks. They form a set — the set of girls wearing white socks. This set inside another set is called a subset. Children should have a variety of similar experiences:—

e.g. Select a set of boys.   Form the subset of boys wearing black shoes.

Select a set of children.   Form the subset of children who come to school by bus.

Select a set of shapes.   Form the subset of circles.

Select a set of beads.   Form the subset of red beads.

In order to reinforce the above experiences some of them could be represented pictorially by the teacher by means of Venn diagrams.

A set of children.
The subset of
children wearing
boots.

Children can move easily to the next stage where more than one subset is formed within a given set. The word 'partition' may be introduced. 'When we sort a set into its subsets we say we **partition** the set.'

e.g. A set of farm animals can be partitioned into:–

> The subset of sheep.
> The subset of horses.
> The subset of cows.
> The subset of pigs.

Individual and group work follows to give the children experiences in partitioning a given set into two or more subsets.

Comment: The above activities provide suitable preparation for examining the components of numbers. (See **N5**).

S5: COMBINING SETS

Situations are presented in which the children form two suitable sets. The sets are then 'combined' or 'put together' to form the union. (It is not necessary to use the word union with the children.)

e.g. 1. Using the children:—

> The set of girls who like beans. ⎱ Putting these two sets together:—
> The set of boys who like beans. ⎰ The set of children who like beans.

2. Using random materials:—

> The set of wooden cubes ⎱ Putting these two sets together:—
> The set of plastic cubes. ⎰ The set of cubes.

3. Using attribute blocks:—

    The set of red squares.   ) Putting these two sets together:—
    The set of red rectangles.) The set of red squares and rectangles.

Discussion should develop to help children appreciate that when we combine two sets we have **more**.

As a further aid to understanding, some of the classwork could be represented by the teacher in the form of Venn diagrams.

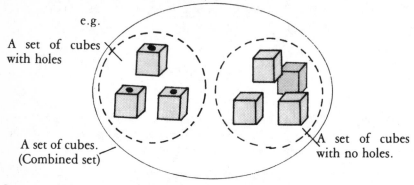

e.g.

A set of cubes with holes

A set of cubes. (Combined set)

A set of cubes with no holes.

Comment: The above activity of combining sets is a preparation for addition. (See **N6**).

S6: GAMES USING ATTRIBUTE BLOCKS

Gate game 1

Select a set of blocks. One of the children is chosen to act as a 'gate-keeper' who will check 'tickets'. The tickets are attribute blocks chosen by the children. Each child in turn selects a ticket and shows it to the gatekeeper who has secretly decided what he will allow to proceed. The first child who can identify correctly what is being collected becomes the new gate-keeper.

Blue

Tickets are presented here

In the illustration the set under consideration is the set of thin circles. The gatekeeper is looking for the attribute 'blue'. It is important to notice that two sets emerge — the set of blocks which have the secret attribute and the set of blocks which do not have it.

Hiding a Block

Select a set of blocks. The teacher or one of the children hides one block while the others close their eyes. The first child who can correctly identify the missing block by all its attributes is the winner. Initially children may need to rearrange the blocks to determine the missing block. Later they should be able to do it by sight.

Games with Logicubes

Logicubes are available from E.S.A. There are four dice in a set, one for each attribute — shape, colour, thickness, size. The markings are the same as those illustrated in section 2 of S3.

Select a set of blocks. Shake one die only, for example 'large'. Children then collect all the blocks with this property. A second die can be introduced and children form the set with the two required properties. Similarly for three dice. If all four dice are used there is only one block to satisfy this set of conditions.

e.g. **The set of yellow blocks**

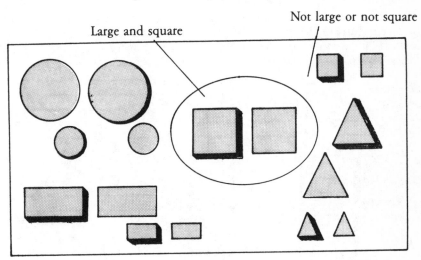

This illustrates the final arrangement of the blocks where two dice have been used to give 'large' and 'square'.

Situations are presented in which the children form two sets, devised by the teacher to involve an intersection. Attribute blocks are particularly suitable for this activity although not essential.

Introductory example:—

Place two large P.E. hoops on the floor. (Do not overlap them)
Label one 'Square' and the other 'Yellow'.
Children select blocks in turn and place them in the appropriate hoop.

The question arises:—

What happens to the **yellow squares?**

Children may make various suggestions:—

'Share them.'
'Don't use them this time.'
'You take them this time, I'll take them next time.'

In each case it must be shown why their suggestion is not satisfactory. Finally some child usually has the idea of overlapping the hoops and the problem is solved. Discussion should follow about the arrangement of the two sets and the word 'intersection' meaning 'in both' is introduced.

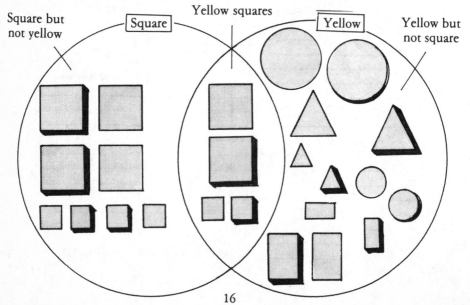

Square but not yellow   Square   Yellow squares   Yellow   Yellow but not square

A wide range of materials can be used for these activities.

Using the children:—

The set of children who have a dog.) Intersection: The children who
The set of children who have a cat.) have a cat and a dog.

Using random materials:—

The set of small cars.   ) Intersection: The small red cars.
The set of small red toys.)

Using attribute blocks:—

The set of thin blocks.) Intersection: The thin triangles.
The set of triangles.   )

Children at this stage could make their own Venn diagrams and record their observations.

S8: FURTHER ATTRIBUTE BLOCK GAMES

Domino Game — 'Difference of one'
Select a set of blocks. The first block of the chain is played and then successive blocks are selected which are different from the previous block in one attribute only.

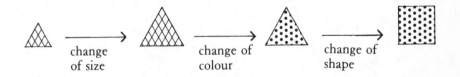

change   change of   change of
of size   colour   shape

The set under consideration in the illustration is the set of thin blocks.

Variations of the Domino Game
Chains can be formed to satisfy:—

(i)   Difference of two, three or four attributes.
(ii) Alternating one and two differences.

17

Gate Game II

The game is played as Gate Game I (see **S6**) but with two gatekeepers. Tickets are shown to Number 1 and those who pass proceed to Number 2.

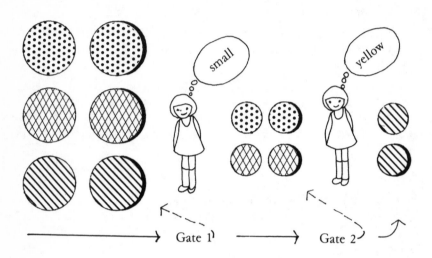

In the illustration the set under consideration is the set of circles. Gatekeeper 1 is looking for the attribute 'small', gatekeeper 2 for the attribute 'yellow'. In this case 3 sets emerge:—

The set of small yellow circles	(Allowed past gate 2)
The set of small circles which are not yellow	(Allowed past gate 1 but not gate 2)
The set of large circles	(Not allowed past gate 1).

NUMBER

N1: SORTING ACTIVITIES — ONE TO ONE CORRESPONDENCE

Experiences in the formation of sets as described in **S1** and **S2** provide the foundation for this next stage. One-to-one correspondence means there is an 'exact match' between two sets.

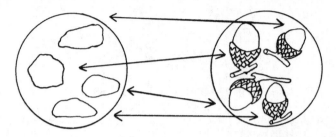

This practical experience of matching is a preparation for counting in which the child must match the number names to the objects in a set.

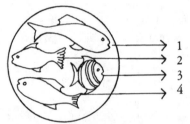

N.B. An ability to recite the number names correctly does not necessarily imply the ability to count.

DEVELOPMENT FOR THE CHILDREN

In the first stage, comparison is made between two sets which do **not** contain the same number of objects. This situation can arise very naturally when children are forming sets. The teacher suggests a comparison:—

> e.g. Look at John's set of cars.
> Look at Jenny's set of shells.

Discussion follows:—

> Who has more, John or Jenny?
> Who has less?
> How many more/less?
> Which objects do not have a 'partner'? Why?

Children match the objects of the two sets in order to answer the questions.

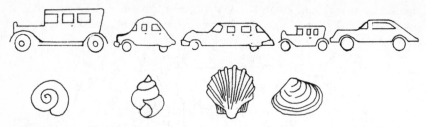

Language:— more, less; many, few; too many, not enough; how many more?

In the second stage children have experience of making an exact one-to-one matching with a wide variety of materials.

    e.g.   (i) Put a cup on each saucer.
                Put a straw in each milk bottle.
                Put a brush in each paint pot.

          (ii) Given a collection of bottles with their corresponding tops, screw the top on each bottle.
                Given a collection of assorted 'pairs,' find the partners.
                Given a collection of Happy Family cards in pairs, find the partners.

    Language:— as many as; enough; the same number.

The real value of these activities lies in the resulting discussion between teacher and child.

N2: CARDINAL NUMBER → 10

When they commence school children usually have a 'nodding-acquaintance' with the number names up to ten. Number rhymes and songs, fairy tales involving number and oral counting in class all contribute further towards the ability to recite the number names in sequence. This, however, does not indicate an understanding of the numbers and much care must be taken to introduce the number symbols in a meaningful way.

Cardinal number is derived from sets of things. Consider:—

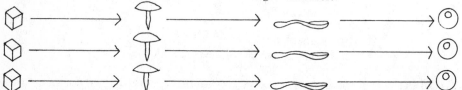

These sets can be put into one-to-one correspondence. There is the same number in each set. 'Threeness' is common to all the sets. This aspect of number is known as cardinal number.

DEVELOPMENT FOR THE CHILDREN

The first numbers
Children will normally have an understanding of 'one' as a single object. They become aware of 'two' through experiences at home and in the classroom and soon discriminate between one and two consistently. It is useful to reinforce these experiences visually by means of charts, at the same time introducing the symbols 1, 2 together with the written words one, two.

Introducing the number three
Suitable number rhymes, songs and stories provide a valuable starting point. Activities in the classroom:—

1. Form sets of 3, using a wide variety of materials.

2. Make a book about 3.

3. A chart about 3.

The three bears

4. Three Unifix cubes

The numbers 4, 5 can be introduced in a similar way.

Consolidating the numbers 1→5

2	5	3	1	4

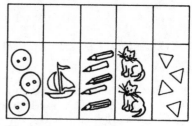

Given the numbers children put out the required set.

Given the sets children put out the required number cards.

When children are confident in the cardinal numbers 1→5 then the numbers 6→10 may be introduced systematically, along the lines indicated above.

A game to consolidate the numbers 1→10

Children play in pairs.

A pack of twenty cards is needed and one die numbered 1 → 10.

(10-sided dice are available from E J Arnold).

On one side of the cards are the numerals 1 → 10, each appearing twice. On the reverse side the same number is represented pictorially:—

    e.g.   4 hens on the reverse side of card 4.

All the cards are placed on the table, pictures facing up. Each child has a number track as indicated below.

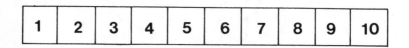

Children toss die in turn and select a card to match the number they have shaken. Partner checks the number on the reverse side and the card is then placed on the child's number track. The winner is the first to complete his track.

FIRST NUMBER PATTERNS

When children have had sufficient experience making sets in a random formation there is value in exploring the patterns of the various numbers. Counters, Unifix cubes, bricks, pegs and peg boards would be suitable for this activity.

e.g.   Patterns of six.

Using pegs and peg boards or Unifix cubes and operational boards one pattern can be selected and repeated in different colours.

An arrangement of each number in twos is particularly useful as it provides an introduction to odd and even numbers and also aids the recognition of bigger numbers by sight.

N.B. Unifix pattern boards are a valuable aid at this stage.

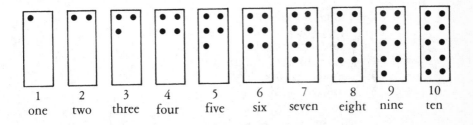

N3: ORDINAL NUMBER → 10   NUMBER LINE → 10

Ordinal number is concerned with putting the numbers in order. It has two aspects:—

(i)   The idea of position — first, second, ..., last.
(ii) The idea of position in relation to other numbers e.g. 5 comes after 4 and before 6.

DEVELOPMENT FOR THE CHILDREN

As children gain confidence in the cardinal numbers 1→5 they need to become aware of the **order** of the numbers. Structured appartus particularly Unifix or Stern, is useful at this stage together with individual number cards and number strips.

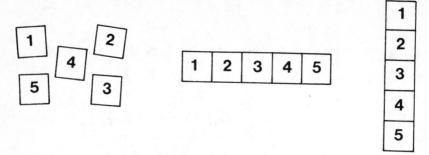

Discussion develops between teacher and children.

  (i) Using individual cards:—
       Find the card with number 1. What number comes next? Put it
       out. Which card has the biggest number? Put it out. What comes
       before 5? Find the card with number 3. What comes after 3,
       before 3?

  (ii) Using number strips:—
       Count along your strip.
       Which number comes first? Point to it.
       Point to the number 3. What comes after 3, before 3?
       Which number is last?

If materials are used alongside some of these activities it helps to bring together the cardinal and ordinal aspects of number and this is essential for a
full understanding of number.

  e.g. Point to the number 2. Put out 2 red cars beside 2.

       What comes after 2? Put out 3 blue dogs beside 3.

       Have you more dogs or cars?

By using Unifix cubes or similar material in the same way the relative value of
each number is clearly visualized.

  Language: First, second, third, ..., last.

             Before, after, one more, one less.

As children's experiences in cardinal number are extended to ten, the ordinal
aspect should be developing at the same time. This leads on to work on the
number line.

Number Line ———→ 10

A large number line should be clearly displayed for classroom use and smaller versions should be available for individual use. At this stage most of the work is oral. It may be helpful for children to have a simple pictorial representation of their first number line as demonstrated below.

Arrangement of spots
may be irregular

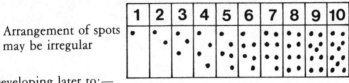

Developing later to:—

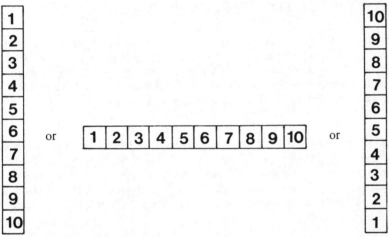

It is best to let the children gain confidence in one version of the number line before introducing a second form.

Some suggestions for use:—

1. Point to given number, tell the number after, before it.
   Point to given number. What number is one more, one less?
2. Point to given number. Tell a number that is greater, less.
3. Given two numbers. Which number is greater, less?
4. What number comes between two given numbers?
5. Two children play together. One shakes die and places counter on number, say 7. Second child follows with, for example, 4.
   Conclusion: 7 is more than 4.
                4 is less than 7.
6. Count forwards, backwards in ones from given number.

25

7. Fill in the blank squares on a number line.
8. Work-cards: 'Which number is greater?'
   Given pairs of numbers child puts a ring around the greater number.
   (Similarly for less).
   The symbols ⟩ (greater than), ⟨ (less than) may be introduced here.

IMPORTANT: The above activities on the number line may begin as soon as the children recognize the symbols 1-10 and should continue alongside further development in number work.

N4: TEST FOR CONSERVATION OF NUMBER → 10

Conservation of number means that the number of objects in a set remains constant regardless of the arrangement. **It is essential that each child be tested individually for conservation of number as progress to the next stage is meaningless without it.** Some children may well have reached conservation at an earlier stage but this is the point where testing is necessary.

Test 1
Ask a child to count out a set, for example eight buttons. Teacher rearranges them by spreading them out, clumping them together and so on. Each time, the child is asked 'How many buttons are there now?' If the child replies eight immediately, without counting, then he has reached conservation of eight. If he needs to count each time he has not yet reached conservation of that number.

Test 2

Here are some kennels. Put one dog at each kennel.

Q. Are there more dogs or kennels?
   Child: Both the same.

Teacher rearranges the dogs, leaving the kennels in the same position.

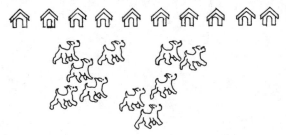

Q. Are there more dogs or kennels now?

Teacher rearranges the kennels, leaving the dogs in the same position.

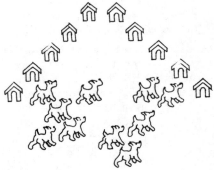

Q. Are there more dogs or kennels now?

When the child is certain that, whatever the arrangement, there are always as many dogs as kennels, the notion of invariance in this situation has been established.

   Any child who is not confident in conservation of number needs more practical work in the preceding activities.

The partitioning of sets into subsets developed in **S4** provides a practical preparation for this concept. Having gained confidence in forming subsets the child is directed to this next stage where attention is focused on the **number of objects** in each set and subset.

To illustrate:—

Partitioning a set   **Components**

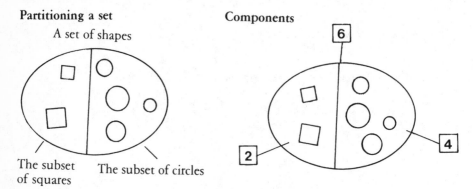

A set of shapes

The subset of squares   The subset of circles

DEVELOPMENT FOR THE CHILDREN

Numbers up to ten are investigated along the lines indicated below. The general approach is introduced by considering 5, 6 proceeding then to larger and smaller numbers.

Materials: Make individual hoops out of cane about 14 cm in diameter. A stick or rod about 16 cm long for each child.

Method: A set of six objects is selected and the child then places them in his hoop. He partitions the set by placing his rod across the hoop giving two subsets. Discussion follows to find out how many objects are in each subset. The rod is then placed in a second position to give a different pair of subsets and so on.

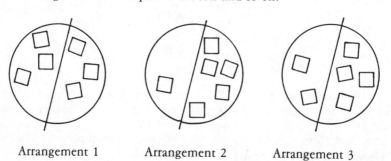

Arrangement 1   Arrangement 2   Arrangement 3

It is important to keep reminding the children that it is the same six objects that give these different arrangements.

Recording: Considerable discussion will be necessary to lead the children to a thorough understanding of this concept. Initially work will be entirely oral, then recording by the teacher and finally by the child. One possible form of recording the above representation is suggested:—

$6 \longrightarrow 3, 3$ $6 \longrightarrow 5, 1$ $6 \longrightarrow 4, 2$

                             $6 \longrightarrow 1, 5$ $6 \longrightarrow 2, 4$

IMPORTANT
The idea of 'number trios' is inherent in this activity and, while children will not be able to record these facts formally, it is worth spending some time orally on this concept.

Example of a number trio: (2,4,6)

$2 + 4 = 6$
$4 + 2 = 6$
$6 - 2 = 4$
$6 - 4 = 2$

Typical questions:—

4 and 2 — how many altogether?
2 and how many make 6?
6, take away 2 — how many left?

Such oral questioning should be in a practical situation, arising from the arrangement in a child's hoop. It helps children begin to form some understanding of the way three such numbers fit together. It is also a very suitable preparation for the next stage of development, namely addition and subtraction.

N6: ADDITION AND SUBTRACTION → 10

ADDITION
Addition is essentially a 'putting together' of sets where attention is focused on the number value of the various sets. Practical preparation for this stage is the **combining of sets** outlined in **S5** and children will benefit from these experiences before being introduced to addition.

The concept of addition will then develop as children have opportunity to handle a wide variety of concrete materials. The symbolic form can only follow when it represents something meaningfully.

Three stages of development can be observed
1. Each set is counted out, the sets are combined and the resulting set is counted.
2. The first set is put out and the second set 'counted on.'
3. Materials are not needed.

Thorough work is needed at each stage and it will often be a long slow process before children reach stage 3.

The introduction of addition
Using the children themselves and random materials the concept of addition is introduced. Emphasis is on understanding the concept and learning the language of addition. Development is as follows:—

    (i)   Demonstration by the teacher
    (ii) Materials handled by children, recording by the teacher.
    (iii) Materials handled by children, recording by the children.

It is important that right from the start children are made aware of the commutative aspect of addition, i.e. $4 + 2 = 2 + 4$.

To the child the action of adding 2 bricks to 4 bricks seems rather different from adding 4 bricks to 2 bricks. However, by careful questioning in a practical situation he begins to abstract this principle.

Some forms of recording are suggested below. Whatever forms are used it is important that children understand what they are recording and that a common policy is agreed upon within each school.

add
4, 3 ———⟶7

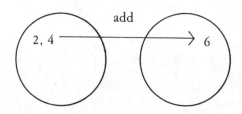

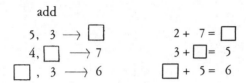

add 3

5 ———→ 8   3 + 5 ——→ 8   5 + 2 = 7

When children understand the operation of addition 'missing number' activities are valuable.

add

5, 3 → ☐   2 + 7 = ☐

4, ☐ —→ 7   3 + ☐ = 5

☐ , 3 —→ 6   ☐ + 5 = 6

Relation between addition and substraction

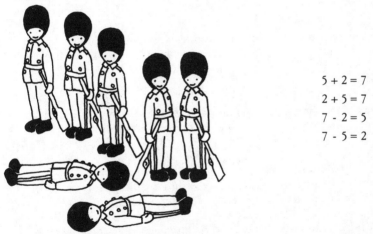

5 + 2 = 7
2 + 5 = 7
7 - 2 = 5
7 - 5 = 2

Initially the idea of subtraction is totally unrelated to addition in a child's mind and it is only fully understood when it is seen as its inverse. Before being introduced to subtraction formally, children should have experience of many varied practical situations similar to the soldier illustration where both the addition and the subtraction facts are discovered orally.

Discussion might develop as follows:—

How many soldiers are standing?

How many soldiers have fallen down?

Add the two sets together.

Tell it another way.

How many soldiers are there altogether?

How many have fallen? — How many are left standing? etc.

A good understanding of the relationship between three such numbers, in this case 2, 5, 7, considerably reduces the number of facts to be committed to memory.

SUBTRACTION

There are three aspects to the concept of subtraction, all three being closely related, but these ideas will only come together in the child's mind after much practical experience.

The three aspects are:—

1. Comparison: Jane has 5 pencils, Edwin has 3 pencils.
   Jane has 2 more than Edwin.
2. Taking away: Neville has 7 sweets. He eats 2.
   How many are left?
3. Complementary addition: Kim has 7 blocks. Clive has 4 blocks.
   How many more must Clive take to have the same number as Kim?

The introduction of subtraction

Situations should be presented and discussion should be developed to draw out the three aspects of subtraction. As in the case of addition three steps emerge:—

   (i)   Demonstration by teacher.
   (ii) Materials handled by children, recording by the teacher.
   (iii) Materials handled by children, recording by children.

Comment: Children often experience difficulty with the concept of subtraction and for this reason it is wise to hasten slowly.

Some forms of recording:—

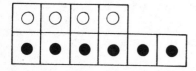

(Comparison aspect)

6 is --- more than 4

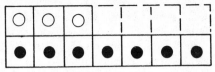

(Complementary addition aspect)

3 and --- make 7.

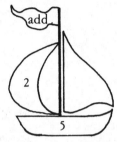

(Complementary addition
aspect)

(Comparison aspect)

Subtract 3

$7 \longrightarrow 4$ $8 - 3 \longrightarrow 5$ $9 - 4 = 5$

Missing number activities follow later:—

$5 - 2 = \square$

$7 - \square = 4$

$\square - 2 = 5$ (Difficult)

N7: CONSOLIDATION OF NUMBER FACTS → 10

Having been introduced to the concepts of components, addition and subtraction as indicated, greater understanding will be gained by exploring the
same concepts with the aid of structured materials. With increased understanding some of the basic number facts should begin to be committed to
memory. The materials referred to here are Unifix (because it is available in
most schools) and Cuisenaire (because its unique structure makes it particularly valuable in certain areas).

Introducing Cuisenaire

Children's first experiences with Cuisenaire should be completely undirected. In this situation they will begin to become aware of some of the relationships between different rods. Because of the nature of the material children may well enjoy this stage for some time. When they have exhausted their own ideas they are ready for a systematic development. A possible approach is suggested:—

1. Put out one of each of the different rods.
   Name them by colour.

2. Arrange the rods in 'stair' formation. Discuss:—
   What colour comes first, last? etc.

3. Hold up the white rod — we call this ONE.
   What do we call the red rod? Why?
   Continue in this way to discover the number value of each rod. (N.B. The number value of the white rod is the only one that needs to be given.) It may be helpful to let children gain confidence in the first five rods and gradually include the remaining ones.

4. Practice is needed to help children become familiar with the number value of the rods in random order.

Components of number using Cuisenaire   'Make a little train'

The child puts out the required rod, say 5, and proceeds to fit as many combinations as possible.

The train of 5

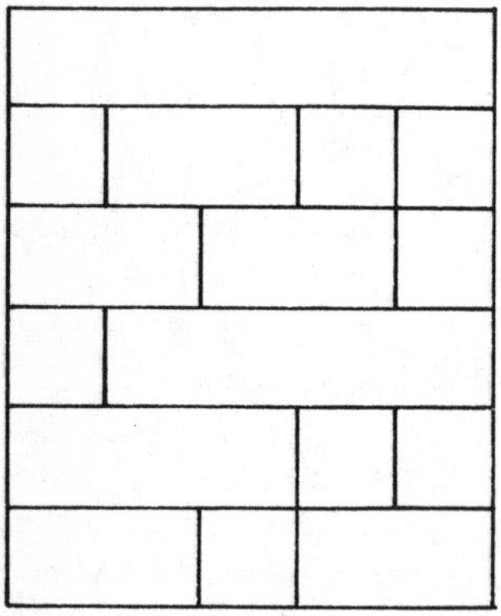

5 ⟶ 1, 2, 1, 1

5 ⟶ 2, 2, 1

5 ⟶ 1, 4

5 ⟶ 3, 1, 1

5 ⟶ 2, 1, 2

Components of number using Cuisenaire   'Step-pattern'.

This is a more structured form of components as illustrated in the diagram.

Step-pattern for 6

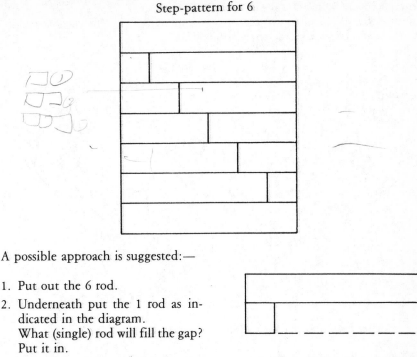

A possible approach is suggested:—

1. Put out the 6 rod.

2. Underneath put the 1 rod as indicated in the diagram.
   What (single) rod will fill the gap?
   Put it in.

3. Under the 1 rod put 2.
   What rod will fill the gap?
   Put it in.

Children continue to place rods until the pattern has been completed. When they understand how to make the step-pattern they can then record it.

The following game can be played later to help children memorize the number facts for each step-pattern. Two children play together using a die. Each child has a card illustrating the step-pattern of some particular number. The pattern of ten is particularly important. Children shake the die in turn, select the corresponding rod and set it in place on their pattern. The winner is the one whose step-pattern is completed first. Eight-sided and ten-sided dice are available for the larger numbers.

Components of number using Unifix   'The story of...'
Children are restricted to **two** colours of Unifix cubes. In this way they form
the pairs of components for any given number.

Example   **The story of 4**

(i)

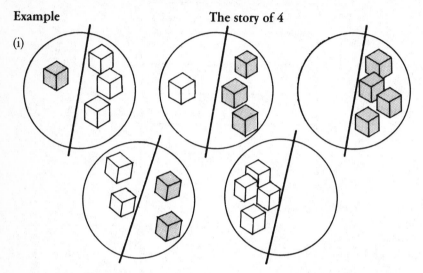

This illustrates the 5 possibilities in making 4 using 2 colours.

Comment: This can be a suitable place to introduce the concept of zero.

(ii)   The cubes of each arrangement are stacked together.
        We must agree to put the same colour on the bottom each time.

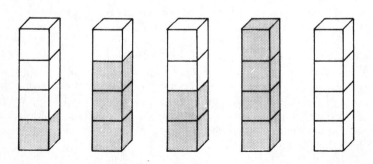

(iii) Rearranged in order:—

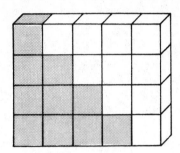

The story of 4.

(iv) Recording:—

4 → 4, 0	4 = 4 + 0
4 → 3, 1	4 = 3 + 1
4 → 2, 2 OR	4 = 2 + 2
4 → 1, 3	4 = 1 + 3
4 → 0, 4	4 = 0 + 4

After practice children should be able to write down the story of a given number without any aids. A good conclusion to this stage is to represent the story of the numbers 1→10 pictorially.

For example:—

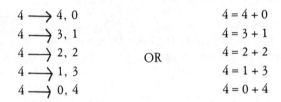

4 = 4 + 0
4 = 3 + 1
4 = 2 + 2
4 = 1 + 3
4 = 0 + 4

Addition — 'adding on' the second number in ones
Unifix is useful at this stage although use should continue to be made of random materials as well. 'Add 1' is clearly the easiest form and as children gain confidence at this point they can progress to adding on 2 and so on.

Addition using Cuisenaire

This leads to the next stage of development where the second number is added on as a whole. The arrangement of rods for addition is illustrated below:—

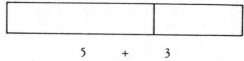

5   +   3

The child must then find the single rod of equivalent length and set it in position:—

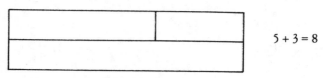

5 + 3 = 8

Cuisenaire illustrates very clearly the commutative aspect of addition and attention should be drawn to this continually. Such experiences in addition together with missing number activities should help children to memorize some of the basic facts.

Addition using the number line

If Cuisenaire is not available a number line and number strips can provide similar experiences to those described on the preceding diagram where again the second number is added on as a whole.

0 1 2 3 4 5 6 7 8 9 10   5 + 3 = 8

| 3 |

A large version for class use and smaller versions for individual use will be found valuable.

N.B. This number line is a progression of the one described earlier in which each square was numbered.

Relation between addition and subtraction using Cuisenaire

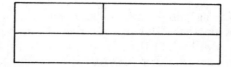

This arrangement of rods provides the following information:—

$$3 + 4 = 7$$
$$4 + 3 = 7$$
$$7 - 3 = 4$$
$$7 - 4 = 3$$

At a later stage the corresponding missing number activities can be investigated:—

$3 + \square = 7$ $7 = 3 + \square$ $7 - \square = 3$

$\square + 4 = 7$ $7 = \square + 4$ $7 - \square = 4$

Equalisation using Cuisenaire

Children may discover many relationships of the type indicated in the diagram:—

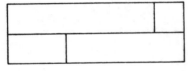

$$5 + 1 = 2 + 4$$

Missing number activities may also be explored:—

e.g. $4 + 3 = 2 + \square$

Some ideas for work-cards in the early stages.

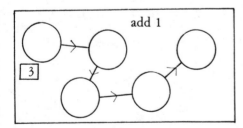

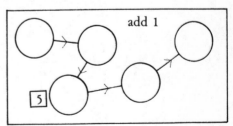

Children put a set of 3 in the first ring as indicated and continue putting sets in each ring according to the rule 'add 1.'

This is a harder version where children have to think 'backwards' to fill the first two rings.

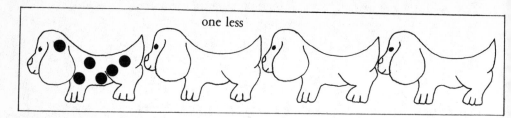

one less

Children put spots on the dogs according to the rule 'one less.' As in the example above the first dog need not always be the one to give the initial clue and the rule may be varied.

$4 = 1 + \boxed{}$

$4 = \boxed{} + 2$

$4 = 3 + \boxed{}$

$4 = \boxed{} + 0$

4   four

Write the next numbers

1   2   3   4 $\boxed{}$ $\boxed{}$

9   8   7   6 $\boxed{}$ $\boxed{}$

Write the missing numbers

4   5 $\boxed{}$ 7 $\boxed{}$ 9

6   5   4 $\boxed{}$ 2 $\boxed{}$

Add 1

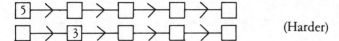

(Harder)

Subtract 1

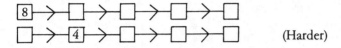

(Harder)

Write the missing numbers

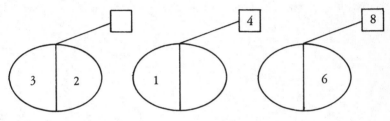

N8: COMPONENTS OF NUMBERS 11 → 15

Children will already be acquainted with numbers beyond ten but it is important to investigate these more closely. **The number combinations up to twenty form the foundation for operations in higher numbers and consequently thorough ground work at this level will make for much easier progress later.**

DEVELOPMENT FOR THE CHILDREN

1. Children count out the required number of objects using a wide variety of materials.

2. Patterns for each number can be explored.

    e.g.   Patterns of 12:—

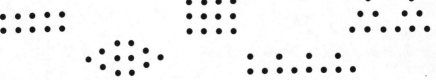

3. Grouping experiences

e.g.   Groupings for 15:—

Grouping in twos

7 groups of 2 and 1 left over.

Grouping in threes

5 groups of 3.

Grouping in fives

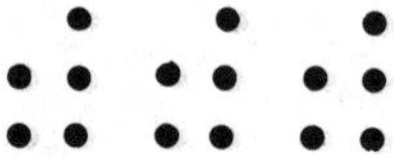

3 groups of 5.

4. Grouping in tens is of special importance and should be approached in a variety of ways.

(i)   Using random materials

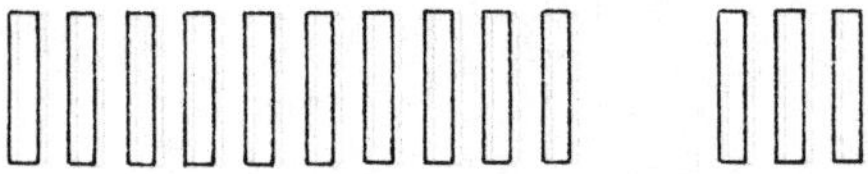

(ii) Using pegs and peg-board 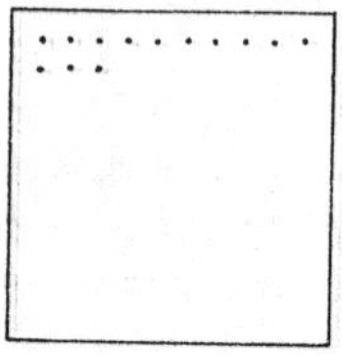   (iii) Using Unifix cubes

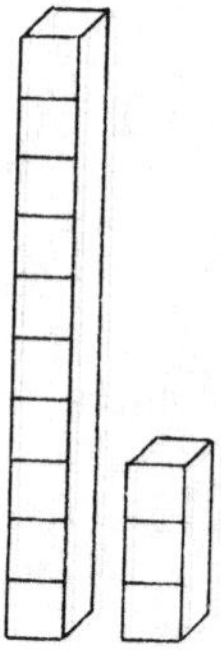

Each arrangement emphasizes that 13 means 1 group of ten and 3 ones.

5. Using Cuisenaire rods children are asked to set out the staircase, one to ten. A new staircase is formed by placing one unit rod on each step.

Q.   What does our new staircase represent?
Ans. Two, three, four, ..., eleven.

Q.   How is eleven made up?
Ans. 1 ten and one.

Similarly by placing a two-rod on each step 12 is seen to be 1 ten and 2 and so on.

Children might enjoy counting the numbers beyond ten as 1 ten and 1, 1 ten and 2, ..., 1 ten and 9, 2 tens, to reinforce these activities.

6. Components

Many of the combinations at this stage are an extension of the basic number facts.

    e.g.   12 + 3 = 15 is an extension of 2 + 3 = 5.

The facts that will have to be committed to memory are listed below and these are the ones that require special emphasis using random materials, Unifix and Cuisenaire.

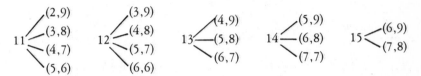

$$11 \begin{cases} (2,9) \\ (3,8) \\ (4,7) \\ (5,6) \end{cases} \quad 12 \begin{cases} (3,9) \\ (4,8) \\ (5,7) \\ (6,6) \end{cases} \quad 13 \begin{cases} (4,9) \\ (5,8) \\ (6,7) \end{cases} \quad 14 \begin{cases} (5,9) \\ (6,8) \\ (7,7) \end{cases} \quad 15 \begin{cases} (6,9) \\ (7,8) \end{cases}$$

Suggestions for work-cards

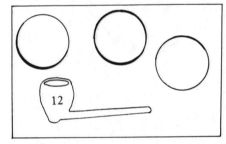

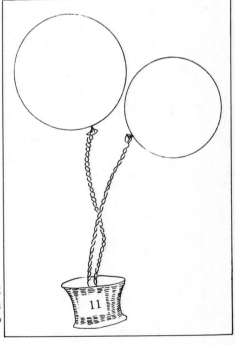

Children count out 12 objects and list their own ideas about 12.

e.g. 12 = 3 + 5 + 4
      12 = 2 + 7 + 3 etc.

(The set is partitioned into three subsets each time).

Children count out 11 objects and list their own ideas about 11. (In this case the set is partitioned into two subsets each time).

43

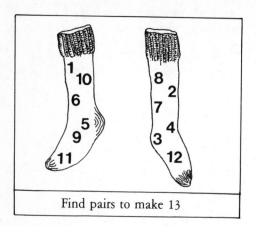

Find pairs to make 13

Children are asked to choose one number from each sock so that the sum of the two numbers will be 13.

Children work in pairs. One child counts out 14 'people' and places them in the house as illustrated. He then closes his eyes while his partner removes some of the people. On opening his eyes he counts the number of people remaining and determines how many were removed. Partner can then check his answer.

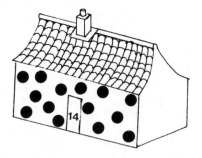

$(4) + \boxed{6} + \triangle = 15$

$\bigcirc + \boxed{10} + \underset{1}{\triangle} = 15$

In each example a number has been chosen from the circle, square and triangle to make the required total.

$(3) + \square + \underset{9}{\triangle} = 15$

Fill in the missing numbers. Make up some ideas of your own.

44

These operations have been introduced in **N6** and examples can now be extended to include numbers beyond 10 in keeping with the development in **N8**. There is clearly a very close link between **N8** and **N9**.

Some suggestions for varying the approach

1. Oral questions:—
   Peter has 12 marbles, he loses 3, how many has he left?
2. Work-cards:—

   $9 + 4 = \square$ $\square = 3 + 8$ $11 - 3 = \square$ $\square = 12 - 2$ $6 + 4 + 3 = \square$

   $10 + \square = 12$ $13 = 6 + \square$ $14 - \square = 7$ $9 = 13 - \square$ $12 - 3 - 4 = \square$

   $\square + 8 = 14$ $15 = \square + 10$ $\square - 5 = 6$ $6 = \square - 6$ $3 + 9 - 1 = \square$

3. Children can 'write a little story' about some of their sums.
4. Equalization:—

   $$6 + 6 = 5 + \square$$
   $$4 + 7 = \square + 3$$
   $$9 + \square = 6 + 8$$
   $$\square + 7 = 9 + 4$$

5. Mappings:—

Add 5	Subtract 4
$3 \longrightarrow$	$10 \longrightarrow$
$6 \longrightarrow$	$12 \longrightarrow$
$9 \longrightarrow$	$15 \longrightarrow$
$7 \longrightarrow$	$11 \longrightarrow$

6. Find as many ideas as you can:—

   $$12 = \square + \square + \square$$
   $$13 = \square + \square - \square$$
   $$14 = \square - \square + \square$$
   $$15 = \square - \square - \square$$

7.

Add the two numbers on either side of the box and record the answer in the box.

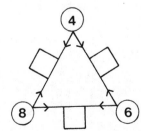

8.

Fill in the missing numbers so that
the sum of the numbers on each side
is the same.

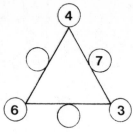

9.

Fill in the missing numbers. (Clearly
a whole range of examples of this
type can be planned. Provided the
three operations are arranged so that
they cancel each other out (i.e. in the
example 2-3 + 1 = 0) the last operation will serve as a check).

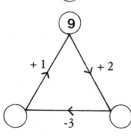

Comment: Assignments in capacity, volume, length, weight, money will
provide further practical experiences in exploring number relationships.

   e.g.   The shelf is 11 straws long.

   My table is 5 straws long.

   The shelf is 6 straws longer than my table.

Some children will assimilate the basic number facts through the wide range
of activities in the classroom. Most, however, will have to commit these facts
to memory. Competitive games can be introduced to make this task more
enjoyable. Two stages are suggested. Stage one is included at this point; stage
two follows later.

Stage one — memorizing the facts → 10

1. Add 1 to any number   e.g.   6 + 1 = 7
                          also   1 + 6 = 7 (Commutative Law)

2. Doubles: 1 + 1, 2 + 2, 3 + 3, 4 + 4, 5 + 5.

3. Add 2 to any number   e.g.   7 + 2 = 9
                         also   2 + 7 = 9

4. Remaining addition facts:—

4 + 3	5 + 3	6 + 3	5 + 4	7 + 3	6 + 4
3 + 4	3 + 5	3 + 6	4 + 5	3 + 7	4 + 6

46

Suitable Games
(1) **Domino game** using addition facts to 10 (For details see **N1** of Section 2.)
(2) **Triangle game**
Twenty-four equilateral triangles are cut out of thin card and ruled as shown:—

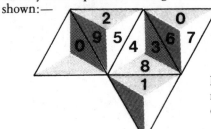

In the diagram adjoining colours match and numbers make a total of 9.

These are coloured in three different colours and numbered (0-10) in random form.

Children are asked to match colours and fit the triangles together in a variety of ways:—

(1) adjoining numbers making a total of 9 (10, 11, 12 etc.).
(2) adjoining numbers adding to give totals which are even.
(3) adjoining numbers adding to give totals which are odd.

N10: EXTEND NUMBER LINE TO 50

The number line is gradually extended to fifty and should be clearly displayed in the classroom.

Visual representations made with cubes, beads etc. should also be displayed. Most of the work is done orally. Some suitable activities are listed:—

1. Recognition of numbers.
2. Count forwards and backwards in ones, from any number.
3. Number after/before any given number— special attention to 10, 20, 30, 40, 50.
4. Add 2 to any number.
   Subtract 2 from any number.
5. Count forwards and backwards in twos, from any number.
6. Count forwards in fives, tens.
7. Odd and even numbers.
8. Workcards involving simple series:—

Write the next 2 numbers						**Fill in the missing numbers**					
29	30	31	32	☐	☐	28	27	26	☐	24	☐
19	18	17	16	☐	☐	32	33	☐	35	☐	37
8	10	12	14	☐	☐	25	23	☐	19	17	☐

Rectangular grids (approximately 30 cm x 15 cm) similar to the one illustrated will be needed for each child. A variety of materials, e.g. cubes, shells, tops, counters etc., should be available. A possible approach is suggested:—

> Count out 24 tops.
> Now place your tops on your squared paper.
> Fill as many rows as you can.
>
> How many rows have you filled?
> How many tops are there on the next row?

Conclusion: We can say that 24 tops make **2** rows of ten and **4** singles.

Children should have frequent practice in this activity until they can say confidently how many tens and how many singles there are in any given number. This understanding can be checked by asking children to take a single object and place it on the square for 11; 29; 32 etc.

The next stage is to introduce the numbered array. A very useful preparatory exercise is to let the children make their own numbered array. Each child will require separate squares numbered 1→50. Under the teacher's direction numbers are then selected in random order and placed on the unnumbered array until it has been completed as illustrated.

1	2	3	4	5	6	7	8	9	10
11	12	13	14	15	16	17	18	19	20
21	22	23	24	25	26	27	28	29	30
31	32	33	34	35	36	37	38	39	40
41	42	43	44	45	46	47	48	49	50

In this arrangement number patterns can be explored. A large display chart is needed for class use together with individual copies for the children. The words row, column will be used. Some suitable activities are listed:—

1. Recognition of numbers.
2. Which number is smallest, largest?
3. Find the numbers which end in 4. What do you notice?
4. Which numbers are in the 7th column?
5. How many columns are there altogether?
6. Find the numbers in the 3rd row. What do you notice?
7. How many rows are there altogether?
8. How many numbers are there in each row?
9. Find all the numbers that begin with 2.
10. Make the pattern of odd, even numbers; pattern of fives, tens.

In order to help children appreciate the relative value of different numbers an activity of estimating and checking can be valuable. Given a collection of objects children first guess how many there are and then check their answer by counting. Children should be encouraged to plan their counting so that the teacher can check it easily.

N12: COMPONENTS OF NUMBERS 16 → 20

The steps listed in **N8** can be followed again for the numbers 16-20 to give children experiences in:—

> counting
> making patterns
> grouping
> components
> work-cards.

The only basic facts that must be committed to memory are:—

$$16 \begin{cases} (7,9) \\ (8,8) \end{cases} \qquad 17 - (8,9) \qquad 18 - (9,9).$$

N13: ADDITION AND SUBTRACTION → 20

By this stage the concepts of addition and subtraction should be firmly established and examples are simply extended to include all the number bonds up to twenty. The activities suggested in **N9** are all applicable again and care must be taken to ensure that all the number facts are covered. In the preparation of work-cards it is good to have a variety of ideas on each card so that children are stimulated to think. Some fresh ideas are listed:—

1.

Add the two numbers on either side of the box and record the answer in the box.

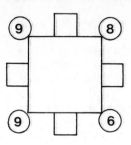

2.

Fill in the missing numbers so that the sum of the three numbers on each side is the same.

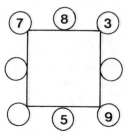

3.

Fill in the missing numbers. (Clearly a whole range of examples of this type can be planned. Provided the four operations are arranged so that they cancel each other out (i.e. in the example 4 + 5-3-6 = 0) the last operation will serve as a check).

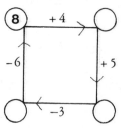

4. Games played with dice:—

Shake your die twice
    (i) add the two numbers together.
    (ii) record the difference between the two numbers.

Shake your die three times
    (i) add the three numbers together.
    (ii) add the largest and smallest numbers and subtract the remaining number.

Stage two — Memorising the facts → 20

1. Revision of facts up to ten (see the end of **N9**).
2. Add 1 to any number.
3. Add 2 to any number.
4. Doubles: 6 + 6, 7 + 7, 8 + 8, 9 + 9, 10 + 10.
5. Near doubles:—

        5 + 6   6 + 7   7 + 8   8 + 9

        6 + 5   7 + 6   8 + 7   9 + 8

6. Add 10 to any number.
7. Add 9 to any number.
8. Remaining facts:—

       3 + 8   4 + 7   4 + 8   5 + 7   5 + 8   6 + 8

       8 + 3   7 + 4   8 + 4   7 + 5   8 + 5   8 + 6

The domino game mentioned in **N9** may be adapted to include all the addition facts to 20.

N14: NUMBER LINE → 100

Reference should first be made to **N10** — the number line 1→50. Children who have worked through that section thoroughly will move easily into the extended number line. A large version of the line should be clearly displayed. (A Philip and Tacey 1→100 Square Wall Chart could be cut into strips to serve the purpose). Visual representations should be made with appropriate materials, e.g. beads, Unifix, cubes etc. Some suitable activities are listed:—

1. Recognition of numbers.
2. Conceal selected numbers to test individual children.
3. Add 1, 2, 3, 10 to any number. Subtract 1, 2, 3, 10 from any number.
4. Count forwards in ones, twos, threes, tens from any number.
   Count backwards in ones, twos, threes, tens from any number.
5. How many tens in 30, 50?
   How many tens in 46? How many ones?
6. Make number strips 1-10 to explore patterns:—

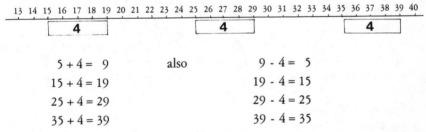

        5 + 4 = 9   also   9 - 4 = 5

      15 + 4 = 19   19 - 4 = 15

      25 + 4 = 29   29 - 4 = 25

      35 + 4 = 39   39 - 4 = 35

N.B. By using the number strip, 4 is added on or subtracted as a whole and not as four ones.

7. Workcards involving series:—

   Count forwards in twos from 49 to 61.
   Count backwards in threes from 74 to 56.
   Write the next 3 numbers.

   83 82 81 80 ☐ ☐ ☐

Find the missing numbers

71 69 ☐ 65 ☐ 61

43 ☐ 49 52 ☐ 58

Spot the clue

17 →15   24 →22   35 → ☐

20 →☐   53 →☐   69 → ☐

N15: 1→100 SQUARE

1	2	3	4	5	6	7	8	9	10
11	12	13	14	15	16	17	18	19	20
21	22	23	24	25	26	27	28	29	30
31	32	33	34	35	36	37	38	39	40
41	42	43	44	45	46	47	48	49	50
51	52	53	54	55	56	57	58	59	60
61	62	63	64	65	66	67	68	69	70
71	72	73	74	75	76	77	78	79	80
81	82	83	84	85	86	87	88	89	90
91	92	93	94	95	96	97	98	99	100

A large display chart is needed for class use together with individual copies for the children. (Philip and Tacey Operational Boards and numbered cards are ideal.) The real value of this arrangement is that it helps to reveal some of the patterns in our number system. As mentioned in N11 for the 1-50 array children should be able to indicate the correct position of any number in a blank 1-100 square before practice on a numbered square. Some suitable activities:—

1. Find any given number.
2. How many columns are there?
3. Explore the columns:—
   Find all the numbers ending in 3. Where are they?
   In which column are the numbers ending in 7?
4. How many rows are there?
5. Explore the rows:—
   What are the numbers in the 2nd row?
   How many numbers begin with 4? Where are they?
   What is the first/last number of the 5th row?

6. Which number is in the 4th row, 5th column?
7. How many tens in 50, 70?
8. Find the numbers with 2 digits the same. Where are they?
9. Number patterns:—

   evens, odds, threes, fives, tens.

   Discuss the resulting patterns.

Addition and subtraction

1. Add 10 to any number.
   Subtract 10 from any number.

2. Add 9 to any number — add 10 and move back one.
   Subtract 9 from any number — subtract 10 and **move on** one.

3. Add 20, 30 etc. to any number.

4. Add any single digit number, 'jumping' method:—

$$4 + 5 = 9$$
$$14 + 5 = 19$$
$$24 + 5 = 29$$

   Subtract any single digit number.

5. Add 2-digit numbers:—

   (i)   32 + 24   (No ten to bridge)
   (ii) 23 + 27   (Landing on one of the tens)
   (iii) 45 + 28   (Bridging the ten)

   Subtract 2-digit numbers:—

   (i)   35 - 12   (No ten to bridge)
   (ii) 30 - 14   (Jumping back from one of the tens)
   (iii) 42 - 17   (Bridging the ten).

N16: HORIZONTAL ADDITION AND SUBTRACTION TO TOTAL OF 99

Children need to experience the full range of activities outlined in **N13**, **N14** and **N15** before they are ready for this stage. Random materials, Unifix, Cuisenaire, the number line and 1-100 square will continue to be of value but should gradually be discarded as understanding develops.

Some representations of 34

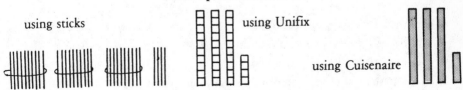

using sticks

using Unifix

using Cuisenaire

using pegs and peg-board

1	2	3	4	5	6	7	8	9	10
11	12	13	14	15	16	17	18	19	20
21	22	23	24	25	26	27	28	29	30
31	32	33	34	35	36	37	38	39	40
41	42	43	44	45	46	47	48	49	50
51	52	53	54	55	56	57	58	59	60
61	62	63	64	65	66	67	68	69	70
71	72	73	74	75	76	77	78	79	80
81	82	83	84	85	86	87	88	89	90
91	92	93	94	95	96	97	98	99	100

using 1-100 square

ADDITION EXTENDED TO TOTAL OF 99

1. Add 10 to multiples of 10 $40 + 10$; $70 + 10$
2. Add multiples of 10 to multiples of 10 $30 + 20$; $40 + 30$
3. Add 10 to mixed numbers $25 + 10$; $56 + 10$
4. Add multiples of 10 to mixed numbers $28 + 20$; $45 + 30$
5. Add two numbers:—   **No ten to bridge**
   - (i) $2 + 7$; $12 + 7$; $22 + 7$; $32 + 7$
   - (ii) $5 + 3$; $5 + 13$; $5 + 23$; $5 + 33$
   - (iii) $3 + 6$; $23 + 46$
   - (iv) $35 + 23 = 50 + 8$ OR $35 + 23 = 35 + 20 + 3$
              $= 58$ $= 55 + 3$
                                          $= 58$

6. Add two numbers:—   **Bridging the ten**
   - (i) $4 + 9$; $14 + 9$; $24 + 9$; $34 + 9$
   - (ii) $6 + 8$; $6 + 18$; $6 + 28$; $6 + 38$
   - (iii) $5 + 7$; $15 + 37$
   - (iv) $48 + 26 = 60 + 14$ OR $48 + 26 = 48 + 20 + 6$
              $= 74$ $= 68 + 6$
                                          $= 74$

SUBTRACTION EXTENDED TO TOTAL OF 99

1. Subtract 10 from multiples of 10 $30 - 10$; $60 - 10$
2. Subtract multiples of 10 from multiples of 10 $40 - 20$; $70 - 30$
3. Subtract 10 from mixed numbers $27 - 10$; $38 - 10$
4. Subtract multiples of 10 from mixed numbers $34 - 20$; $53 - 30$

5. Subtract two numbers:—   **No ten to bridge**

   (i)   7 - 4;   17 - 4;   27 - 4;   37 - 4

   (ii)   8 - 3;   38 - 13

   (iii)   46 - 22 = 46 - 20 - 2
                  = 26 - 2
                  = 24

6. Subtract two numbers:—   **Bridging the ten**

   (i)   12 - 8;   22 - 8;   32 - 8;   42 - 8

   (ii)   14 - 9;   34 - 19

   (iii)   53 - 36 = 53 - 30 - 6
                  = 23 - 6
                  = 17

N17: PREPARATION FOR PLACE VALUE

'Place value is a highly mathematical concept which is much more difficult for children to form than, say, the concept of length. In the past work on it has commonly been done too soon and too quickly; children have learnt procedures for getting the right answers with only a glimmering of understanding or, in many cases, with none at all. Until he reaches the stage of being able to add mentally two numbers with a total of less than 100 a child is not ready for systematic work on place value.

In our number system we exchange in tens but if, with suitable material, a child is given experience of exchanging in threes or fours or fives he sees a variety of examples from which to begin to abstract the concept of place value and eventually he can reach a greater understanding than if he works in base 10 only.' (Northern Ireland Primary Education Teachers' Guide.)

The place value system uses some important ideas in recording numbers:—

    1. successive grouping
    2. zero as a place holder
    3. digits representing the larger groupings appear to the left.

These concepts can be developed with the aid of unstructured and structured materials:

    Stage 1: Grouping and exchanging using random materials.
    Stage 2: Games and operations using multibase materials.
    Stage 3: Operations using an abacus.

STAGE 1

1. Experiences in grouping
Using a variety of materials children are introduced to the idea of grouping.

e.g. Count out 9 tops.

Grouping in fours we have:—

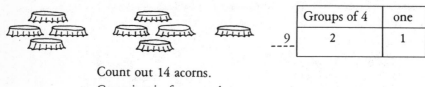

Groups of 4	one
2	1

Count out 14 acorns.

Grouping in fours we have:—

Groups of 4	ones
3	2

Initially it is best to group in one number only each day. Over a period of time children should have experiences in grouping in threes, fours, fives, sixes.

2. Grouping a given number in several ways

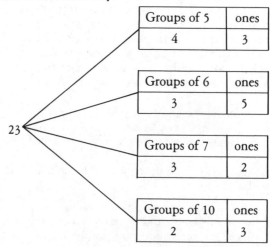

Groups of 5	ones
4	3

Groups of 6	ones
3	5

Groups of 7	ones
3	2

Groups of 10	ones
2	3

3. Grouping and exchanging

(i) Involving first grouping only:—

e.g. 5 conkers can be exchanged for 1 spool.

Count out 13 conkers and group in fives.

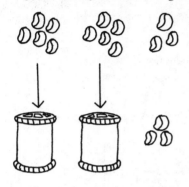

Arrangement after
first grouping.

Arrangement after
exchange.

13 conkers can be exchanged for

spools	conkers
2	3

(ii) Involving second grouping:—

e.g. 3 beads can be exchanged for 1 stick
      3 sticks can be exchanged for 1 brick

Count out 22 beads.

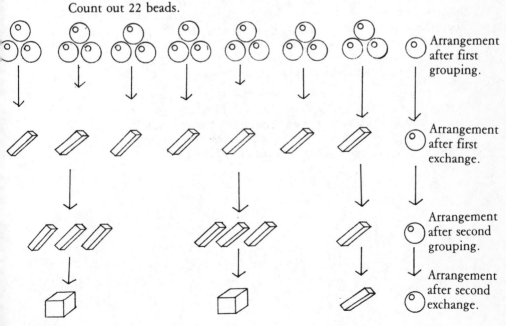

Arrangement
after first
grouping.

Arrangement
after first
exchange.

Arrangement
after second
grouping.

Arrangement
after second
exchange.

57

	bricks	stick	bead
22 beads can be exchanged for	2	1	1

N.B. When second and third groupings are introduced it is essential that the grouping number remains unchanged for each particular example, i.e. grouping in threes throughout, grouping in fours throughout etc.

4. A game involving grouping and exchanging

Materials: Buttons (first grouping), tops (second grouping), hats (third grouping), rings (fourth grouping).

Dice numbered as indicated in the following table:—

grouping in 3's	1, 2, 1, 2, 1, 2
grouping in 4's	1, 2, 3, 1, 2, 3
grouping in 5's	1, 2, 3, 3, 4, 4	etc.

Procedure

The game may be played in pairs.

First the grouping number must be chosen — for this example, 3. Children take turns throwing the die and collecting the corresponding number of buttons each time. As soon as a child has 3 buttons he exchanges these for 1 top. The game continues, throwing for buttons all the time. When 3 tops have been acquired these are exchanged for 1 hat. The winner is the first to get a ring.

In games involving larger groupings the winner may be the first to get a hat.

These activities outlined as stage 1, give children the experience of grouping and exchanging in a variety of ways and help towards an understanding of our place value system which groups in tens successively. Stages 2 and 3 (already defined) are developed in detail in **N2** of Section 2.

PICTORIAL REPRESENTATION

'One picture is worth a thousand words'
Pictorial representation is a method of presenting information in visual form. Discussion must always accompany such activities in order to interpret the various graphs as fully as possible. In this way relationships can be explored and concepts clarified.

PR1: REPRESENTATION OF ONE OR TWO SETS IN 3D FORM

The simplest form of pictorial representation is one-to-one correspondence where there is one object for each child. It is important that every child is involved at this stage. Clearly if each child takes a bead, say, then there will be the **same number** of beads as children. However, inequality is of more significance than equality in the early stages. Comparison involving only two rows or columns is sufficient initially.

Example: 'Comparing the number of girls and boys in the class'

(a) Each child takes a brick and   OR   (b) Each child takes a
places it in position   building cup.

The real value of such comparisons will be determined by the resulting discussions.

Language: more, less; greater, fewer.
Suitable materials: Building blocks, beads, match boxes, interlocking toys, Unifix, poppet beads, pegs and peg board.

PR2: REPRESENTATION OF TWO SETS IN A VARIETY OF WAYS

Comparison is still made between two sets but new forms of representation are introduced: Mapping, Venn Diagram, Pictograph, Block Graph.

This provides a progression from the three-dimensional stage to the two-dimensional and ultimately to the more abstract block graph. This section is best explained by means of an example.

IMPORTANT: It is much more valuable to represent one set of data in four ways than to represent four sets of data in only one way.

TOPIC: What age are you?

1. **Three-dimensional representation**

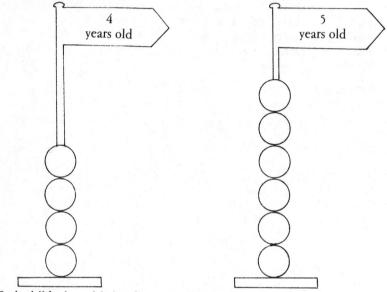

Each child places his bead on the correct rod.

2. **Mapping**   **'is'**

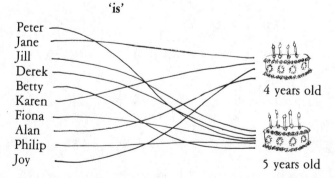

Each child draws a line from his name to his age.

60

3. **Venn Diagram**

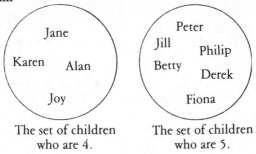

The set of children   The set of children
who are 4.   who are 5.

Children stick their names into the correct set.

4. **Pictograph**

4 years old	☺	☺	☺	☺		
5 years old	☺	☺	☺	☺	☺	☺
Number of children	**1**	**2**	**3**	**4**	**5**	**6**

Each child makes a small picture and sticks it in position.

5. **Blockgraph**

Children move easily into this representation after they have had considerable experience in pictographs. Representation can be horizontal or vertical.

6		▨
5		▨
4	▩	▨
3	▩	▨
2	▩	▨
1	▩	▨
	age 4	age 5

PR2: REPRESENTATION OF TWO SETS IN A VARIETY OF WAYS (cont'd)

Typical questions for class discussion:—
1. Check understanding of each representation.
   e.g. Pointing to the three-dimensional representation for 4-year olds — what can you say about the children who put beads on this rod? Peter, where did you put your bead? Why?
2. Comparisons:—
   e.g. Are there more children who are four or more who are five? How many more? Look at the sets — which set has less?
3. Counting:—
   e.g. Looking at pictograph — how many children are four? How many are five?

(**Comment:** If these questions are asked for each representation the same numbers 'turn up' each time and this can be helpful in leading children towards conservation of number.)

Some more suitable topics:—
1. Children wearing socks/tights.
2. Children wearing laced/slip-on shoes.
3. Children who have/have not crisps for break.
4. Children whose Mummy goes out to work/works at home.

PR3: REPRESENTATION OF THREE OR FOUR SETS

A similar approach is used as in **PR2** but topics selected involve three or more possibilities. The greatest value will still be gained by representing one topic in three or four ways and discussing the results as fully as possible.

Some suitable topics:—
1. Children who ... go home for dinner.
   go to the canteen.
   bring a packed lunch.
2. Children who ... walk to school.
   come by bus.
   come by car.
3. Shoe sizes.
4. Number of children in the family.
5. Birthdays.

PR4: INDIVIDUAL ACTIVITIES IN PICTORIAL REPRESENTATION

As children are gaining understanding in graphical work they can be encouraged to attempt some simple recording at an individual level. In this way they can progress to an ability to make their own graphs on a given topic and also read information from a given graph.

Further suitable topics:—
1. Types of pets.
2. Bed-times.
3. Types of coats.
4. Favourite colours.
5. Favourite form of travelling.
6. Favourite school song.

A final comment: Pictorial Representation provides an interesting and attractive means of developing and reinforcing the following mathematical concepts:—
1. One to one correspondence.
2. Comparisons and the language of inequalities.
3. Conservation of number.
4. Set language.
5. General computation based on particular data.

SHAPE — THREE DIMENSIONAL

3D1: UNDIRECTED PLAY

Sand and water play, use of constructional toys, model-making and similar activities will give children the opportunity to handle many objects in a variety of situations. These informal experiences are important in laying the foundation for subsequent work.

3D2: SORTING SHAPES

Materials: Sets of three-dimensional shapes — coloured if possible.
Familiar containers of the same shape, e.g. tins, boxes, food packets.

Given a collection of three-dimensional shapes children are asked to sort them in a variety of ways in order to become aware of their properties.

e.g. those that roll/do not roll
those that slide/do not slide
those that build/do not build
hollow/solid.

In this way similarities and differences will be observed.

N.B. This particular activity might be linked with **S2** in the development of SETS.

3D3: PLACING SIMILAR SHAPES IN ORDER

(i) Given a set of similar shapes children are required to order according to size.

(ii) Given a set of similar shapes children order according to one property and re-order according to another property.

e.g. Given a set of cylinders
(a) order according to height
(b) order according to thickness.

3D4: NAMING SHAPES: CUBE, CUBOID, SPHERE, CYLINDER

A possible approach is suggested. Show the children a shape, e.g. a box (i.e. cuboid). Ask them to find similar shapes about the classroom. Their experiences in sorting should provide a good preparation for this activity. The shape can then be named CUBOID and attention directed to its faces, edges and corners. Care must be taken to describe the properties accurately. Inspection of some of the faces will lead to the naming of two-dimensional shapes. (See 2D4). Other shapes may be introduced in a similar way.

Some activities

1. Collecting cubes, cuboids, spheres, cylinders.
2. Placing a shape in the child's hands behind his back and asking him to name it by feeling.
3. Making patterns by printing with different shapes.
   e.g. printing with a match-box gives a pattern of rectangles.
4. Tracing round the different faces of a cube or cuboid and naming them.
5. Taking a cuboid container (e.g. a suitably shaped box) and unfolding it to see how it was made. Repeating for other shapes.
6. Providing cardboard cylinders for children to discover the shape of the curved surface when opened out.

SHAPE — TWO DIMENSIONAL

2D1: UNDIRECTED PLAY

Children should have experience of handling and playing with a wide variety of two-dimensional material. Coloured plastic, wooden and cardboard shapes should be provided, each shape appearing in several sizes. Patterns and simple representations will be made in this undirected situation.

2D2: SORTING SHAPES

As in **3D2**, children are given a collection of two-dimensional shapes and are asked to sort them in a variety of ways in order to become aware of their properties.

e.g.   those with straight edges / curved edges
           those with 3 corners / 4 corners
           those with 3 sides / 4 sides.

N.B. This activity might be linked with **S2** in the development of SETS.

2D3: MAKING PICTURES AND PATTERNS

The experiences outlined in **2D1** and **2D2** should prepare children for a more controlled activity of making pictures and patterns. Several forms are suggested:—

(1) Using the shapes provided
(2) Using flannelgraph or plastic sheets
(3) Using gummed shapes for more permanent form
(4) (Coming later). Tracing round shapes.

2D4: NAMING FACES OF 3D SHAPES

By inspecting the faces of a cube and cuboid the square and rectangle may be introduced. (See **3D4**). By inspecting the end faces of a cylinder circles are introduced. When children are fairly confident in recognising these three shapes the triangle may be introduced. Accurate description of the properties of each shape is important.

2D4: NAMING FACES OF 3D SHAPES (cont'd)

Some activities:—
1. Collecting squares, circles, rectangles, triangles.
2. Placing a collection of shapes in a bag — the child picks out the required shape by feeling.
3. Finding shapes in the environment.
4. Introducing attribute blocks. (See **S3** in the development of SETS.)

2D5: TESSELLATION OF SHAPES

Materials: Sets (of about 12 pieces) of each shape.
Shapes which might be included:—
Squares, rectangles, triangles, hexagons etc.

When shapes fit together without leaving a gap or overlapping they are said to tessellate. Brick walls, tiled walls, floor and ceiling tiles could serve as an introduction to this idea.

Some activities:—
1. Finding out which shapes tessellate.
2. Making tile patterns by tracing and colouring or by cutting gummed paper and sticking.
3. Using rectangles to see how many ways tile patterns may be made.

A follow-up to these activities would be the use of arbitrary units to measure area. (See **A5** of Area.)

2D6: FITTING SHAPES TO MAKE NEW SHAPES

Materials: Geoboards
Sets of various shapes.

Some discoveries will already have been made in the tessellating experiences but these can be developed further:—
(1) Use squares to make bigger squares.
(2) Use squares to make rectangles.
(3) Use rectangles to make bigger rectangles.
(4) Use rectangles to make squares (length and breadth must be related, e.g. length three times breadth).
(5) Use (equilateral) triangles to make bigger triangles.
(6) Use (equilateral) triangles to make a hexagon.

2D7: SYMMETRY

The idea of symmetry comes naturally to young children. Much of their play activity, painting and picture making reveals symmetrical qualities. The environment will provide plenty of introductory material:—

> e.g. clothes
> books
> shapes on floor, ceiling
> doors and windows
> leaves and flowers

Some activities:—

1. Finding symmetrical shapes in the classroom.
2. Making ink and paint blots as illustrated.

3. Making a symmetrical pattern using pegs and peg-board. This could take the form of a game where one child places a peg and the partner copies the pattern on the other half of the board.

4. Folding a piece of paper in two. Tearing or cutting out a shape, opening up to show that the shape and the hole are both symmetrical.

 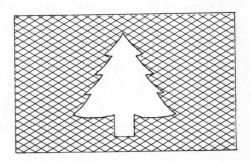

5. Folding a piece of paper in two and opening up. Drawing a simple shape on one side of the fold. Copying the shape on the other side.

GENERAL INTRODUCTION TO MEASUREMENT

With respect to non-numerical mathematics much of the work with younger children must be left rather 'loose' and connections only made where these are obvious. What is important is that children get a rich and varied range of experiences which will, at some later stage, cohere into mathematics.

There are three basic ideas in measurement:—

   (i)   the choice of a unit
   (ii) comparison
   (iii) counting

A unit is chosen and then compared with the object to be measured. The number of times the unit is required is called the measurement of the object. It is important to note that **all measurement is approximate**. Children should be taught to be as accurate as possible within the limits of the units under consideration.

In developing the various aspects of measurement three main stages emerge:—

STAGE I: **PREMEASURING STAGE**
1. Comparison of two objects, unequal with respect to the property under consideration. Suitable **vocabulary** is introduced which will help the children in the formation of the various concepts.
2. **Ordering** of three or more objects.
3. **Equivalence** of two objects.
4. **Conservation** experiences.

STAGE II: Use of **ARBITRARY UNITS** for measuring.

STAGE III: Use of **STANDARD UNITS** for measuring.
(With regard to Area this stage will not be reached in the Infant Section).

WORKCARDS: For each topic a few sample workcards are suggested. These are intended to serve as a guide in preparing sets of cards to cover each aspect of the topic. The teacher will adapt these ideas to suit the needs of her own particular children. Workcards should be clear, concise and attractive. Reading content and recording should be appropriate to the child's ability.

CAPACITY/VOLUME

Please read the General Introduction to Measurement preceding this section.

Definitions: Capacity — The amount of space in a hollow container.

Volume — The measurement of the space occupied by a solid shape.

C/V1: SAND AND WATER PLAY

Materials: Sand — wet and dry
Buckets, tins, cups, washing-up liquid containers, spades, rakes, ladles, spoons, sieves, funnels.

Water
Containers of various shapes and sizes, tubing, sieves, jugs, funnels, corks, sponges, wood, stones.

Undirected play with a wide variety of materials is needed to lay the foundations of measuring. Children should encounter both aspects of volume — the amount of space a solid occupies and the amount of space in a hollow container.

Experiences of filling three-dimensional space with sand and water will eventually lead children to the concepts of capacity and volume. The meaning of 'full' must be clearly demonstrated. Informal discussion should direct their attention along the following lines:—

Size and shape of the containers and relationships between them.

The look of a container and its shape inside.

The shape water takes when poured into containers.

Experience of emptying a jug full of water into container, then returning water to find the jug full again.

Language: Full, empty; how much; how much more/less; how many; holds more/less; amount.

C/V2: COMPARISON OF TWO CONTAINERS OF UNEQUAL CAPACITY

Initially containers selected should be obviously different in size.

Children are required to estimate first which container holds more and then check their conclusions:—

(i) By filling one container and transferring to the other.

(ii) By filling each container using a smaller container and counting.

(iii) By filling both containers and tipping contents into two identical containers for comparison.

Further experiences should involve less obvious comparisons, e.g. a tall thin container and a short fat container.

C/V3: PUTTING SEVERAL CONTAINERS IN ORDER

Order by handling. Check by one of the methods above. 'Nesting' play-materials are very useful here.

Language: Holds most/least; biggest/smallest amount.

C/V4: CONSERVATION EXPERIENCES

Equivalence of capacity — volume
'Holds the same as far as I can see'
'Takes the same amount of space'

Children are presented with three or four containers and asked to find out which two hold the same amount of sand, water or blocks. It is important for children to discover that the amount can be the same while the shape is different. This is a helpful step on the way to conservation.

Conservation of capacity — volume

Test 1: Volume of water remains unchanged when poured into different jars.

> **Materials required:—**
> A jug of liquid, two identical glasses, one tall narrow jar, one short fat jar.
> Pour liquid into one of the glasses.
> Ask the child to pour the same amount into the other glass.

Q. Have the two glasses got the same amount of liquid?
Ask child to pour liquid from his glass into the tall (or short) jar. Put this beside the other glass.

Q. Have the glass and jar got the same amount of liquid? Why?

Test 2: Volume of shape made by cubes remains unchanged when cubes are rearranged.

> **Materials required:** 24 cubes.
> Ask the child to make two blocks which look the same.

Q. Which takes up more space?
Move one set of cubes to a new shape.

Q. Do the two sets still take up the same amount of space? Why?

Children who are unsure at any point of these tests need more experience in the preceding activities.

C/V5: USE OF ARBITRARY UNITS

More meaningful activities can now be provided using arbitrary units for measuring capacity and volume. In each case the subheading is illustrated by means of a work-card. Clearly a series of cards can be planned along similar lines.

ACTIVITIES INVOLVING ARBITRARY UNITS
(1) Using different arbitrary units

fill →

☐ egg cups ♉ ⟶ the jar 🍶

fill →

☐ cubes ⬜ ⟶ the box ▭

(2) Using different arbitrary units, guess first

You need:—

∽ spoon   rice   tub

I **guess** the tub holds ☐ spoonfuls
I **counted** ☐

(3) Using the same units with different containers

How many boxes will it hold?

tin ☐

tidy box ☐

case ☐

(4) Using different units with the same container

☐ cups
☐ jars
☐ bottles

How many will **fill** it?

basin

71

C/V5: USE OF ARBITRARY UNITS (cont'd)

(5) Using a graduated measure

A 'home-made' measure can be introduced
marked off in, say, jugfuls. Children can then
use it for measuring the capacity of various
containers. This is a useful preparation for the
next stage.

Comment: Many of these activities give rise to the idea of comparison.

> e.g. How good was your guess?
> How many more boxes in the tin than in the tidy box?

Initially children may make these observations orally. Later they can be encouraged to record them.

Interesting activities can also be planned involving ideas of both capacity and weight.

> e.g. Weigh: one jug of sand, rice, salt.
> Discuss your results.

C/V6: STANDARD UNITS

Discussion of the preceding activities should help children to appreciate the necessity of having units which are the same for everyone, i.e. standard units.

ACTIVITIES INVOLVING STANDARD UNITS

1. **Introducing the litre**

   Children already have had experience in handling litre measures. At this stage the name may be introduced.

   (i) Estimate how many beakers of water, cups of sand will fill one litre measure.

   (ii) Find containers that hold ... just over one litre.

   > under one litre.
   > about one litre.

2. **Using the litre and half-litre**

   Guess the capacity of various containers.
   Check your answer and discuss.

AREA

Please read the General Introduction to Measurement preceding **C/V1**.

Definition: Area is the measurement of the 'surface covered' by a certain region.

AI: PAINTING AND COVERING SURFACES WITH PAPER

Materials: Paper — of various shapes and sizes; paint, chalk, crayons; gummed paper, scrap material; printing materials.

Finding area might be described as a 'covering-up' exercise. Children's first experience of area arises quite naturally from activities in painting, picture and pattern making, model-making. Discussion will largely be centred on comparisons of shape and size.

A2: COMPARISON OF TWO SURFACES

Comparison is made by fitting one surface over the other. Discussion is very important at this stage to lead children to a clear understanding of the meaning of area. Materials with rough surfaces would be particularly useful so that children could 'feel' the actual amount of surface. Attention will again be drawn to shape and size.

Typical questions:—

> Will the table-cloth cover the table?
> Is this piece of wallpaper big enough to make a cover for my book?
> Will our chart fit into this space on the board?
> Is that enough material to make a curtain for the play-house?

A3: ORDERING SIMILAR 2D SHAPES

In choosing shapes, different colours are used so that identical areas are not associated with identical colours. Some shapes will have one or more identical dimensions but be dissimilar in area.

A4: CONSERVATION EXPERIENCES

Equivalence of area
'Covers about the same amount of surface'
'The same area as far as I can see'

Two approaches are suggested:—
(i) From a given set of shapes children pick out shapes that fit over one another 'exactly'.
(ii) They use more than one piece to cover the surface of a selected shape.

Conservation of area
Test 1: Take two postcards and place on the table.

> Q. Do the cards cover the same amount of table?
>   Tear one card in two, replace on table with the pieces apart.
> Q. Do the pieces of card cover the same amount of table as the whole card?

73

Tear each of the two pieces to make four and repeat the question. Similarly for eight pieces.

Test 2: You will need three rectangles

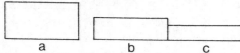

Q. Does the rectangle (a) have the same amount of surface as b and c together?

You can move the shapes if you like.

OR These are three fields.

Q. Does this field have more grass than these two fields?

You can move the shapes if you like.

If children are unsure at any point of these tests they need further experience in the preceding activities.

A5: USE OF ARBITRARY UNITS

To introduce the need for arbitrary units a problem may be presented in which children are asked to compare a long narrow surface with a short wide surface. An arbitrary unit, say tiles, could be provided to help children find an answer. Such experiences provide a good preparation for measuring the total area of various surfaces using arbitrary units.

Initially children seem happiest handling three-dimensional units to cover surface area, later experience being with two-dimensional units. They should already have had experience involving tessellations so that they know which shapes fit together without leaving spaces (See **2D5**). Where 'odd bits' occur useful discussion can arise over various methods of approximation.

ACTIVITIES INVOLVING ARBITRARY UNITS
Materials: Various boxes; books; newspapers, paper bags, school paper; stamps; dusters; tiles.

Geometrical shapes — plastic or card (All in sufficient number to cover surface in question).

In each case the sub-heading is illustrated by means of a work-card. Clearly a series of cards can be planned along similar lines.

(1) Using different arbitrary units

> **Cover** the table with shoe-boxes.
> Write:
> ☐ shoe boxes cover my table.

74

(2) **Using different arbitrary units, guess first**

> **Cover** the cloakroom floor with paper bags.
> I guess ☐
> I counted ☐

(3) **Using the same unit with different surfaces**

> How many [books] will cover it?
> window-sill ☐
> shelf ☐
> shoe-rack ☐

(4) **Using different units with the same surface**

> cover the surface of
> ☐ squares
> ☐ triangles ── plasticene board
> ☐ tablets

Comment: Attention should be drawn to the idea of comparison.

e.g. Why did you need more books for the window-sill than the shoe-rack?

What did you use most when you covered the plasticene board?

Initially children may make these observations orally. Later they can be encouraged to record them.

A6: CALCULATION OF AREAS USING SQUARED PAPER

Materials: Squared paper with a 2 cm grid.

(1) Make a garden using one square.
How many ways can you do it?

Now do it with 2, 3, 4 ... squares.

Draw a picture of your ideas.
What did you discover?

(2) Trace round objects on squared paper to calculate their area.
Discuss what is to be done about the bits.

LENGTH

Please read the General Introduction to Measurement preceding **C/V1**.

L1: COMPARISON OF TWO UNEQUAL LENGTHS

Initially objects should be chosen so that they are clearly different in length only but later other differences should be included.

Typical questions:—

Two pencils:	which pencil is long/short?
Two children:	which child is tall/small?
Two ribbons:	which ribbon is wide/narrow?
Book on shelf/floor:	which book is high/low?

It is easier at first for children to use the words long, short etc. although these are not absolute but relative. They should move quickly to an ability to use the comparative forms — longer, shorter etc. In asking questions it is important to draw out all aspects present in any comparison. For example children need to appreciate that if the blue pencil is **longer than** the red one then it follows that the red pencil is **shorter than** the blue one.

Further suggestions:—
Find objects longer than this straw.
Find objects shorter than this straw.

I am a mouse — what is tall to me?
I am a giant — what is small to me?

Build a tower taller than my tower.
Build a train longer than my train.

Language: Long, short; tall, small; broad, narrow; thick, thin; high, low; near, far.

Comparatives: longer, shorter etc.

L2: ORDERING MATERIALS FOR LENGTH, WIDTH OR HEIGHT

Ordering can be done by eye and checked by direct comparison. Differences, however, should still be very definite.

Language: Superlatives: longest, shortest etc.

Finding a go-between
Two objects require to be compared but cannot be moved side by side. The problem is solved by introducing a 'go-between' and comparing it with each object in turn.

L2: ORDERING MATERIALS FOR LENGTH, WIDTH OR HEIGHT (cont'd)

e.g.   Two model monsters — which monster is taller?

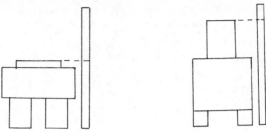

L3: CONSERVATION EXPERIENCES

Equivalence of length
'The same length — as far as I can see.'
Children are required to find an object the 'same' length, width etc. as the one provided.

Language: As long as; as tall as etc.

Conservation of length

Test:

(a) Q.   Which pencil is longer?   a
    Ans. Both the same
(b) Q.   Which pencil is longer?   b

If children are hesitant at all they need more practice in the preceding sections.

L4: USE OF ARBITRARY UNITS

Situations should be presented to help children see the need for some form of measuring:—

Typical questions:—
Would the cupboard fit into that space beside the shelf?
We cannot move it — how will we find out?

In the playground, two children stand at some distance from the group and in different directions. How can we find who is further away?

Two children, almost the same height — who is taller?

Having seen the need for some way of measuring length, children can be given experiences in measuring with a wide range of arbitrary units. Right from the start they should be encouraged to be as accurate as possible. At this stage, parts of a unit may be spoken of as 'nearly', 'just over', 'and a bit'.

ACTIVITIES INVOLVING ARBITRARY UNITS

Materials: Both rigid and flexible — sticks, canes, spills, pens, pencils, interlocking toys, ribbons, tapes, strings etc.

In each case the sub-heading is illustrated by means of a work-card. Clearly a series of cards can be planned along similar lines.

(1) Using different arbitrary units

Measure with sticks
The **length** of the table is ☐ sticks.

Measure with building cups
The **height** of the shelf is ☐ building cups

(2) Using different arbitrary units, guess first

Use canes to measure the **length** of the corridor.
Guess first.

(3) Using the same unit with different objects

Measure with unifix cubes

	guess	count
Length of pencil	☐	☐
Width of jotter	☐	☐
Height of box	☐	☐

(4) Using different units with the same object

The mat is ☐ bricks **wide.**
The mat is ☐ lollipop sticks **wide.**
Did you use **more** bricks or **more** sticks?
Why?

Comment: The idea of comparison is present in many of these examples and should be discussed orally with the children and later can be recorded.

L5: PARTS OF THE BODY USED FOR MEASURING

Working in pairs children could take their own personal measurements using string or tape. They could then compare the length of their span, cubit, foot, stride with those of their partner. Further practice in measuring can be given using the span, cubit, foot, stride as units.

> I **count** the **length** of the floor is ☐ strides.
>
> I **guess** the **width** of the floor is ☐ strides.
>
> I count the width is ☐ strides.
>
> My guess was ...

> Measure the **length** and **width** of the newspaper in **spans**.
>
> Record your answers.
>
> Compare with your friend.

These activities lead very naturally into the next section.

L6: STANDARD UNITS

When children are familiar with the use of arbitrary units for measuring length they can be led to a discussion of the fact that the same distance has been measured as, say,

24 strides (for John)
27 strides (for Julie)
18 strides (for teacher)

Through careful questioning children come to realize the need for some unit that is the same for everyone.

ACTIVITIES INVOLVING STANDARD UNITS
(1) **Introducing the metre**
Find objects longer than one metre.
Find objects shorter than one metre.
Find objects about the same length as one metre.
(2) **Using metres for measuring**
Guess the length of various distances and objects.
Check your answer and discuss.
(3) **Introducing the centimetre**
Situations will arise where it is necessary to measure with a unit smaller than a metre. The centimetre is introduced and children discover there are 100 centimetres in one metre.

(4) **Using centimetres for measuring**
Measure: various lengths
         personal measurements
         curved and twisted lines
(5) **Using metres and centimetres**
Measure: Heights of children.
         Long jump distances.
Materials: Metre-stick:— unmarked, ½ m divisions, ¼ m divisions, trundle wheel; metre tape.
         Rulers:— 20cm, 30cm.

WEIGHT

Please read the General Introduction to Measurement preceding C/V1.

W1: COMPARISON OF TWO OBJECTS OF UNEQUAL WEIGHT

Materials: Everyday articles, as varied as possible, e.g. familiar food packets; pieces of wood, metal; stones; plasticene; dough.
Balances.

Before children can commence to measure weight they must have some idea of heavy, light, heavier, lighter and so on. It is also important that experiences are provided so that the **size** of an object is not confused with its weight. Initially one object should be a good deal heavier than the other.

(1) **Comparison is made by direct handling**
   (i) Objects of similar volume, differing in weight only. This avoids any possibility of ambiguity when the basic vocabulary is introduced.

      'The green box is heavy.
      The yellow box is light.'

      'The green box is heavier than the yellow box.
      The yellow box is lighter than the green box.'

   (ii) Objects of different volume and different weight (weight related to size)

Language: Heavy, light; heavier than, lighter than; weighs more, weighs less.

(2) **Using a balance to compare weights**
Objects are compared by
   (i) handling
   (ii) placing on pans.

Children discover that the lower pan contains the heavier object; the higher pan contains the lighter object.

(3) Comparison of two objects, weight not related to size
Compare by handling.
Check by balancing.

W2: ORDERING THREE OR MORE OBJECTS BY WEIGHT

Order by handling.
Check by balancing.
(i) Identical containers, differing only in weight.
(ii) Assorted parcels differing in shape, size and weight.
Language: Superlatives: heaviest, lightest; weighs most, weighs least.

W3: CONSERVATION EXPERIENCES

Equivalence of weight
'The same weight as far as I can see'

Children make a ball of plasticene the 'same' weight as given object by making the scales balance.
Language: Weighs the same as; equal weight; balance.

Conservation of weight
Test: Take two balls of plasticine of equal weight and volume. Place on balance — both the same weight.
Remove one ball and roll into a long sausage shape.
Q. Which weighs more, the ball or the sausage?

Roll sausage until it is longer and thinner.
Repeat the question.

The child who is unsure at any point needs more practice in the preceding sections.

Note: It may be helpful to encourage the child to take away some plasticene from the 'heavier' one to make them both the same. Such experiences of taking off, putting on and checking help him to reorganize his thinking and finally achieve conservation.

W4: USE OF ARBITRARY UNITS

Consider the situation where two objects have been placed on the scale pans, one object being heavier than the other. Children are asked to find how much heavier is one object than the other. Some arbitrary unit is introduced, for example nails, and hence the difference is measured. Note, it is only the difference that is known, not the actual weight. This activity should be repeated a number of times to enable the children to accept that the number of nails is a measure of the difference in weight.

Next, children could be asked to guess how many nails it would take to balance the heavier object. The true balance is then made and discussion follows.

ACTIVITIES INVOLVING ARBITRARY UNITS

Materials: Familiar objects in the classroom of suitable size and weight.

Units: Marbles, pebbles, conkers, shells, tops, sticks, lego, beads, peas, beans, buttons.

In each case the sub-heading is illustrated by means of a work-card. Clearly a series of cards can be planned along similar lines.

(1) **Using different arbitrary units**

$$\boxed{} \quad \text{shells} \xrightarrow{\textbf{balance}} \text{a ball.}$$
$$\boxed{} \quad \text{tops} \longrightarrow \text{a pencil.}$$

(2) **Using different arbitrary units, guess first**

Take nails ⊤ to **balance** your pencil-case

My guess is ☐ nails
My count is ☐ nails

(3) **Using the same unit with different objects**

Balance with marbles.

☐ marbles balance the tin.

☐ marbles balance the orange.

The tin is heavier / lighter than the orange.

(4) **Using different units with the same object**

The toy soldier **weighs**
☐ beans
☐ peas
☐ pebbles

Make a graph of your answers.

Comment: Comparisons should be made where appropriate.

W5: MYSTERY PARCELS

Several parcels are prepared which are similar in size but of different weight. Parcels may be identified by means of a colour or letter.

Children put the parcels in order by handling and check their findings by successive balancing or by measuring the weight of each parcel using arbitrary units. For a more difficult version of this activity parcels may be of differing size and prepared so that a larger parcel is lighter than a smaller parcel.

W6: STANDARD UNITS

Materials: Various containers filled with sand, rice etc.
Weights: ½-kilogram; 200-gram;
100-gram; 50-gram.

Once again, after discussion, children will agree there is a need to have units that everyone knows. It is a good idea to begin with the half-kilogram as this is a weight children can handle fairly easily.

ACTIVITIES INVOLVING STANDARD UNITS
(1) **Introducing the half-kilo**
Find objects that weigh more than half a kilogram.
Find objects that weigh less than half a kilogram.
Find objects that weigh about half a kilogram.
(2) **Introducing grams**
Several weights of 100 g and 50 g should be available for children to discover the relationship between grams and the half kilogram.
(3) **Using grams**
Guess the weight of various objects.
Check your answer and discuss.

TIME

The concept of time is a very difficult one for young children living, as they do, in the present. Activities must be provided to give experiences in the passing of time and leading to the idea that time is continuous.

T1: EVENTS ASSOCIATED WITH TIME

One of the first 'time words' to become meaningful to the child is **NOW** with its opposite **NOT NOW**. Certain events familiar to the child are associated with time:—

> lunch-time, tea-time
> time to get up, time for bed
> Daddy goes to work, Daddy comes home.

General discussion of these topics provides the first stage in an understanding of time.

Language: now, early, late, later, before, soon.

T2: DAY, NIGHT. TODAY, TOMORROW, YESTERDAY. DAYS OF WEEK

A day for the child begins with morning. A routine follows — get up, wash, dress, have breakfast ... and so one.

The day finishes at night with supper and bed.

This type of daily routine is probably the first measure of time to have meaning.

Today, yesterday and tomorrow form the next development together with the days of the week.

T3: COMPARISON OF TWO INTERVALS OF TIME

As the span of attention of the average young child is small the time intervals involved must be very brief. All the activities will be measured and compared purely by the children paying attention. In this way children begin to become aware of longer and shorter intervals.

Some suggestions

(i) Listening to two pieces of music, one bright and quick, the other slow (to aid identification).
   Q. Which piece took the longer/shorter time?

(ii) Two different activities: One child walks the length of the room, the other walks round the room.
   Q. Which took longer?

(iii) Two children doing the same job: Fill tins with beads.
   Q. Who finished first?
   Who took longer?

Language: Longer than, not as long as, shorter than, quicker, slower.

T4: RECOGNITION OF SPECIAL TIMES ON THE CLOCK FACE

A teaching clock is used to make children aware of particular times in the school day:—

School starts; time for television; break-time; time for P.E., lunch-time. Some of these may be illustrated.

Time for school

Time for P.E.

T5: USE OF ARBITRARY UNITS TO MEASURE TIME

Materials: Egg-timer, sand-clock, water-clock, candle-clock, metronome, pendulum.

ACTIVITIES INVOLVING ARBITRARY UNITS
(1) **How long does it take?**
    e.g. How many swings of the pendulum while the children say a nursery rhyme?
    How many turns of the egg-timer while your friend walks round the playground?
(2) **How many can you do in the time?**
    e.g. How many skips can you do in 20 drips of the water-clock?
    How many bounces of the ball in one turn of the egg-timer?
(3) As for (1) and (2) but children must **guess first.**
(4) **Comparison of two time intervals**
    (i) Two different jobs done by the same child:—

> Use the water-clock
>
> 1. Change my shoes ☐ drips
> 2. Put on my coat ☐ drips
> I was **quicker** at ....

85

(ii) Two different children doing the same job:—

> Use a **metronome** to time your partner packing away all the blocks.
>
> **Write:** My partner took ☐ beats.
>
> Now you do it.
>
> **Write:** I took ☐ beats.
>
> Who took longer?
>
> **Write:** I was $\begin{matrix}\text{quicker}\\\text{slower}\end{matrix}$ than my partner

Such comparisons will help children begin to develop an idea of what the measure of 'speed' is.

T6: MONTHS OF THE YEAR. TELLING THE TIME — THE HOUR

The months of the year are memorized and children learn to tell the date. A first simple calendar might be made as illustrated. Later on the more common arrangement in weeks could be used.

Comment: This provides a valuable link with ordinal number.

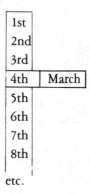

The easiest form of telling the time is the hour and children may have practice in

(i)   telling the time on the teaching clock
(ii) making required time on individual clocks
(iii) drawing in the hands on stamped clock faces

T7: ACTIVITIES INVOLVING THE PASSAGE OF TIME

Introducing seconds and minutes
A clock with a sweep seconds hand is needed.

Children count in seconds, following the clock. Then they turn their backs and attempt to estimate a certain number of seconds. Similarly the minute is introduced and children attempt to estimate one minute.

After children have become conversant with the second and minute and have discussed how difficult it is to keep an accurate count of each, a stop-watch can be introduced.

Activities involving seconds and minutes
      How long does it take?
e.g. How many seconds to build a tower of 12 bricks?
       How many minutes to run round the playground?

      How many can you do in the time?
e.g. How many strides in 15 seconds?
       How many jumps in 2 minutes?

As before, children should be encouraged to estimate and make comparisons in these activities.

Further ideas of **speed** can be developed in some of the comparisons:—

e.g. A track is marked in the playground.
      A child walks round while being timed.
      Next time he walks faster.

Q. Which way took longer?
      Did he take more or less time when walking faster?

      Next time the child runs round the track.

      Questions are repeated.

Careful questioning is needed to help children realize that the faster they move the shorter the time they take.

T8: NUMBER PATTERNS IN THE CALENDAR

Sun	Mon	Tues	Wed	Thurs	Fri	Sat
		1	2	3	4	5
6	7	8	9	10	11	12
13	14	15	16	17	18	19
20	21	22	23	24	25	26
27	28	29	30	31		

Discuss a calendar month with the children.

Emphasize the pattern of repeated days. Record the dates of consecutive Sundays. Repeat the activity for other days of the week encouraging children to spot the pattern of 7's.

Recognition of the half-hour, quarter past and quarter to the hour using:—

    the teaching clock
    individual clocks
    stamped clock faces.

MONEY

To a child money has no connection with measuring. The idea of money as measuring the exchange value of goods will be beyond him for a long time. He simply knows that a price is attached to goods and he must know what coins to offer. In contrast to other forms of measurement the different coins are already familiar to him. What he needs is practice in finding equivalences within coins and in matching coins to price. Exchanging and shopping activities give wide and useful experience of numbers and can follow the child's growing ability to deal with numbers.

M1: COIN RECOGNITION

The coins 1p, 2p, 5p, 10p should be handled and recognized. Children should use real coins whenever possible.

M2: SIMPLE SHOPPING ACTIVITIES

An attractive display of items is required with prices clearly marked.
    (i) Exchange one coin for one item.
    (ii) Discuss ways of selecting coins to make 3p, 4p, 6p, 7p, 8p, 9p. One item, value not greater than 10p, can be purchased and correct coins given in exchange.

M3: RELATIONSHIPS BETWEEN COINS → 10p

Investigation could develop along the following lines:—

(1) Finding equivalences up to 6p

	Use 1p coins ⬤ to make
3p	
5p	

Use 1p coins  and 2p coins 	
4p	
6p	

Put out the coins

(2) Finding equivalences up to 10p

Find 2 coins to make 7p	
Find 3 coins to make 8p	

Make up the right amount

9p	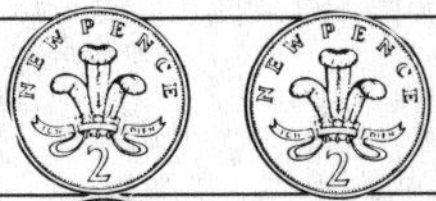
10p	

Put out the coins

(3) **Represent a given amount in several ways**

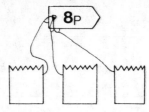

Charts made with paper coins are a valuable aid.

M4: SHOPPING ACTIVITIES

Materials: Actual shop and money.
Price list and individual shopping cards.

Comment: Examples can be extended to keep pace with children's development in number.

(i)   Buy two items, total cost not greater than 15p.
(ii)   Buy one item. Give change out of 10p.
Buy one item. Give change out of 15p.
(iii) Buy two items. Give change out of 15p.
(iv)   Spend an exact amount of money in two different ways.

M5: MONEY GAMES

Game 1
Materials: Die numbered 1-6.
Coins.

Shake die. Number on die indicates number of 1p coins to be taken. Keep shaking for 1p's exchanging where possible for 2p, 5p, or 10p.
The winner is the first child to acquire 50p.

Game 2   As game 1 — in reverse.
Begin with 50p and give away 1p's until nothing remains.

Game 3
Materials: 1 card for each child as illustrated.
Die marked in new pence.
Coins.

Children may play in groups of two or three. The die is tossed and the corresponding coin is selected and placed in position on the child's card. As soon as one section is completed the coins are exchanged for a 10p coin, counting the money as a check. When all five 10p coins have been won, these are exchanged for 50p. The winner is the first child to reach 50p.

N.B. This is a self-corrective game.

Game 3

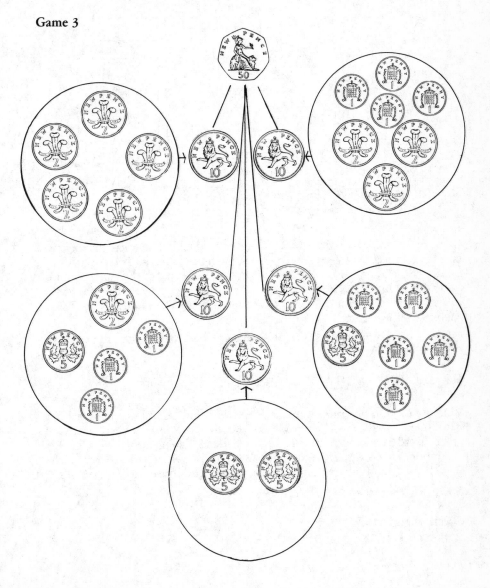

Game 4

Materials: A set of cards similar to those illustrated.
Die marked in new pence.
Coins.

Cards are placed face down on the table and children select the agreed number of cards, 3 or 4 say, and set these in front of them. The die is tossed in turn and children select the appropriate coin or coins of the corresponding value. These may be placed on one card or shared over several. The aim of the game is to collect enough coins to pay for each item. The winner is the first to complete all his cards.

Comment: The prices on the cards can be graded to suit the ability of the children.

M6: SHOPPING ACTIVITIES → 50p

When interest in one shop wanes a new shop could be planned or possibly a Bank or Post Office. Activities are similar to those listed above, extended gradually to include the buying of three items and giving change of 50p ('counting on' method). Sometimes children are required to record the answer using the least number of coins, sometimes in two different ways.

Some other ideas:—
'Sale On' — 2p off all goods!
Check takings at 'closing time.'
Simple stocktaking.

Section 2

 r—red

 b—blue

y—yellow

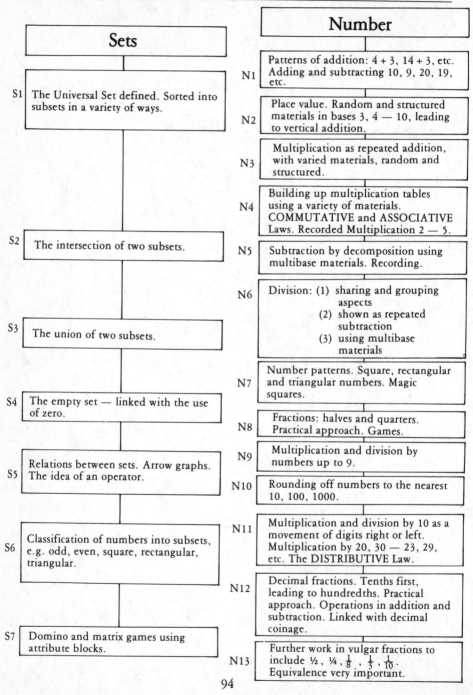

Sets

S1 The Universal Set defined. Sorted into subsets in a variety of ways.

S2 The intersection of two subsets.

S3 The union of two subsets.

S4 The empty set — linked with the use of zero.

S5 Relations between sets. Arrow graphs. The idea of an operator.

S6 Classification of numbers into subsets, e.g. odd, even, square, rectangular, triangular.

S7 Domino and matrix games using attribute blocks.

Number

N1 Patterns of addition: 4 + 3, 14 + 3, etc. Adding and subtracting 10, 9, 20, 19, etc.

N2 Place value. Random and structured materials in bases 3, 4 — 10, leading to vertical addition.

N3 Multiplication as repeated addition, with varied materials, random and structured.

N4 Building up multiplication tables using a variety of materials. COMMUTATIVE and ASSOCIATIVE Laws. Recorded Multiplication 2 — 5.

N5 Subtraction by decomposition using multibase materials. Recording.

N6 Division: (1) sharing and grouping aspects
(2) shown as repeated subtraction
(3) using multibase materials

N7 Number patterns. Square, rectangular and triangular numbers. Magic squares.

N8 Fractions: halves and quarters. Practical approach. Games.

N9 Multiplication and division by numbers up to 9.

N10 Rounding off numbers to the nearest 10, 100, 1000.

N11 Multiplication and division by 10 as a movement of digits right or left. Multiplication by 20, 30 — 23, 29, etc. The DISTRIBUTIVE Law.

N12 Decimal fractions. Tenths first, leading to hundredths. Practical approach. Operations in addition and subtraction. Linked with decimal coinage.

N13 Further work in vulgar fractions to include ½, ¼, $\frac{1}{8}$, $\frac{1}{3}$, $\frac{1}{10}$. Equivalence very important.

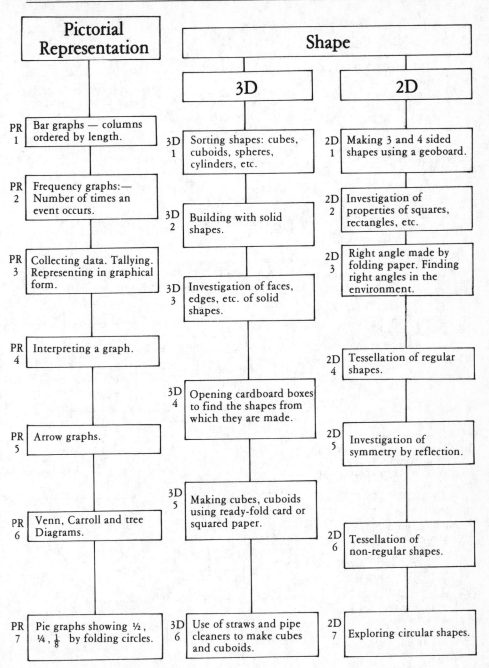

Pictorial Representation

Shape	
3D	**2D**

PR 1 — Bar graphs — columns ordered by length.

PR 2 — Frequency graphs:— Number of times an event occurs.

PR 3 — Collecting data. Tallying. Representing in graphical form.

PR 4 — Interpreting a graph.

PR 5 — Arrow graphs.

PR 6 — Venn, Carroll and tree Diagrams.

PR 7 — Pie graphs showing ½, ¼, $\frac{1}{8}$ by folding circles.

3D 1 — Sorting shapes: cubes, cuboids, spheres, cylinders, etc.

3D 2 — Building with solid shapes.

3D 3 — Investigation of faces, edges, etc. of solid shapes.

3D 4 — Opening cardboard boxes to find the shapes from which they are made.

3D 5 — Making cubes, cuboids using ready-fold card or squared paper.

3D 6 — Use of straws and pipe cleaners to make cubes and cuboids.

2D 1 — Making 3 and 4 sided shapes using a geoboard.

2D 2 — Investigation of properties of squares, rectangles, etc.

2D 3 — Right angle made by folding paper. Finding right angles in the environment.

2D 4 — Tessellation of regular shapes.

2D 5 — Investigation of symmetry by reflection.

2D 6 — Tessellation of non-regular shapes.

2D 7 — Exploring circular shapes.

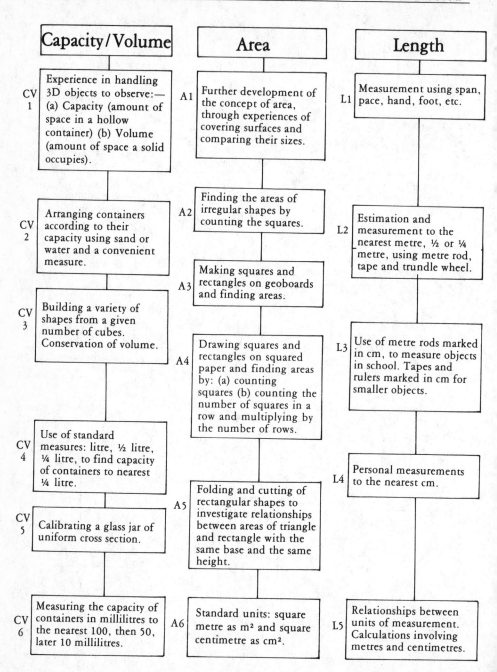

Capacity / Volume

CV 1 — Experience in handling 3D objects to observe:— (a) Capacity (amount of space in a hollow container) (b) Volume (amount of space a solid occupies).

CV 2 — Arranging containers according to their capacity using sand or water and a convenient measure.

CV 3 — Building a variety of shapes from a given number of cubes. Conservation of volume.

CV 4 — Use of standard measures: litre, ½ litre, ¼ litre, to find capacity of containers to nearest ¼ litre.

CV 5 — Calibrating a glass jar of uniform cross section.

CV 6 — Measuring the capacity of containers in millilitres to the nearest 100, then 50, later 10 millilitres.

Area

A1 — Further development of the concept of area, through experiences of covering surfaces and comparing their sizes.

A2 — Finding the areas of irregular shapes by counting the squares.

A3 — Making squares and rectangles on geoboards and finding areas.

A4 — Drawing squares and rectangles on squared paper and finding areas by: (a) counting squares (b) counting the number of squares in a row and multiplying by the number of rows.

A5 — Folding and cutting of rectangular shapes to investigate relationships between areas of triangle and rectangle with the same base and the same height.

A6 — Standard units: square metre as m² and square centimetre as cm².

Length

L1 — Measurement using span, pace, hand, foot, etc.

L2 — Estimation and measurement to the nearest metre, ½ or ¼ metre, using metre rod, tape and trundle wheel.

L3 — Use of metre rods marked in cm, to measure objects in school. Tapes and rulers marked in cm for smaller objects.

L4 — Personal measurements to the nearest cm.

L5 — Relationships between units of measurement. Calculations involving metres and centimetres.

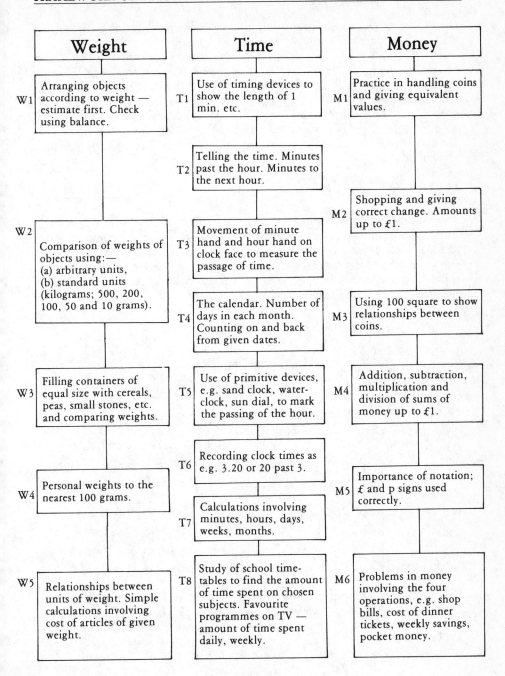

Weight

W1 — Arranging objects according to weight — estimate first. Check using balance.

W2 — Comparison of weights of objects using:—
(a) arbitrary units,
(b) standard units (kilograms; 500, 200, 100, 50 and 10 grams).

W3 — Filling containers of equal size with cereals, peas, small stones, etc. and comparing weights.

W4 — Personal weights to the nearest 100 grams.

W5 — Relationships between units of weight. Simple calculations involving cost of articles of given weight.

Time

T1 — Use of timing devices to show the length of 1 min. etc.

T2 — Telling the time. Minutes past the hour. Minutes to the next hour.

T3 — Movement of minute hand and hour hand on clock face to measure the passage of time.

T4 — The calendar. Number of days in each month. Counting on and back from given dates.

T5 — Use of primitive devices, e.g. sand clock, water-clock, sun dial, to mark the passing of the hour.

T6 — Recording clock times as e.g. 3.20 or 20 past 3.

T7 — Calculations involving minutes, hours, days, weeks, months.

T8 — Study of school time-tables to find the amount of time spent on chosen subjects. Favourite programmes on TV — amount of time spent daily, weekly.

Money

M1 — Practice in handling coins and giving equivalent values.

M2 — Shopping and giving correct change. Amounts up to £1.

M3 — Using 100 square to show relationships between coins.

M4 — Addition, subtraction, multiplication and division of sums of money up to £1.

M5 — Importance of notation; £ and p signs used correctly.

M6 — Problems in money involving the four operations, e.g. shop bills, cost of dinner tickets, weekly savings, pocket money.

SETS

Sorting activities provide opportunities for the development of **set language** through the discussion of the properties of the objects which have been sorted. If children have not experienced the activities outlined in the infant section of this guide, it is vital that they should do so at this stage. Even if sorting has been an important part of the mathematical programme, it is necessary to extend the idea of sorting and classifying to a wider range of objects and eventually to the investigation of numerical situations. It cannot be over-emphasized that at the primary level, the language and logic of sets are appropriate, but the formal manipulation of the symbols of sets is not recommended.

S1: THE UNIVERSAL SET

The universal set was defined for the teacher in **S2** of the infant section. Children should now realize that when we speak of the universal set, we are simply referring to the complete collection under consideration at any particular time and not to all the other objects in the universe. Objects which form the universal set, may be placed on a rectangular sheet of paper or cardboard as shown in the diagram below.

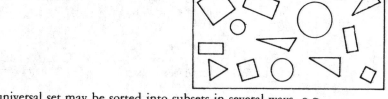

This universal set may be sorted into subsets in several ways, e.g.

(1) for colour

R : The subset of red shapes
B : The subset of blue shapes
Y : The subset of yellow shapes

(2) for shape

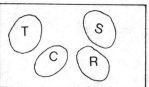

T : The subset of triangles
S : The subset of squares
R : The subset of rectangles
C : The subset of circles

N.B. Subsets are sometimes loosely referred to as sets, though they are, in fact, subsets of the universal set which may also be called the universe.

The complement of a subset consists of those members which belong to the universal set, but do not belong to the subset as shown in the diagram. It is sometimes referred to as the difference set. (See over.)

Universal set of shapes

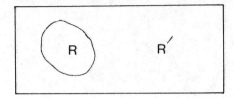

R : The subset of red shapes.

R′ : The complement of R:— The shapes which are 'not red'.

This method of sorting provides a variety of subsets with corresponding complements, e.g. square/not square; yellow/not yellow; four-sided/not four-sided.

There are several ways of representing the sorting process, three of which are illustrated.

(a) **The Venn Diagram**, takes its name from the logician, John Venn, who invented this form of representation. It is most important that the outer rectangle, is present in a Venn diagram, since there will always be at least two regions to be filled.

Universal set of shapes

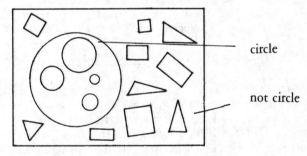

circle

not circle

(b) **The Carroll Diagram**, takes its name from Lewis Carroll, author of 'Alice in Wonderland', a famous mathematician.

circle   not circle

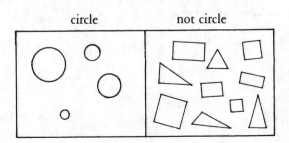

(c) **The Tree Diagram** is a third way of representing the same process of sorting.

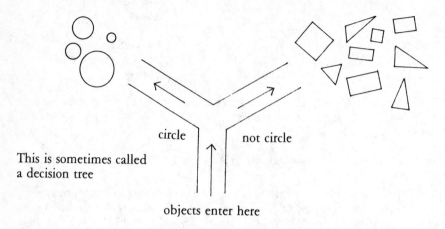

circle   not circle

This is sometimes called a decision tree

objects enter here

The class of children might be the universal set under consideration, sorted into two subsets in a variety of ways, e.g. wearing glasses/not wearing glasses; wearing school uniform/not wearing school uniform; having a birthday this month/not having a birthday this month. The representation of these subsets may again be shown by Venn, Carroll or tree diagrams.

S2: THE INTERSECTION OF TWO SUBSETS

In each of the activities mentioned, children have sorted the universal set into two disjoint sets, i.e. sets which have no members in common. Sometimes objects or children belong in both sets and this is illustrated as an intersection or overlap. Children were introduced to this in a practical way in the infant section, **S7**. The idea of intersection may now be developed to include a wider range of materials and recording may take any, or all, of the three ways illustrated. Each is simply a different representation of the same idea, e.g. the universal set, the collection of coloured shapes is sorted into the subset of triangles and the subset of red shapes.

Venn diagram

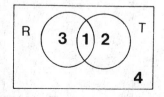

1. Red triangles.
2. Triangles but not red.
3. Red but not triangles.
4. Not red and not triangles.

Carroll diagram

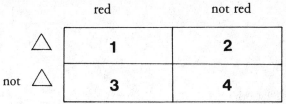

Tree diagram

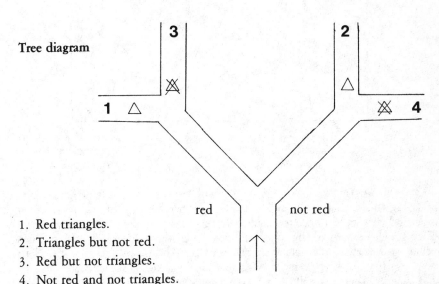

1. Red triangles.
2. Triangles but not red.
3. Red but not triangles.
4. Not red and not triangles.

Each of the diagrams illustrated has four regions to be filled and it is important that children can describe the shapes in each region by reference to the attributes they possess or do not possess. When an X is put on a word, e.g. red, it simply means 'not red'. An X on a symbol, e.g. ⊗ means 'not circle'.

S3: THE UNION OF TWO SUBSETS

In **S5** of the infant section, the union of two sets was demonstrated as the putting together of 'disjoint' sets (having no members in common) and was thus linked with addition. The union of the set of boys in the class and the set of girls in the class was the set of children in the class.

The two subsets to be combined may have members in common, forming an intersection, as shown in the diagram on next page.

Universal set of shapes

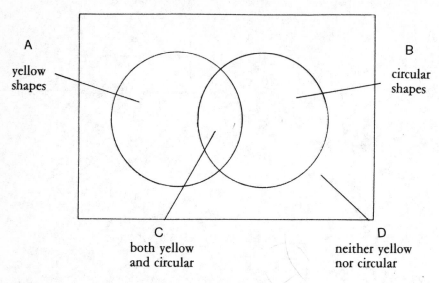

A
yellow
shapes

B
circular
shapes

C
both yellow
and circular

D
neither yellow
nor circular

Sometimes we want to know the members of both sets together. Another way of saying this is that the members of the new set are in A **or** in B. Children may find this difficult to understand at first, because they cannot see that a piece which belongs to the union set may be either yellow or circular or both yellow and circular. To help towards an understanding of this concept, both sets A and B may be put into a box and children asked to select pieces in turn and describe them. It will soon become apparent that each piece chosen was either yellow or circular or both yellow and circular. If pieces are common to both sets, they only appear **once** in the union.

S4: THE EMPTY SET

When children first make sets, each has members, but there are occasions when there are no members of a particular set, e.g. the set of children in the playground may be empty because all the children are inside; the set of pennies may be empty, either because the child has spent all his money, or has no pennies in his pocket money. The state of 'not having any' corresponds to the empty set. It is always an abstraction and the child may have difficulty in comprehending this if he thinks only in terms of the physical objects which form any set. The number corresponding to the empty set is zero.

If the universe is the set of numbers 1 → 10, the diagram below shows an empty subset.

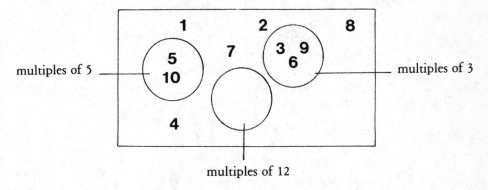

multiples of 12

Other examples of empty sets:__
1. The set of children in your class who are under four years of age.
2. The set of numbers between 11 and 19 which are multiples of 10.
3. The set of children in the class who have beards.
4. The set of grandfathers in the classroom.

The absurdity of some of these may be amusing and yet constructive as they lead to the idea of contradiction.

S5: RELATIONS BETWEEN SETS

See P.R.5

A. Relations **between the members of a set** may be represented by an arrow graph, e.g.

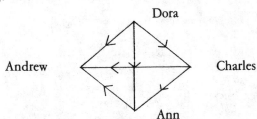

The relation or arrow ——→ reads 'is older than'. Other relationships, e.g. 'is the brother of', 'is taller than', 'weighs less than', etc. may also be shown by arrow graphs.

B. Relations **between the members of different sets** may also be illustrated by arrow graphs, e.g.

(1)

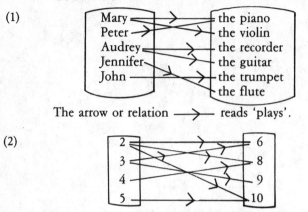

The arrow or relation ——→— reads 'plays'.

(2)

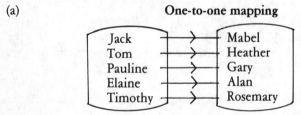

The arrow or relation ——→— reads 'is a factor of'.

Mappings are special kinds of relations between sets and may be illustrated by diagrams (a) or (b) shown below:—

(a)   **One-to-one mapping**

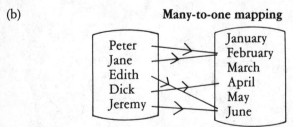

The arrow reads 'is the partner of'. There is **only one arrow leaving each member of the first set** and only one arriving at each member of the second set. This is called a one-to-one correspondence or mapping. Sets with this relationship are said to be 'equivalent' (not to be confused with 'equal').

(b)   **Many-to-one mapping**

The arrow reads 'was born in'. There is **only one arrow leaving each member of the first set**, but more than one arriving at some of the members of the second set. This is referred to as a many-to-one mapping.

To summarize: a mapping is a relation in which:—

(1) Each member of the first set must be used once and only once.

(2) To each member of the first set there corresponds one and only one member of the second set.

(3) It is not essential for each member of the second set to be used.

N.B. Diagrams (1) and (2) from the previous section do not satisfy these rules and consequently may not be called mappings.

When the operations of addition, subtraction, multiplication and division are performed on sets of numbers, the resultant set may be thought of in terms of a relation:—

e.g.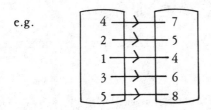

Here the arrow reads 'add three gives'.

S6: CLASSIFICATION OF NUMBERS

If we choose as our universal set, the numbers $1 \rightarrow 50$, there are many different subsets which may be formed, e.g. odd and even numbers, multiples of 3, 4, etc. square, rectangular and triangular numbers, etc. Before children represent these sets in diagrammatic form, they should have become familiar with them in practical situations through the handling of concrete materials, (refer to **N7**).

The numbers $1 \rightarrow 50$ might be written on squares or circles of cardboard and put on a sheet of paper representing the universe. Loops made of cord, cardboard, plastic, etc. should be given to the children to help them to sort these numbers as directed.

Universal set: $1 \rightarrow 50$

e.g.
(a)

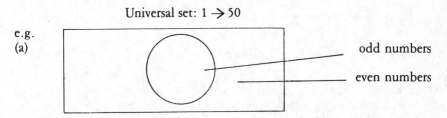

odd numbers

even numbers

In this example one set is the complement of the other.

(b)

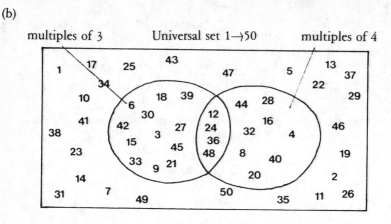

In diagram (b) there is an intersection as the numbers 12, 24, 36, 48 are common to both sets.

(c)

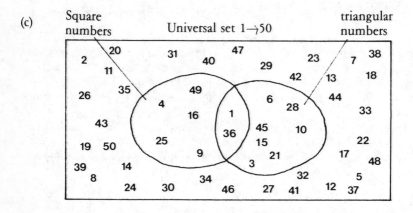

In diagram (c) there is also an intersection as numbers 1 and 36 belong to both sets.

These are only three, of a number of sorting activities which children may attempt, but again, it must be stressed that there is no value in sorting abstract numbers, unless children have become familiar with their properties through practical situations.

Attribute blocks were introduced in the infant section of the guide and may be used again at this stage. Random material for sorting activities is particularly useful in the early stages, but has its limitations, e.g. one object may be multi-coloured, or another, part wood and part metal. Structured materials, such as attribute blocks, where the attributes are readily seen, are a valuable asset to set work. Teachers should check that children are familiar with the similarities and differences between the pieces and should play again some of the games described in **S6** and **S8** of the infant section. The desk size sets with forty-eight pieces may replace the larger shapes used in the infant classes.

There are four variables in the set:—

1. Shape (circle, square, rectangle, triangle).
2. Colour (red, yellow, blue).
3. Size (large, small).
4. Thickness (thick, thin).

This may be described as a $4 \times 3 \times 2 \times 2$ system. It is important that **teachers** should be able to form smaller systems as children often find the complete universe too complex:—

(a) 12 blocks as a 4×3 system.

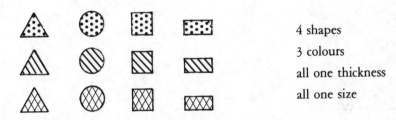

4 shapes

3 colours

all one thickness

all one size

(b) 12 blocks as a $3 \times 2 \times 2$ system.

3 colours

2 sizes

2 thicknesses

all one shape

107

(c) An alternative 3 × 2 × 2 system

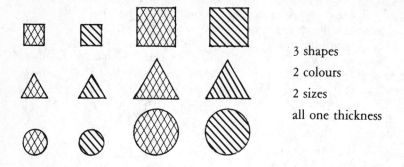

3 shapes

2 colours

2 sizes

all one thickness

(d) 8 blocks as 4 × 2 system

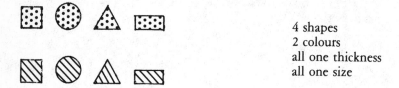

4 shapes
2 colours
all one thickness
all one size

(e) 8 blocks as 2 × 2 × 2 system

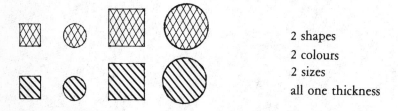

2 shapes
2 colours
2 sizes
all one thickness

Older children may be asked to form these sub-systems and to make some of their own using cards on which they print, e.g.

(1) four different objects in three different colours giving a 4 × 3 system;

(2) three shapes in four colours and two sizes giving a 3 × 4 × 2 system.

Cards may also be purchased, e.g. Red Indian Card Game, Truck Games or attribute card games.

If attribute blocks are not available for the following games, they may be played using the cards.

(1) **Domino Game.** Children play in pairs or groups with selected blocks or cards and arrange them in a chain so that each piece is different from its neighbour in **one** way only, e.g.

One difference chain

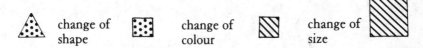

change of shape   change of colour   change of size

Chains may also be formed so that there are two or three attribute differences between any block and its neighbour.

(2) **Two-dimensional domino game.** This is an extension of the previous game. The starting piece is placed in the centre and others are placed horizontally or vertically so that there is a one attribute difference between any two adjacent pieces.

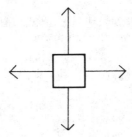

Variations might be any of the following:—

(a) horizontally — a one attribute difference
     vertically   — a two attribute difference
(b) horizontally — a two attribute difference
     vertically   — a one attribute difference
(c) a two attribute difference in both directions

(3) **Placing pieces on a matrix**

(a)

The teacher selects twelve blocks from either a 4 × 3 system (4 shapes, 3 colours, one size and one thickness) or a 3 × 2 × 2 system (3 shapes in 2 colours, 2 sizes and one thickness) and asks children to arrange these on the grid so that horizontally or vertically there is one attribute difference between any two adjacent blocks.

109

(b) Variations on this may be similar to those suggested in no. (2).

(c) Grids may be made to accommodate 4 × 2 systems; 2 × 2 × 2 systems, etc. and suitable blocks selected to place on these.

(d) A 3 × 4 system (3 colours, 4 shapes, one size, one thickness) may be placed in the following diagram so that no two adjacent pieces will be the same colour.

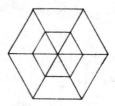

(e) Using a 2 × 3 system of blocks (e.g. small thin squares and circles in red, yellow and blue) place them on the following diagram:—

a one attribute difference ⟨——→

a two attribute difference ⟨===⟩

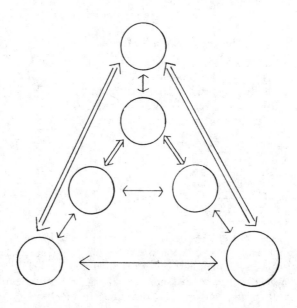

NUMBER

N1: PATTERNS OF ADDITION

At all stages of the work it is necessary to consolidate and extend what has already been done. Children are probably familiar with the patterns 4 + 3, 14 + 3, etc. but at this stage, quick responses to oral questions would be expected. The development of concepts is all important, but the practising of skills must not be neglected. Games may be devised to help in the consolidation of extended addition.

e.g.
(1) Can you find the missing word?

20	17	14	26	15	11	23	18	16	20	14	32	19	34	26	17	16
21	24	22	23	10	16	25	31	15	24	11	14	31	10	25	19	30
23	19	13	22	29	30	28	17	13	21	24	27	18	15	22	20	21

Shade or colour the squares which give the answers to the following:—

12 + 8	14 + 7	15 + 8
19 + 7	16 + 6	16 + 7
14 + 9	18 + 7	19 + 9
17 + 7	13 + 8	14 + 6
18 + 8	18 + 6	19 + 8
13 + 9	13 + 7	17 + 5
19 + 5	15 + 6	16 + 9

If this game is printed on thin card and laminated, it is possible to use it again and again, provided a felt-tipped pen is used and the surface wiped clean each time.

(2) Cards may be prepared in the following manner:—

CUT →

25	18+8
26	14+7
21	19+9
28	13+7
20	15+9
24	12+7
19	19+8
27	18+7

Any number of facts may be included providing the answer to the last question, e.g. 18 + 7, appears on the first card. The cards are cut where indicated and used to play the following games:—

111

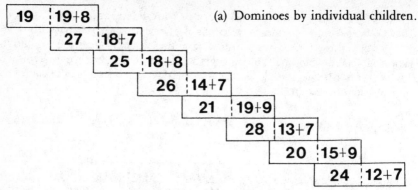

(a) Dominoes by individual children.

19	19+8
27	18+7
25	18+8
26	14+7
21	19+9
28	13+7
20	15+9
24	12+7

(b) 'domino' chains by children working in pairs.

| 27 | 19+9 | 28 | 13+7 | 20 | 15+6 | 21 | 12+7 | 19 | 19+8 |

(c) 'closed shapes' as an activity for individual children or groups.

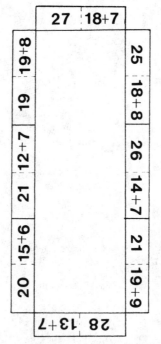

Work on the '100' square was introduced in the infant section of the guide (N15). Revision of the activities outlined there would be beneficial, particularly the addition and subtraction of 10, 9, 20, 19, etc.

N2: PLACE VALUE (For a fuller development view the 'Place Value' video available from the audio visual department, Queen's University Belfast.)

Place value is a highly abstract mathematical concept which takes much longer to form than, e.g. the concept of length. It is for this reason that systematic work on place value has been left until children are familiar with what has gone before and can confidently add mentally two numbers, e.g. 16 + 27 (total less than 100).

To form, e.g. the concept of colour, children see a variety of colours; to understand the concept of place value, children need to work in several bases and develop the habit of grouping and exchanging in each of these. N17 of the infant section suggests a suitable introduction to more formal work on place value and teachers should check that children are familiar with the grouping and exchanging activities outlined there, before attempting what follows.

(1) **Grouping** a variety of materials, e.g. beads, shells, bottle tops, bobbins, sticks, cones, etc, in threes, fours, fives, sixes, sevens, etc.

Recording a group of 14, e.g. as

fives	ones
2	4

or

fours	ones
3	2

(2) **Exchanging** a group of, e.g. 7 shells for spools, 3 shells exchanging for 1 spool. Record:

spools	shells
2	1

Exchange the same group, this time giving 4 shells in exchange for 1 spool. Record:

spools	shells
1	3

Exchange, e.g. 14 shells, giving 3 in exchange for 1 spool; 3 spools exchanging for 1 bobbin. Record:

bobbins	spools	shells
1	1	2

(3) **Free play** with Dienes' M.A.B., Tillich's bricks or any plastic multibase material in bases 3, 4, 5, 6, 10. Let children exhaust their own ideas, for only then will they concentrate on the directed activity. If these structured materials are not available, Unifix cubes, Centicubes or Minicubes may be used, the structuring being done by the children.

(4) **Dice Games**. Dice may be numbered as follows:—

Base 3: 0, 1, 2, 0, 1, 2 (1, 2, 1, 2, 1, 2 is an alternative suggestion as it avoids the frustration of missing a turn).
Base 4: 0, 1, 2, 3, 2, 3
Base 5: 0, 1, 2, 3, 4, 4
Base 6: 0, 1, 2, 3, 4, 5
Base 10: 0 → 9 using ten-sided dice. (available from E.J. Arnold).

(a) First throw is for blocks, second for flats, third for longs and fourth for units. The winner is the player with most wood at the end of the last round. The aim is to establish the relative values of the pieces. The game is over after the first round of throws, if any one player has one block more than any of the others (a fact not immediately obvious to the children),

e.g.
in base 6
1 block is greater than 5 flats, 5 longs and 5 units, i.e. 1000 $>$ 555 (read as one, zero, zero, zero)
in base 4
1 block is greater than 3 flats, 3 longs and 3 units, i.e. 1000 $>$ 333 (again read as one, zero, zero, zero)
in base 10
1 block is greater than 9 flats, 9 longs and 9 units, i.e. 1000 $>$ 999 (this may be read as one thousand)

(b) This time the game is played in reverse, and it is the last round of throws which determines the winner.

(c) Throw dice and pick up unit pieces each time. Keep exchanging for larger pieces. The winner is the person who gets a block first (or in larger bases, a flat). This is a particularly useful game as it is the preparation for addition in any base.

(d) Give each child a flat. The number indicated on the dice when thrown is the number of units to be given away. This involves changing to smaller pieces. The winner is the person who gets rid of his wood first, but an exact throw is required in the final stage. In the smaller bases, start with a block. This game prepares children for the decomposition method of subtraction.

(5) **Addition** is the operation of 'putting together' and children put out the materials indicated by the 'sum' on the blackboard (or work card) on a card measuring approximately 20 cms by 15 cms, illustrated below:—

```
  B F L U
    2 2 2          (1)
+   1 2 2 base 3
  1 1 2 1
```

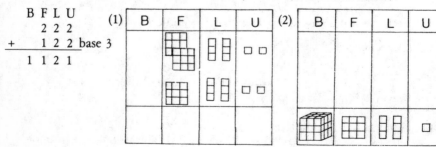

The pieces are brought together in their columns and exchanges made as follows: 3 units for 1 long; 3 longs for 1 flat; 3 flats for 1 block. The result is depicted in diagram (2) on previous page and recorded as 1121.

Children working with material, grouping and exchanging, move quickly into four places and need not be restricted, as was often the case, to 'tens and units'. Teachers plan their own progression but the motto 'Hasten slowly', is applicable with such a difficult concept as place value.

While the games are played in a variety of bases, the directed activitires may be carried out in bases 3 and 4, as they are easy to handle, share around more economically and cost less. The concepts may be formed using these and by the time examples are worked in other bases, including 10, the material is usually discarded. If some children need material in bases, 5, 6 and 10, then larger cards are necessary.

Materials in base 3 and base 4 are available through the 'Nicolas Burdett' catalogue.

Extended materials in bases 3 and 4 are also available and show the structuring of the base to the fifth place (long block). (E.S.A. Catalogue).

An abacus may be introduced to the children and used for counting forwards and backwards singly or in twos. Addition as grouping and exchanging may again be demonstrated. A simple abacus may be made by pushing counting sticks into a block of plasticine or dowel rods into a block of wood.

e.g.

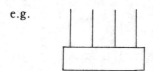

Work on the abacus is a progression on the previous activities as the material is no longer structured. Coloured blocks, beads, or tablets may be used and a colour sequence planned, e.g. three yellows on the first rod (to the right) might be exchanged for one green on the second rod; three greens for one blue on the third rod; three blues for one red on the fourth rod.

Children should be encouraged to count in sequence on the abacus, e.g. in base 3, one yellow is put on the rod on the extreme right, another and another. These three yellows are exchanged for one green. At this stage it is important to check that the next one added is yellow and not green as frequently happens. It is very important to give practice in building up the structure from the **unit** pieces and equally important to give away only unit pieces one at a time until all have been removed. This involves changing reds to blues, blues to greens, greens to yellows and is excellent preparation for work in decomposition.

Abacus boards are useful at this stage. They are made of plastic and have rows of pegs on which children put coloured tablets. The arrangement is very similar to the recording that children will be doing, and is the final stage in the preparation for written calculations. Position 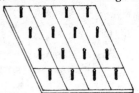 or place is very important, colour being the only aid employed. Work, similar to that with structured apparatus should be attempted. It is only by a variety of experiences that the concept of place value can eventually be formed.

N3: MULTIPLICATION AS REPEATED ADDITION

The grouping activities already mentioned in the guide (**N17**) of the infant section and **N2** of this section) form part of the practical preparation necessary before any formal work in multiplication is attempted. As soon as children are able to add together small numbers, the idea of multiplication can be introduced as repeated addition, e.g.

(a)

2 + 2 + 2	= 6
3 sets of 2	= 6
3 (2)	= 6
and finally	
3 × 2	= 6

(b)

3 + 3 + 3	= 9
3 sets of 3	= 9
3 (3)	= 9
and finally	
3 × 3	= 9

Recognising two objects, e.g. as one (two) is difficult and it is only after much experience in grouping and counting the groups that children begin to understand that 'one' may describe a group of two, three, four, etc. There are two variables which children have to identify:—

(a) the number of groups;

(b) the number of objects in each group.

Until they can do this easily and quickly, formal work in multiplication should not be attempted.

Cuisenaire rods might be used in the early stages and the rods called by their colour names. Three red rods measure 6 units; three green ones measure 9. Later, these rods may be referred to as 'twos' and 'threes'. Unifix materials grouped together in twos, threes, fours, etc. with two colours alternating are also useful. These may be placed on the number track and children quickly read off the answers e.g. 4(3), 5(3), etc. Again it must be stressed that the more varied the experiences, the more thorough will be the grasp of the concept. Many of these grouping activities may be done earlier by brighter children, but reinforcement is needed before proceeding to more formal work.

N4: MULTIPLICATION TABLES, ETC.

Tables are essential tools without which children are not properly equipped to deal with mathematics in any competent fashion. 'Rote' learning is no longer advocated, as more interesting and efficient ways have been discovered, but by the end of the P.5 year most children should give quick and correct responses to addition and multiplication tables.

In **N6** of the infant section reference was made to the **commutative law**, i.e. $4 + 5 = 5 + 4$. This law also applies to multiplication, and children should become aware of it through a wide variety of examples and much discussion. (The word itself should not be used.) Neither subtraction nor division possesses this commutative property, i.e. $5 - 4$ is not the same as $4 - 5$; $12 \div 4$ is not the same as $4 \div 12$.

e.g.
(a) Group 12 buttons as:—

4 sets of 3 or 3 sets of 4

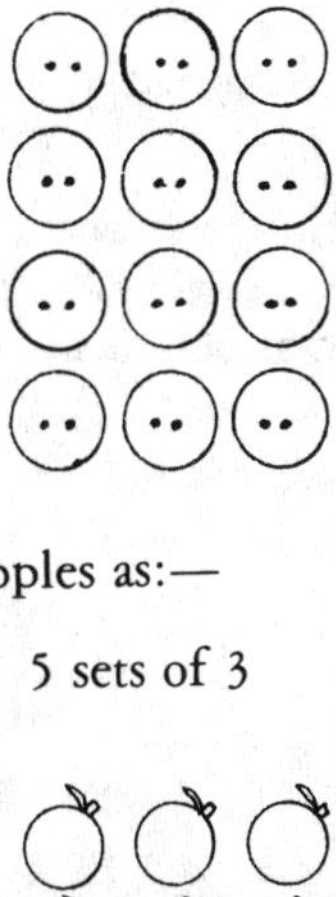

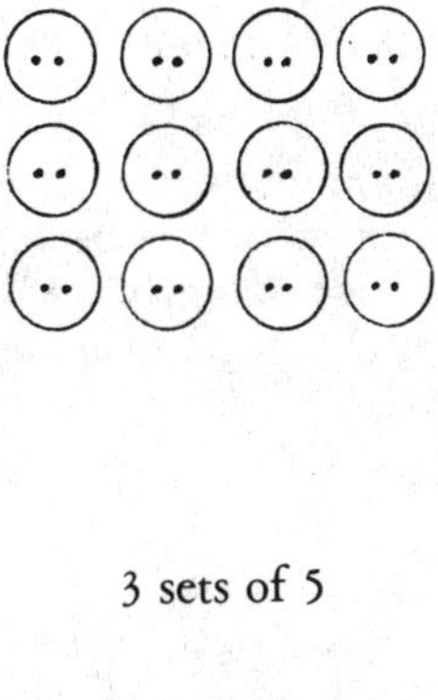

(b) Group 15 apples as:—

5 sets of 3 or 3 sets of 5

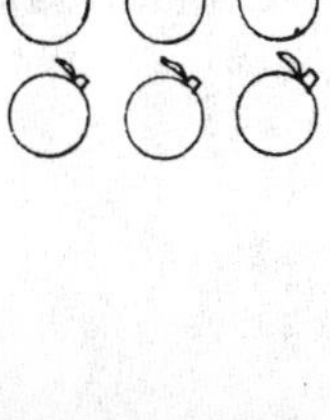

(c) Squared paper to show the 'pattern' aspect:—

| 4 sets of 3 | 3 sets of 4 | 5 sets of 3 | 3 sets of 5 |

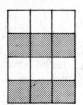 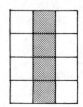 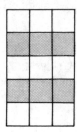 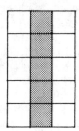

(d) The number line.

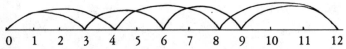

The number line demonstrates that 12 is made up of:—

3 sets of 4   or   4 sets of 3.

By using the commutative law for multiplication, the number of facts which must be known is reduced considerably as the table below shows. 1 × 2 does not appear in the second column because its mathematical equivalent 2 × 1 is in column one. Other spaces are empty for a similar reason.

```
1 × 1
2 × 1   2 × 2
3 × 1   3 × 2   3 × 3
4 × 1   4 × 2   4 × 3   4 × 4
5 × 1   5 × 2   5 × 3   5 × 4   5 × 5
6 × 1   6 × 2   6 × 3   6 × 4   6 × 5   6 × 6
7 × 1   7 × 2   7 × 3   7 × 4   7 × 5   7 × 6   7 × 7
8 × 1   8 × 2   8 × 3   8 × 4   8 × 5   8 × 6   8 × 7   8 × 8
9 × 1   9 × 2   9 × 3   9 × 4   9 × 5   9 × 6   9 × 7   9 × 8   9 × 9
```

Colouring patterns on the blank 100 square and numbering them helps to familiarize children with the numbers in that particular table. It is possible to arrange more than one pattern on the square as it is only necessary to colour 10 units of each.

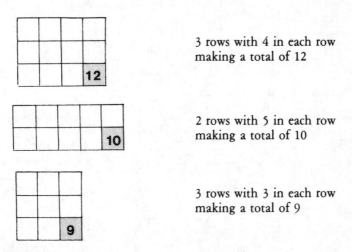

Pattern of threes

pattern of sixes

Linking the table of 10's with 5's

2's with 4's and 8's

3's with 6's and 9's

often helps in the assimilation of table facts. Seven is not related to the others and is best left to the last.

Table facts may be built up using squared paper, e.g.

3 rows with 4 in each row
making a total of 12

2 rows with 5 in each row
making a total of 10

3 rows with 3 in each row
making a total of 9

Children might be asked to cut out rectangles to represent all the multiplication facts as illustrated. When these are placed against the top left-hand corner of a grid the 'multiplication square' appears.

1	2	3	4	5	6	7	8	9	10
2	4								
3		9							
4			16						
5				25					
6									
7		21			42				
8						56			
9							72		
10								90	100

Only a few rectangles have been placed on this grid, but it is obvious how each space represents the bottom right hand corner of a rectangle and children can record the number of squares on it.

On a blank square children might be asked to fill in the numbers in the bottom right hand corner of all square shapes,

e.g.

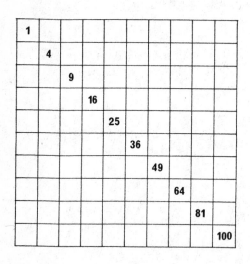

1									
	4								
		9							
			16						
				25					
					36				
						49			
							64		
								81	
									100

This produces the 'square' numbers which form the diagonal of the blank square. Keeping in mind that $3 \times 4 = 4 \times 3$, etc. they might proceed to fill in the rectangles in pairs.

For further information read the Teachers' Notes for the BBC programme 'It's Maths!' Number 3, written by Alistair McIntosh, Principal Mathematics Adviser for Leicestershire.

The final result looks like this:—

1	2	3	4	5	6	7	8	9	10
2	4	6	8	10	12	14	16	18	20
3	6	9	12	15	18	21	24	27	30
4	8	12	16	20	24	28	32	36	40
5	10	15	20	25	30	35	40	45	50
6	12	18	24	30	36	42	48	54	60
7	14	21	28	35	42	49	56	63	70
8	16	24	32	40	48	56	64	72	80
9	18	27	36	45	54	63	72	81	90
10	20	30	40	50	60	70	80	90	100

The multiplication square may be built up systematically from a blank square and children may begin at the top or bottom. e.g.

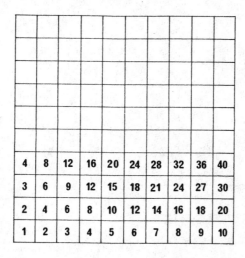

As children fill in the squares, they are in effect writing out multiplication tables.

A set of patterns, which children find fascinating, can be obtained by colouring the squares containing the numbers exactly divisible by 2, by 3, by 4, etc.

1	2	3	4	5	6	7	8	9	10
2	4	6	8	10	12	14	16	18	20
3	6	9	12	15	18	21	24	27	30
4	8	12	16	20	24	28	32	36	40
5	10	15	20	25	30	35	40	45	50
6	12	18	24	30	36	42	48	54	60
7	14	21	28	35	42	49	56	63	70
8	16	24	32	40	48	56	64	72	80
9	18	27	36	45	54	63	72	81	90
10	20	30	40	50	60	70	80	90	100

Multiples of 3.

Multiplication was introduced as repeated addition; it could now be linked with division, e.g.

3 rows with 5 in each row make 15.

How many threes in fifteen? How many fives in fifteen? These questions draw attention to the grouping aspect of division. As children are learning multiplication tables, e.g. $4 \times 5 = 20$, they should be able to complete the following:—

$$4 \times \Box = 20$$
$$\Box \times 5 = 20$$
$$20 = 4 \times \Box$$
$$20 = \Box \times 5$$

which is in effect, saying, 'How many fours (or fives) in twenty?

The associative law is worth mentioning here, but only the principle should be demonstrated to children, e.g. in the addition of $3 + 5 + 7$, the order does not matter and it is easier to add $3 + 7$ and then 5. With multiplication this also applies, e.g. $4 \times 9 \times 5 = 4 \times 5 \times 9$ or 20×9 which is easier than 36×5.

If children have an understanding of the concept of multiplication through many and varied concrete experiences, they are ready for recorded work and at first this might be limited to the numbers $2 \rightarrow 5$. It is best to involve the children in a problem solving situation, e.g. a farmer planted 4 rows of cabbages with 85 plants in each row. How many altogether? When children can explain what they are doing, e.g. 32×5, as e.g. 32 children in a class, each receiving 5 sweets, they are ready for some practice examples. From time to time they should be asked to put a story to the numbers and symbols.

N5: SUBTRACTION

The three aspects of subtraction which children meet are outlined in **N6** of the infant section:—

1. comparison
2. taking away
3. complementary addition

It is necessary at this stage to teach a method of **written subtraction** which will be used throughout the school. As 'decomposition' may be demonstrated by the use of multibase materials, it is the method suggested here.

In using this material for demonstrating the process, it is easier to deal only with the second aspect, viz. 'taking away'.

The example to be considered:

$$\begin{array}{c c c c} B & F & L & U \\ & 3 & 2 & 1 \\ - & 1 & 2 & 3 \end{array} \quad \text{base 4}$$

Children put out the material indicated by the numbers on the top line, i.e. 3 flats, 2 longs and 1 unit.

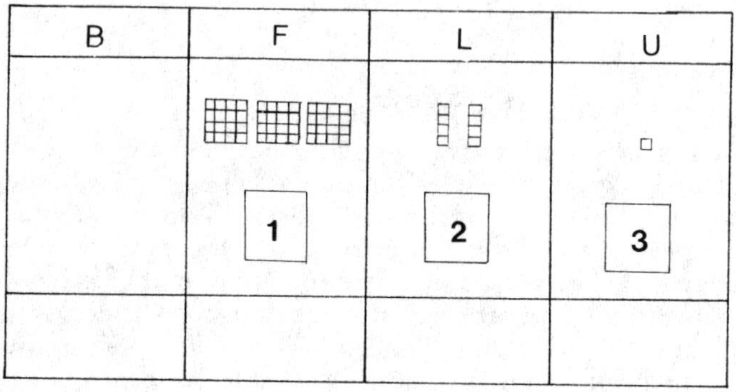

B	F	L	U
	1	2	3

The amount to be taken away is written on cards which are placed underneath. The question is asked: 'Can you give away 3 units?'

Children suggest exchanging 1 long for 4 units, giving away 3 and having 2(1 + 1) left. (Material placed as shown on the next diagram).

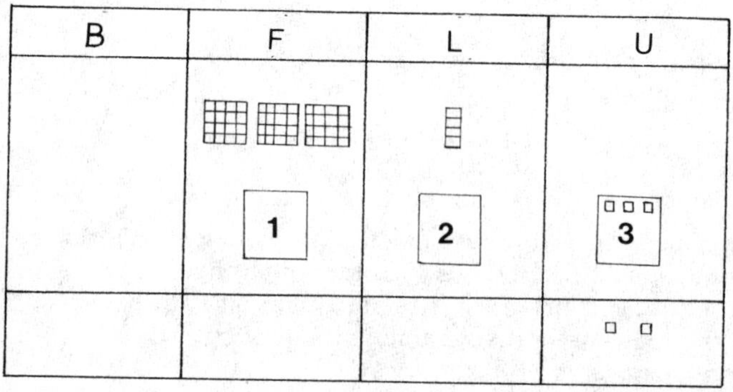

B	F	L	U
	1	2	3

The next question is: 'Can you give away 2 longs?' The suggestion of exchanging 1 flat for 4 longs is given. Children do this, giving away 2 longs and having 3(2 + 1) left. Again material given away is put on the card marked 2 and what is left, in the answer space below.

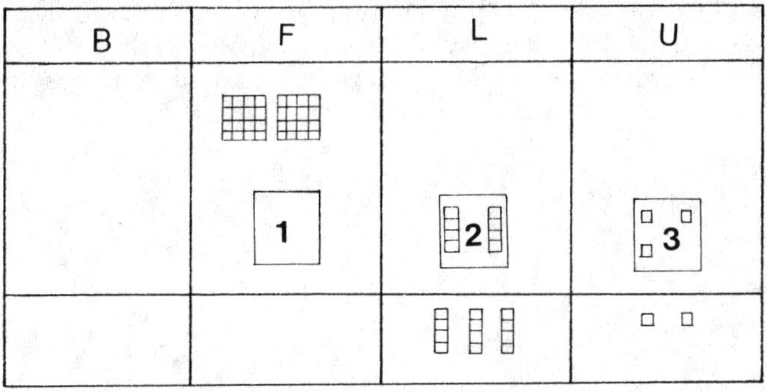

B	F	L	U
	▦ ▦		
	1	**2**	**3**
		❚ ❚ ❚	□ □

The last question is: 'Can you give away 1 flat?' Children can do this without exchanging and place the material as shown below.

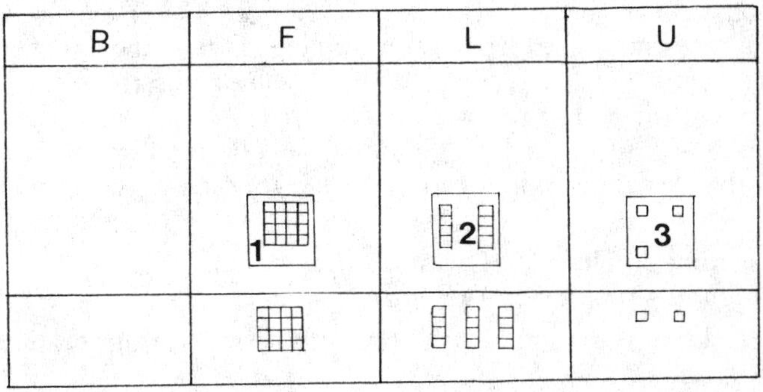

B	F	L	U
	1	**2**	**3**
	▦	❚ ❚ ❚	□ □

The answer recorded by the teacher on the blackboard is 1 flat, 3 longs and 2 units.

As addition and subtraction are inverse processes, the material may be added and exchanged and the original amount left on the board.

At first the recording is done by the teacher at the end of the operation. A progression from this is to record each step as the children work. Eventually children will work from cards, remembering to put out material for the top line, only, exchanging, giving away and recording answers.

When zero appears as, e.g.

B	F	L	U	
2	1	0	1	Base 3
−	1	2	2	

Children have no longs, but readily exchange a flat for 3 longs. **One** of these is exchanged for 3 units, and 2 given away. Much practice with zero in different positions is necessary before children grasp the concept. The principle of exchanging **one** for the base number when moving to the right or the base number for **one** when moving left, is established for all multibase work.

N6: DIVISION

The two aspects of division to be considered are:—

(a) Sharing or partition
(b) Grouping or quotition.

Children have experienced the '**sharing**' or 'partition' aspect when they share out sweets with their friends, though often they are not aware either of the number of sweets to be shared or the number of children involved. Sharing becomes a mathematical experience only when children know, e.g. that there are twelve sweets and four people, a check being made to see that each has three sweets at the end of the transaction.

The problem is turned into a '**grouping**' or 'quotition' one if the question is asked: 'How many children can get 4 sweets each if there are 12 in the bag?'

A sharing problem: Divide 12 into 4 equal parts.
A grouping problem: How many 4's in 12?

If children think of division as the inverse process to multiplication the two aspects are related.

e.g. $4 \times 3 = 12$
$4 \times n = 12$ 4 times what number is 12? (sharing)
$n \times 4 = 12$ how many 4's make 12? (grouping)

Much practice, oral and written, to establish division as the inverse of multiplication is necessary, e.g. $5 \times 6 = 30$. How many fives in 30? How many sixes? Five times what number is 30? Six times what number is 30?

The sharing and grouping aspects may be illustrated using Venn diagrams. The universal set of twelve triangles is divided into three equivalent subsets, each containing four triangles.

Sharing

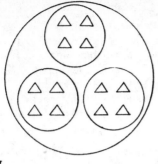

Here the '**sharing**' process is illustrated. Three subsets were provided and the triangles shared equally among them.

Grouping

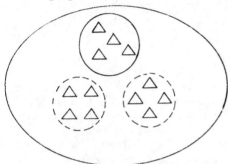

This diagram illustrates the '**grouping**' process. This time the size of the subset is given as 4 and the problem is finding how many subsets there are. This links with the grouping activities already experienced in the preparation for place value.

Work with number rods, e.g. Cuisenaire, Unifix, etc. demonstrates the 'grouping' process, e.g.

9		
3	3	3

Counting backwards on a number line also illustrates this process and may be recorded as:—

Repeated subtraction. The question asked: How many 6's in 24?

```
e.g.      24
        -  6
          18
        -  6        The answer is 4, as 6 was removed
          12        4 times from 24.
        -  6
           6
        -  6
           0
```

Recording using multibase materials

In the early stages of recording, multibase materials provide an excellent model for the 'sharing' process and if the 'long division' pattern is established, then division by 20, 30, 31, etc. present few problems in the upper end of the primary school (or lower secondary). Sharing may be done in various bases, but the recording in base 10 is very important.

Children are given a quantity of material and asked to share it equally among, e.g. three people.

```
              F L U
  e.g.        0 4 8        Check-up
          3 |1 4 6          48                    48
            1 2 +           48        or        × 3
            ─────           48                  ─────
              2 6           48                   144
              2 4          + 2                   + 2
              ───          ────                  ────
                2          146                   146
```

The question asked is: 'Can you share 1 flat among 3 people?' Children, who have had multibase experiences in addition and subtraction, readily suggest exchanging 1 flat for 10 longs, adding to the 4 already there, making 14 longs to be shared. Each person gets 4 and 2 are left. The 4 is recorded above the line as shown. The next question is: 'How many fours have you given away?' The reply: 'Three', leads to check-up: 'three fours are twelve'. The 12 is recorded underneath the 14, and subtracted, leaving 2. The 2 longs left over are exchanged for 20 units, the 6 units already there being added to make 26 units. When shared, each person has 8 units, the 8 being recorded above the line in the correct position. The check-up is: 'Three eights are twenty-four', 24 being recorded under the 26, and subtracted, leaving 2 units as a remainder. If this pattern is followed, it gets rid of the jargon: 'Three goes into 14' or 'Three into one won't go'. It is necessary to provide children with practical situations where division becomes meaningful. Multiplication is used to check the answer as it is the inverse process of division.

Once children have established this pattern for division they can dispense with the material and rely on their knowledge of table facts to continue, though they still think in terms of material to be shared and exchanged if they are going to relate the prcess in any meaningful way to place value.

Much practice is needed to establish multiplication facts and their inverses and filling empty boxes can test the understanding of the concepts, e.g.

$$5 \times 4 \ = \ \square$$

$$4 \times 5 \ = \ \square$$

$$5 \times \square \ = \ 20$$

$$\square \times 5 \ = \ 20$$

Children should recognise division in its various forms.

e.g.

$$\frac{24}{4}\,; \qquad 24 \div 4\,; \qquad 4 \times \square = 24\,; \qquad \square \times 4 = 24$$

Arranging multiples of numbers 2 → 9 in a rectangular form, as illustrated below, is an aid to learning multiplication and division facts, but is particularly useful when concentrating on division.

e.g.

1	2	3
4	5	6
7	8	9
10	11	12
13	14	15
16	17	18
19	20	21
22	23	24
25	26	27
28	29	30

1	2	3	4
5	6	7	8
9	10	11	12
13	14	15	16
17	18	19	20
21	22	23	24
25	26	27	28
29	30	31	32
33	34	35	36
37	38	39	40

Children can quickly give the answers to the following:—

How many threes in
6 → 2
18 →
30 →
24 →
etc.

How many fours in
8 → 2
24 →
36 →
28 →
etc.

Later: how many threes in
14 → 4 rem. 2
20 →
17 →
11 →
etc.

Later: how many fours in
11 → 2 rem. 3
22 →
30 →
19 →
etc.

(a) Square Numbers

Children have already experienced patterns in number, e.g. odd and even, multiples of 3, 4, etc. patterns of addition, etc. As they built up the multiplication square they were aware of square patterns and discovered them along the diagonal. These squares were cut out of squared paper and numbered as shown :—

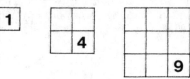

They may also be made using a variety of materials, e.g. Multipegs and grids, pegs and pegboards, small coloured squares, Centicubes, or the flats of multibase materials.

Their growth may be shown by the following diagram built up using pegs on pegboards or counters on a square grid.

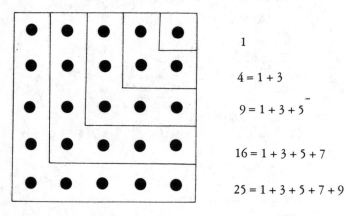

1

$4 = 1 + 3$

$9 = 1 + 3 + 5$

$16 = 1 + 3 + 5 + 7$

$25 = 1 + 3 + 5 + 7 + 9$

All square numbers may be obtained by adding consecutive odd numbers, beginning at 1 (2 terms for the square of 2; 3 terms for the square of 3, etc.).

(b) Rectangular Numbers

Children cut out rectangular shapes to illustrate multiplication tables and the numbers on the bottom right hand corner may be called rectangular numbers, e.g.

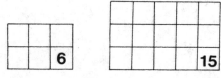

These rectangular numbers may be built up using counters. Unifix cubes, squares, Multipegs and grids, etc.

3 sets of 2	2 sets of 3	3 sets of 5	5 sets of 3
0 0	0 0 0	0 0 0 0 0	0 0 0
0 0	0 0 0	0 0 0 0 0	0 0 0
0 0		0 0 0 0 0	0 0 0
			0 0 0
			0 0 0

A selection here shows the commutative aspect of multiplication already mentioned (**N4**).

Numbers which cannot be arranged in rectangular form are called prime numbers (see **N4** of Section 3).

(c) Triangular Numbers

Counters, unit cubes, buttons, etc. which can be arranged in triangular shapes, represent triangular numbers.

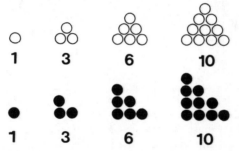

Each row in a triangle has one more counter or cube than the one above.

The triangular numbers adjacent to each other produce a square number, when added together.

e.g.

$$1 + 3 = 4 \qquad 3 + 6 = 9 \qquad 6 + 10 = 16$$
$$= 2 \times 2 \qquad = 3 \times 3 \qquad = 4 \times 4$$
$$= 2^2 \qquad = 3^2 \qquad = 4^2$$

With the exception of one and three all triangular numbers are also rectangular numbers, e.g.

	6			**10**	
			0		
0			0 0		
0 0	0 0 0		0 0 0	0 0 0 0 0	
0 0 0	0 0 0		0 0 0 0	0 0 0 0 0	

8	1	6
3	5	7
4	9	2

(d) **Magic Squares** (For a fuller development read 'Number Patterns' published by the Queen's University Teachers' Centre.)

This is a 3 × 3 magic square. The totals of columns, rows and diagonals are fifteen. Variations of this may be made by adding the same number to each element, or by multiplying or dividing each element by the same number. Families of magic squares are thus generated in which the essential pattern is the same as the original square.

These form excellent practice in addition and extended addition. Some squares should be left empty, but at least one complete row, rolumn or diagonal must be kept in order to indicate the totals required.

e.g.　(a)

13		11
	10	
9		7

(b)

		18
9		21
		6

N8: FRACTIONS

At this stage children will have some idea of the meaning of a half though often it is a very hazy one. Experiences to show that halves are exactly the same size are essential and may be related to the sharing of cubes, counters, etc; the colouring of shapes drawn on squared paper; the handling of plastic shapes already cut in half (circles, squares, hexagons). The minute hand of the clock at six, shows the face in two halves.

Practice in doubling and halving is also relevant and could be illustrated as shown.

(a)　　halved is ⟶　　　　　　(b)　　doubled is ⟶

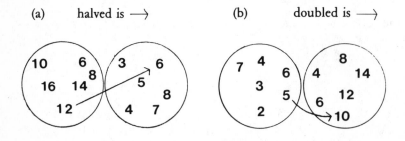

Children are asked to fill in the missing arrows.

132

Colouring half of each square is a useful occupation,

e.g.

and leads on to the idea of quarters, which may be thought of as halves, cut exactly in two (or halved).

Experience in handling fractions, often in a game situation, is essential for an understanding of the concept. For each game, it is necessary to cut four squares measuring 8 cm. × 8 cm., preferably in two colours (pink and blue). Arnold's thick card (BD146 or 147) is ideal for this purpose.

These are cut as follows:—

    1. A pink square cut in half →

    2. A pink square cut in half →

    3. A blue square cut in quarters →

    4. A blue square cut in quarters →

These pieces will be placed on a card like the one shown:—

16 cm

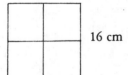

16 cm

Each child has one of these and a set of the fraction pieces.

A six-sided die (cube from multibase wood will do) is marked as follows: ½, ¼, ¾, ½, ¼, ¾.

As a preparation for the game, children are asked to put out, e.g., ¾ in as many ways as possible:—

    ¼ + ¼ + ¼ (using the square pieces)
    ¼ + ¼ + ¼ (using the triangular pieces)
    ½ + ¼ (using square pieces)
    ½ + ¼ (using triangular pieces)

The game is played in pairs each child throwing the die in turn. If ½ is thrown, an appropriate piece is put on the square. The aim is to fill the four squares completely and the first to do so is the winner. The game may be played in reverse, children giving away the fractions indicated, until squares are empty.

Squares with area 16 cm² may be drawn on squared paper and children asked to divide them into quarters in as many ways as possible.

e.g.

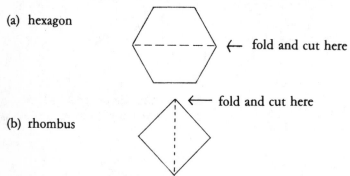

Folding paper strips in halves and quarters, cutting and comparing sizes is a useful activity, leading to the idea of equivalence, e.g. $\frac{2}{4} = \frac{1}{2}$

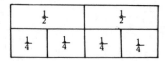

Folding and cutting may be extended to other shapes, e.g.

(a) hexagon

← fold and cut here

← fold and cut here

(b) rhombus

The need for fractional parts arises in a practical way when children are measuring and discover that the length of the room is more than four metres but not quite five. At first they are content to say four and a bit, but later, see the need for writing halves, quarters and tenths. At this stage we are not so much concerned with the notation as the understanding of the concept, and the more varied and interesting the activities we devise, the more thorough will be the understanding.

Multiplication and division have already been outlined in **N3**, **N4** and **N6**. This section is an extension of the work suggested there and attention is drawn again to the fact that concepts are formed slowly by using varied materials in practical situations. It is important to introduce the operation of multiplication and division in story form:—

e.g. (1) 35 children each collect 6 tin tops. How many tin tops altogether?

or (2) Share 128 coloured counters equally among 8 children.

Eventually, a practice stage is reached where children are working out examples such as (a) 376 × 7 or (b) 207 ÷ 9 but they should be able to tell a story about any example worked on paper.

Table practice will be necessary so that children respond quickly to questions asked, but there are many more interesting ways of consolidating multiplication and division facts than rhyming tables in sequence. The games mentioned in **N1** may be adapted and used for this purpose. Cards are now made out with multiplication tables.

e.g.

36	5 × 8		
	40	3 × 6	
		18	7 × 5
			35	4 × 9

Multiplying triangles like the one illustrated give further practice

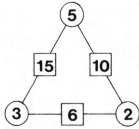

At first one circle is left empty, e.g.

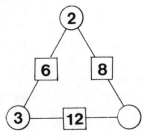

Then all three circles have to be filled, e.g.

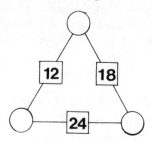

In the development of multiplication and division, children may be introduced to the terms 'factor' and 'product'. The 'factor, product' game may be prepared from equilateral triangles — 10 for the factor set and 10 for the product set.

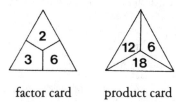

factor card   product card

The factor cards are coloured, e.g. blue, and the product cards, e.g. yellow. Children play a factor card and try to match any side with an appropriate product card.

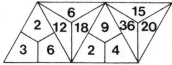

The game continues by matching product cards to factor cards and vice versa. Children are practising multiplication and division facts as they say, e.g. $2 \times 6 = 12$ or what are the factors of 36?

N10: ROUNDING OFF NUMBERS TO NEAREST 10, 100, 1000

This is a useful activity and one which needs practice. It may be summarised as follows:—

1. **Rounding to the nearest 10**
   Numbers, e.g. $41 \rightarrow 44$ (inclusive) become 40.
   Numbers $45 \rightarrow 49$ (inclusive) become 50.
   Under **5** go backwards; **5 and over** go forwards.

2. **Rounding off to the nearest 100**
   Numbers, e.g. 301 — 349 (inclusive) become 300
   Numbers   350 — 399 (inclusive) become 400
   Under **50** go backwards; **50 and over** go forwards.

3. **Rounding off to nearest 1000**
   Numbers, e.g. 5001 — 5499 (inclusive) become 5000
   Numbers   5500 — 5999 (inclusive) become 6000
   Under **500** go backwards; **500 and over** go forwards.

N11: MULTIPLICATION AND DIVISION BY 10

It is most important that children should see this as a movement of material in the early stages when working with multibase materials. It is much easier to demonstrate in bases 3 or 4 as the examples require fewer pieces than, e.g. base 10.

Children might be asked to put out the materials indicated by the following and add:—

(a)
```
     B F L U                    B F L U
       1 2 2    base 3            1 1 2    base 3
       1 2 2                      1 1 2
       1 2 2                      1 1 2
     ───────                    ───────
     1 2 2 0                    1 1 2 0
```

Adding three times in base 3 is really × 3 or more correctly by 10 (one zero).

(b)
```
     B F L U                    B F L U
       1 2 3                      2 3 1
       1 2 3    base 4            2 3 1    base 4
       1 2 3                      2 3 1
       1 2 3                      2 3 1
     ───────                    ───────
     1 2 3 0                    2 3 1 0
```

This demonstrates multiplying by 4 or by 10 (one zero). Each time there is a grouping of materials, an exchanging and recording and the final result shows a movement of digits one place to the left. It may be necessary to demonstrate × 10 in base 10 so that children will think of this as a movement of digits and so cancel the prevailing idea that to multiply by 10 means adding zero (usually added to the right of the number, revealing the lack of understanding of 'place' value).

Division by 10 may also be demonstrated using multibase materials in bases 3, 4, etc.

```
        B F L U                        B F L U
          1 2 2    base 3                2 3 2    base 4
       3 ┌─────                       4 ┌─────
         │1 2 2 0                        │2 3 2 0
       (or 10)                        (or 10)
```

These examples show that dividing by 10 is a movement of digits one place to the right. Many examples using concrete materials are necessary before children grasp the concept. When they do, progress to multiplication and division by 20, 30, 40, etc. is possible. If children link 2 with 20, 3 with 30, etc. few problems arise.

(a)   56
        × 2
       ———
        112

Children are asked to **work** the example (a) on the left and **write the answer** to (b) on the right.

(b)   56|
        × 20|
       ————

As 20 is ten times 2, this is simply a matter of multiplying 112 by 10 or moving digits one place to the left. It is often necessary to draw a line in (b) so that children are forced to move to the left and not add zero to the right.

(c)   76
        × 3
       ———

Work out example (c). Use this to write the answer to (d)

         76|
        × 30|
       ————

Division by 20, 30, etc. if modelled on the pattern already given in **N6** (3), should present few problems.

```
        F L U
        0 1 8
      ————————
e.g.  20| 3 7 6
        -2 0
      ————————
        1 7 6
       -1 6 0
      ————————
          1 6
```

It is still advisable to **think** of 376 in terms of actual material to be shared — flats, longs and units in base 10 or hundreds, tens and units.

The question is asked: 'Can I share 3 flats among 20 people?' The suggestion is made of exchanging them for 30 longs and adding the 7 already there, making a total of 37 to be shared. One is given to each and 17 are left which are exchanged for 170 units, 6 added, making a total of 176. These are shared and 16 remain.

Much practice is needed in exchanging flats for longs and longs for units or in multiplying by 10, so cards may be prepared, e.g.

	flats		longs
	3	$\longrightarrow$	30
	7	$\longrightarrow$	
	6	$\longrightarrow$	
	10	$\longrightarrow$	
	12	$\longrightarrow$	etc.

longs		units		hundreds		tens
5	$\longrightarrow$	50		6	$\longrightarrow$	60
8	$\longrightarrow$			8	$\longrightarrow$	
9	$\longrightarrow$			11	$\longrightarrow$	
13	$\longrightarrow$			23	$\longrightarrow$	
25	$\longrightarrow$	etc.		46	$\longrightarrow$	etc.

Eventually this leads to recording of multiplication and division by 10.

× 10		÷ 10	
6	$\longrightarrow$	50	$\longrightarrow$
9	$\longrightarrow$	60	$\longrightarrow$
18	$\longrightarrow$	150	$\longrightarrow$
76	$\longrightarrow$	36	$\longrightarrow$
101	$\longrightarrow$		
110	$\longrightarrow$	etc.	

This leads into decimal fractions developed in **N12**.

An alternative method of division is repeated subtraction, mentioned in **N6(2)**.

e.g.

$$
\begin{array}{r}
18 \\
20 \quad 376 \\
-200 \quad \text{10 each} \\
\hline
176 \\
-100 \quad \text{5 each} \\
\hline
76 \\
-60 \quad \text{3 each} \\
\hline
16
\end{array}
$$

}18

The distributive law may be demonstrated using Unifix materials, blocks, counters, etc.

e.g.
(a)

```
0 0 0 0|0 0      4 rows of 6 may be partitioned as:—
0 0 0 0|0 0      4 rows of (4 + 2)
0 0 0 0|0 0      or 4 rows of 4 + 4 rows of 2
0 0 0 0|0 0
```

(b)

```
X X X X X X X X X X|X X X X
X X X X X X X X X X|X X X X
X X X X X X X X X X|X X X X
```

3 rows with 14 in each row may be partitioned as:—
3 rows of (10 + 4)
or 3 rows of 10 + 3 rows of 4.

N11: MULTIPLICATION AND DIVISION BY 10 (cont'd)

It is understanding of this law that enables children to multiply, e.g. 56 by 37 in an intelligible way.

56			56	
× 37			× 37	
1680	30 times	or	392	7 times
392	7 times		1680	30 times
2072	37 times		2072	37 times

N12: DECIMAL FRACTIONS

We may think of decimal fractions as an extension of place value and as already indicated in **N11**, division of numbers by 10 leads into this area. If children have developed the concept of place value by engaging in the activities suggested in **N2**, **N3**, **N5**, **N6** and **N11**, then they have reached the final stage in understanding, i.e. position alone determined the value of a number.

	100	10	1	$^1/_{10}$
	0 0 0	0 0 0 0	0 0 0 0 0	
÷ 10 →		0 0 0	0 0 0 0	0 0 0 0 0

On cards, similar to the one above, children place counters or buttons, Centicubes, etc. to represent numbers. 345 e.g. is shown by placing three buttons in the 100's column, four in the 10's column and five in the units' column. Multiplication by 10 may be shown as a movement of each group, one place to the left. Similarly, division by 10, may be shown as a movement one place to the right as shown in the diagram above, i.e. $345 \div 10 = 34\,\frac{5}{10}$. The thick line divides the whole numbers from the fractions, but is replaced by a decimal point in recording, e.g. 34.5, the decimal point indicating where the units' digit is. It is standard practice to write 0.6 rather than .6, the zero acting as a warning that a decimal point follows.

The earlier work in multiplying and dividing by 10 forms a suitable link with decimal fractions and children may record,

e.g. $\frac{1}{10}$ of the following

100 p $\longrightarrow$	10 p
50 g $\longrightarrow$	
600 m $\longrightarrow$	
70 cm $\longrightarrow$	etc.

The odometer of a car shows tenths of a kilometre in colour and children might show the following distances by drawing odometers and filling in the numbers. (tenths in red).

e.g.   4.1 $\longrightarrow$ coloured red.

⬚ ⬚ ⬚ ⬚ **4** **1**   etc.

10.6 $\longrightarrow$

325.3 $\longrightarrow$

24513.7 $\longrightarrow$

Boxes, holding exactly ten pencils, may be taken as the unit and each pencil as   (0.1). Recordings may be made, e.g.

56 pencils as 5.6 (5 full boxes and 6 pencils)

37 pencils as

54 pencils as   (children fill in empty spaces)

63 pencils as

or   4.6 boxes as 46 pencils

3.2 boxes as

5.9 boxes as

7.5 boxes as

Children have probably been introduced to decimal fractions in a practical way when measuring heights or counting money, but in both cases the relationship is between the unit and the hundredth and the recording is always to two decimal places, e.g. 4 pounds 20 must be written as £4.20, and not as £4.2. Similarly, 3 metres 40 centimetres would be recorded as 3.40 metres. Not until children have a fuller understanding of decimal fractions can they relate 4.2 as being equivalent to 4.20.

Simple operations in addition and subtraction of decimal fractions may be attempted. If children are encouraged to group and exchange as they did with whole numbers, they should experience little or no difficulty with examples (a) and (b).

(a)

```
    T U . t
    1 4 . 6
+   1 3 . 5
    1 8 . 9
    ─────────
    4 7 . 0
```

Children add the tenths and get a total of 20. Ten of these exchange for 1 unit, so 20 exchange for 2. This is added to the units' column and addition proceeds.

(b)

```
    T U . t
    5 6̶ . 3
-   1 4 . 6
    ─────────
    4 1 . 7
```

The question asked is: 'Can I give away 6 tenths? The suggestion is given of exchanging 1 unit for ten tenths giving away 6, leaving 4 which is added to the 3 and recorded as 7, etc.

Decimal fractions will continue to occupy an important place not only in mathematics, but in business and industry. For this reason it must be stressed that a thorough understanding of them is of vital importance.

N13: VULGAR FRACTIONS

The ideas developed in **N8** might be extended to include $\frac{1}{8}$, $\frac{1}{3}$, $\frac{1}{6}$, $\frac{1}{10}$. The fraction game described there may be played using halves, quarters and eighths. Two extra squares, each cut into eighths are required for each set.

e.g.

The markings on the dice are, e.g. ½, ¼, $\frac{1}{8}$, ¾, $\frac{3}{8}$, $\frac{5}{8}$. As children play the fraction pieces on the blank squares provided, they are gaining experience in relationships and equivalence of fractions.

A similar game might be devised using circular plastic shapes (commercially produced) cut into halves, thirds and sixths. As children throw the dice (marked ½, $\frac{1}{3}$, $\frac{1}{6}$, $\frac{2}{3}$, $\frac{5}{6}$, $\frac{4}{6}$) they place the appropriate pieces on circles (drawn on cards) until they are completely filled. A subtraction game may be played by removing pieces one by one, until the circles are empty. Experience in equivalence is gained as children exchange, e.g. $\frac{1}{3}$ for $\frac{2}{6}$, or $\frac{3}{6}$ for ½.

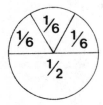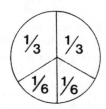

Fraction dominoes can be cut out of stiff card and fractions marked as follows:—

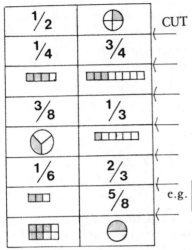

These may be played in a similar way to 'Dominoes' described in **N1**. They help children to identify each individual fraction. Another set, stressing equivalence may also be prepared where, e.g. ½ appears as $\frac{2}{4}$ or $\frac{4}{8}$ or $\frac{3}{6}$, etc. Children might match,

e.g.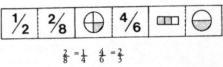

$$\frac{2}{8} = \frac{1}{4} \qquad \frac{4}{6} = \frac{2}{3}$$

Squares can be divided into eighths in numerous ways, six of which are illustrated below. If these are drawn on squared paper each measuring 4 × 4 (total of 16 small squares) sub-divisions are easier to mark.

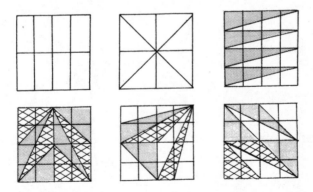

Tenths have already been introduced in **N12** as decimal fractions, but may also be linked with halves and fifths, e.g.

$$\frac{1}{2} = \frac{5}{10}$$
$$\frac{1}{5} = \frac{2}{10}$$

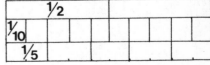

Measuring rods (metres) are usually sub-divided into tenths of a metre and practical work using these helps to develop the understanding of tenths both as vulgar and decimal fractions.

The 100 square coloured in strips of ten is another visual aid to the understanding of tenths.

$\frac{1}{10}$

When linked with decimal coinage tenths become our 10p. coins and so $\frac{3}{10}$ of £1 may be written as 30p, $\frac{4}{10}$ of £1 as 40p, etc. The emphasis at this stage is on practical activities which help children to understand the meaning of fractional parts and their equivalences.

PICTORIAL REPRESENTATION

PR1: BAR GRAPHS

In the infant section of the guide, children were introduced to block graphs where individual squares were coloured to represent data — types of pets.

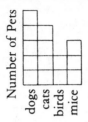

The bar or column graph is a similar form of representation, but in this graph, the complete rectangle is coloured and it is the length or height of the column which gives the information required.

e.g. (a)

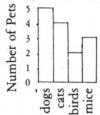

The representation may also be in horizontal form.

e.g. (b)

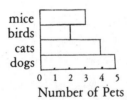

Again, it must be stressed that graphs are a means of communicating information clearly and concisely; they are not just drawings to be displayed. The discussion generated by the teacher is a very important part of all graphical work.

Various topics for pictorial representation will arise naturally in the classroom and may include some of the following:—

1. Favourite drinks (milk, tea, lemonade, etc).
2. Favourite sports (football, hockey, netball, rounders, etc).
3. Heights of a set of dolls (to nearest cm).
4. Sizes of feet to the nearest cm.
5. Favourite breakfast cereals.

145

PR2: FREQUENCY GRAPHS

Frequency simply means the number of times an event occurs, e.g. in diagrams (a) and (b) in **PR1**, the number of dogs was 5, so 5 was the frequency for dogs; 4 was the frequency for cats, etc.

The following are examples of frequency graphs:—

e.g. (a) **Family size in a class**

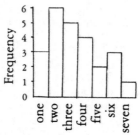

Number of children in the family

The family of seven occurs once, while the family of two occurs six times.

(b) **A graph to show the frequency of various shoe sizes**

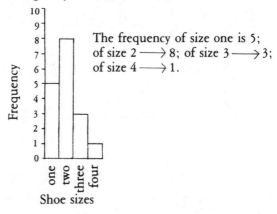

The frequency of size one is 5; of size 2 ⟶ 8; of size 3 ⟶ 3; of size 4 ⟶ 1.

PR3: COLLECTING DATA, ETC.

To record the number of times an event occurs, children may be introduced to the following method of tallying:—

e.g.

The counting has been in groups of 5 represented ////.

Event (vehicles passing)	Tally	Frequency
Lorries	//// //// /	11
Cars	//// ///	8
Buses	//	2
Motor cycles	//// /	6

146

The graphical representation of the facts is shown below:—

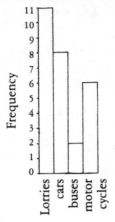

PR4: INTERPRETING A GRAPH

As already stated, graphs are a means of communicating information, but in order that this may be effective, children must be given opportunities not only to draw graphs, but to read information from those already drawn. No graph on the wall of a classroom has fulfilled its usefulness to the maximum unless comments are made about it and correct answers given to questions asked.

The following is one example of a graph presented to children, with a set of questions to test their ability to interpret it.

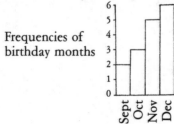

Frequencies of birthday months

1. What would be a suitable label for this graph?
2. What information does the vertical axis give? — the horizontal?
3. Does the graph refer to a class, a school or a town?
4. In which month were most children born?
5. In which month were 2 children born?
6. Comment on the statement, 'December is the month when most children are born'.

147

Arrow graphs may be used to show relationships within a family,

e.g. (a)

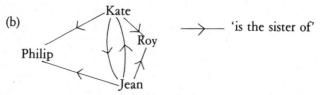

The arrow shows the relation-ship 'is the brother of'.

(b)

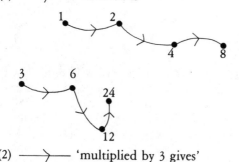

$\longrightarrow$ — 'is the sister of'

Arrow graphs may also be used to show relationships between numbers,

i.e. (1) $\longrightarrow$ — 'doubled is'

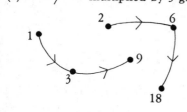

(2) $\longrightarrow$ — 'multiplied by 3 gives'

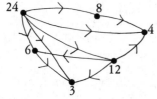

$12 \longleftarrow 4$

(3) $\longrightarrow$ — 'can be divided exactly by'

This is a more complex diagram, but if children go in the direction of the arrows and repeat what the arrows stand for, there should be no difficulty in interpreting the graph.

The children might be asked to complete the following diagrams:—

(a)  'is greater than'

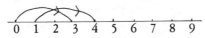

(b) 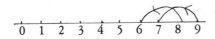 'add 3 gives'

(c)   'subtract 2 gives'

(d) ———>— 'is less than'

PR6: VENN, CARROLL AND TREE DIAGRAMS

In S1, attribute blocks were sorted in a variety of ways using Venn, Carroll and tree diagrams. This practical approach is essential before children attempt any abstract representations using these diagrams.

Children might be asked to interpret the following diagrams by answering the questions posed:—

(a) **Venn Diagram**

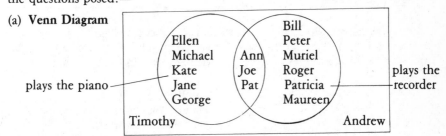

1. How many children play the recorder? the piano?
2. Name the children who play both.
3. What can you say about Andrew and Timothy?

149

(b) Carroll Diagram

	Rides a Bicycle	Cannot ride a Bicycle
swims	Jack Betty Robert	Dorothy Jean Tom
cannot swim	James Rosemary Paul	

1. Name the children who can swim and ride a bicycle.
2. Who can swim but can't ride a bicycle?
3. Who can ride a bicycle but can't swim?
4. What does the empty set tell us?

(c) Tree Diagram

Sorting a box of foreign coins

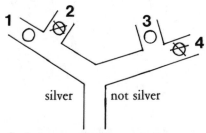

1. Where would you find the round, silver coins?
2. Describe the coins at number 4.
3. Where would you find the coins which are silver and not round.
4. Describe the coins at number 3.

PR7: PIE GRAPHS

These are graphs which represent data using a circle divided into sectors. Halves, quarters and eighths, which can be produced by folding circular shapes give easy examples which are particularly suitable at the initial stage.

e.g. (a)

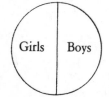

Children in a class

Half of the children are boys; half of the children are girls.

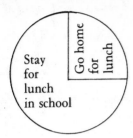

One quarter of the children go home for lunch; three quarters of the children have lunch in school.

(c) **The use of land on a farm**

¼ of the farm produces barley;
⅛ of the farm produces potatoes;
the remainder ⅝ is used for grazing.

This form of representation has its limitations at primary level as it involves angular measurement and the use of a protractor.

SHAPE — THREE DIMENSIONAL

3D1: SORTING SHAPES

Solid shapes are prominent in the environment and a study of these usually precedes the work with 2D shapes. Sets of solids should be available for sorting and should include commercially produced shapes as well as scrap material collected by the teacher. Food containers can provide examples of cubes, cylinders or cuboids; roofs and gables are shaped like triangular prisms (also Toblerone chocolate boxes); marbles, beads, balls etc. are examples of spheres; ice-cream cones, fir cones etc illustrate solid conical shapes.

Sorting in a variety of ways, to highlight some particular property is a useful activity.

e.g. (a) shapes that roll; shapes that slide; shapes that do both.

(b) shapes with curved faces; square faces; rectangular faces; triangular faces.

(c) shapes with the same number of faces; same number of edges.

3D2: BUILDING WITH SOLID SHAPES

Children need to explore the possibility of building with cubes, cylinders, cuboids etc. In discussion draw attention to the fact that the properties of the solids determine the kind of building that can be made.

The following questions may help children in their investigation:—

(a) **Cube**   What shapes can you make by fitting together 2 cubes?

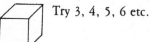

Try 3, 4, 5, 6 etc.

(b) **Cuboid**

In how many ways can you fit 2 cuboids together? Are your new shapes still cuboids? Try building 3, 4, 5, 6 etc.

(c) **Cylinder**

Put one cylinder on top of another. What is the new shape called? Try building horizontally as well as vertically.

What do you notice?

(d) **Sphere**   (e) **Cone**   (f) **Prism**   (g) **Pyramid**

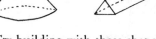

Try building with these shapes.
What did you discover?

3D3: INVESTIGATION OF FACES, EDGES ETC OF SOLID SHAPES

As children handle and sort **3D** objects they begin to investigate the 'faces' of the shapes.

Questions to stimulate the investigation

(1) Find the shapes with all faces square. Name them.

(2) Name other shapes with six rectangular faces.
(3) Some of the cartons have square faces and some have rectangular faces. Sort and name them.
(4) Describe the faces of the soup tins.
(5) Name all the shapes with curved surfaces.

Children are invited to count the edges of each shape in turn and record their results.

Questions

(1) How many edges has a cube? Mark each as you count.
(2) Find another shape with the same number of edges and name it.
(3) How many edges has the 'Toblerone' carton?
(4) Count the edges of the pyramid etc.

3D4: OPENING CARDBOARD BOXES TO FIND THE SHAPES FROM WHICH THEY ARE MADE

Investigation of 'faces' of shapes leads naturally into the activity of opening out cardboard shapes to find out how they were made. Children open corn-flakes packets, chocolate cartons (prisms), 'Smarties' boxes (cylinders) etc and put them together again.

The record of the result might appear as shown below.

Number of each 2D shape used to make the following 3D shapes

	□	▭	◯	△
cube	6	–	–	–
cuboid	–	6	–	–
cylinder	–	1	2	–
prism	–	3	–	2

3D5: MAKING CUBES, CUBOIDS ETC

Ready-fold card, produced by Philip & Tacey is a suitable medium to use in the early stages of construction as it folds easily and retains its shape. Children may use their opened shapes (**3D4**) to help them plan the pattern or 'net' of the shape they wish to make. They will find that it is not necessary to join up six different squares to form a cube; it may be made from one piece. Later this leads to the investigation of how many different 'nets' will fold to make cubes. Cuboids may also be made from one piece in a variety of ways. Children may wish to make open boxes or boxes with lids. If interest is sustained, children may wish to make cylinders (open or closed), cone shapes etc.

3D6: USE OF STRAWS AND PIPE CLEANERS TO MAKE CUBES AND CUBOIDS

Straws and pipe cleaners may also be used to construct shapes. This is a more difficult construction and may be limited, at this stage, to cubes and cuboids. The pipe cleaners are used to link together the framework of the shapes.

e.g.

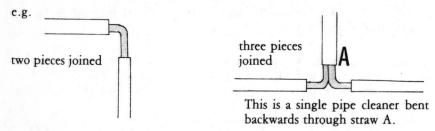

two pieces joined

three pieces joined **A**

This is a single pipe cleaner bent backwards through straw A.

If children are making a cube they need twelve pieces of straw all the same length.

For a cuboid they also need twelve pieces, either four each of three different lengths, or eight of one length and four of another:—

e.g. (1)   (2)

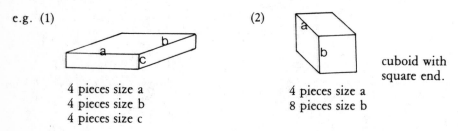

4 pieces size a
4 pieces size b
4 pieces size c

4 pieces size a
8 pieces size b

cuboid with square end.

Constructing **3D** shapes helps children towards an awareness of their properties.

SHAPE — TWO DIMENSIONAL

2D1: MAKING SHAPES ON A GEOBOARD

Geoboards may be made of 9 mm plywood and brass-headed escutcheon pins. It is possible to buy transparent plastic ones which may be used on the overhead projector. The nine-pin geoboard is suitable at this stage.

The pins are spaced 4 cm apart.

e.g.

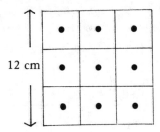

12 cm

(a) Triangular Shapes
Ask children to make a three-sided figure on the geoboard and check that they know its name — triangle.

Questions
1. What is the largest triangle you can make?
2. What is the smallest triangle you can make? How many of this size can you make?
3. How many different triangular shapes can you make?
4. Copy these on to dotted paper.

In the early stages, children will not produce all that are illustrated.

(1)

At first children will make a random arrangement, but should be encouraged to plan the work, e.g. find all that have two pins on the bottom row; all that have three pins, etc.

In drawing triangles on dotted paper, children may produce some which are identical in size and shape, but differently positioned on the paper, e.g.

(2)

155

To convince them that these pairs are the same shape and size, it may be necessary to cut one out and fit it over the other. The next stage in the investigation might be to take each of the triangles (illustrated in (1)) in turn and find how many of each of these can be made on the nine-pin geoboard.

Four-sided shapes

Children are asked to make a four-sided figure on the geoboard; then as many **different** four-sided figures as possible.

e.g.
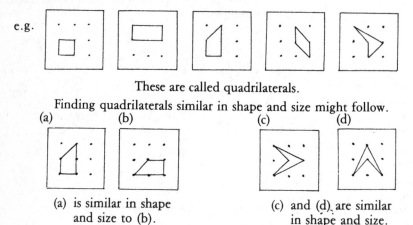

These are called quadrilaterals.

Finding quadrilaterals similar in shape and size might follow.

(a)   (b)   (c)   (d)

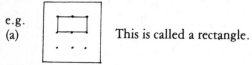

(a) is similar in shape and size to (b).

(c) and (d) are similar in shape and size.

2D2: INVESTIGATION OF PROPERTIES OF SQUARES, RECTANGLES ETC.

Children made 4-sided figures (**2D1**) and called them quadrilaterals. They now learn that some quadrilaterals have special names and properties

e.g.
(a)
    This is called a rectangle.

Question

How many rectangles can you make on the geoboard? Copy them on to spotted paper.

Children are becoming aware of the properties, i.e. opposite sides equal and 'square' angles.

(b)
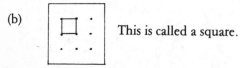
    This is called a square.

2D2: INVESTIGATION OF PROPERTIES OF SQUARES, RECTANGLES ETC. (cont'd)

Questions
1. How many squares the same size as this can you make on your geoboard?
2. How many different sized squares can you make?
3. How many squares can you make altogether?

Again, an awareness of the properties of a square is developing, through experiences in making and contrasting with other four-sided shapes.

2D3: MAKING A RIGHT ANGLE

As children make various four-sided figures, their attention is drawn, not only to the sides, but also to the angles of the shapes. Squares and rectangles may be identified by their 'square' corners. This is a suitable stage to show children how to make a right angle by folding paper. A piece of torn paper is folded in two,

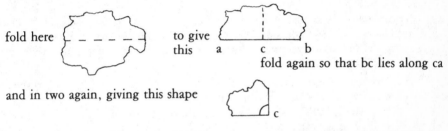

fold here   to give
              this   a   c   b

fold again so that bc lies along ca

and in two again, giving this shape

The angle at c is a right angle. Children can use it to check right angles which occur in the classroom and in the shapes already made on geoboards and transferred to paper.

When opened it
appears like this

This shows four right angles fitted together. Two of the folded shapes put together demonstrate that two right angles make a straight line,

e.g.

Three fitted together give the angles at the corner of a room.

157

2D3: MAKING A RIGHT ANGLE (cont'd)

Four fitted together complete the circle.

Angles may be measured in terms of right angles, e.g. greater than a right angle; less than a right angle; less than two right angles (tessellating activities of **2D4**) etc.

To develop the concept of an angle not only as a static measure but as a measure of turning, children can rotate the folded paper by putting a pin in the centre and turning until X returns home again.

If we call this a whole turn, then a right angle is a quarter turn and a straight line is a half turn.

These measures are quite sufficient for all early work on shape and help children to form the concept of an angle as a measure of the amount of turning. If further development of the topic is thought necessary, refer to **2D5** and **2D6** of section 3.

Read **Towards Mathematics** page 116, by J A Glenn and D A Sturgess published by Schofield and Sims.

'It's Maths' BBC TV Programme Autumn Term Teachers' Notes, page 9, by Alistair McIntosh.

2D4: TESSELLATION OF REGULAR SHAPES

Regular shapes are those whose angles and sides are all equal. Children investigate the tessellating properties of regular shapes:—

e.g. (1) **Square** (a) 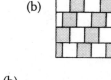 (b)

(2) **Equilateral triangle**

(a)   (b)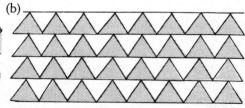

(3) Regular hexagon

(a)   (b)

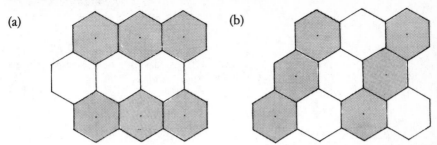

Children discover that the square, the equilateral triangle and the hexagon fit together without any spaces between. The investigation may also include the following regular shapes which do **not** tessellate.

(1) **Regular pentagon**

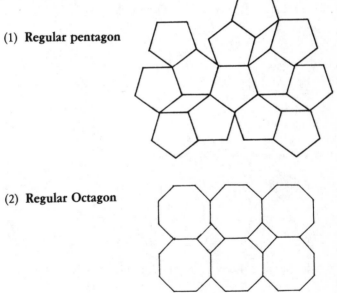

(2) **Regular Octagon**

As tessellation activities may be used to study angle properties, children might be asked to suggest a reason why some of these shapes fitted together while others left spaces between. Fitting the pieces together on the 'right angle tester' illustrated in **2D3** might spark off an investigation which would eventually lead to the assertion that the angles of tessellating shapes at O make a total of four right angles as shown on following page.

e.g.

The lines ab and cd may be produced by folding paper and the words 'horizontal' and 'vertical' used to describe them.

Equilateral triangles are fitted together at the intersection O. Six of these completely cover the four right angles.

2D5: INVESTIGATION OF SYMMETRY BY REFLECTION

In **2D7** of the infant section, children were introduced to symmetrical patterns by (1) ink blobs on paper, (2) by folding and cutting paper. Similar activities may be included here to develop the concept,

e.g. Take a piece of paper and fold it in half.

(a)

draw a wavy line
and cut along it.

open out the paper to
produce the pattern (above).

(b) Put an ink blob on a piece of paper.

Ink
blob

Fold
paper

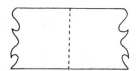

Open to reveal a
symmetrical pattern.

Each shape has a fold down the middle called the **line of symmetry** or **mirror line**.

Children try to find mirror lines in shapes studied,

e.g.

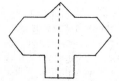

Pegboards and pegs or multigrids and pegs (supplied by E J Arnold Ltd) are suitable media for exploring mirror patterns. Children may be given one half of a shape or pattern and asked to complete it:—

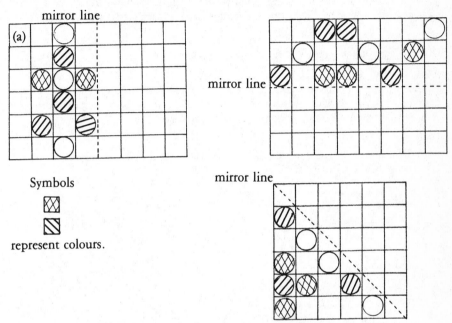

Symbols

represent colours.

All the examples illustrated show symmetry by **reflection**.

Children can devise games to be played on peg boards, multi grids, or squared paper. The line of symmetry (mirror line) is marked and each player takes turns to put a peg on the board.

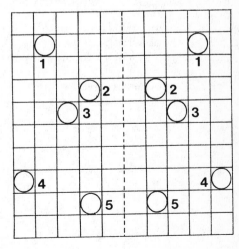

161

The first player puts a peg in position 1. The second player places a similar one in a similar position on his side of the mirror line. Player two puts a second peg in position and player one matches it on his side. He places a third peg on his side which is matched by player two on the other side. Each player matches what his opponent has played and then places a peg for his opponent to match. The game continues as long as interest is sustained.

2D6: TESSELLATION OF NON-REGULAR SHAPES

Regular shapes were defined in **2D4** as those having equal sides and equal angles. Shapes outside this set may be termed non-regular shapes. Some of these may be investigated for tessellating properties.

e.g.

(1) **Rectangles:** Many patterns of rectangular tessellations are possible, some of which are illustrated.

e.g. (a)   (b)

(c)   (d)

(2) **Triangles:** Equilateral triangles, being regular shapes, were illustrated in **2D4**. Children may use different shaped triangles, e.g. isosceles, right-angled, scalene (names not important at this stage).

e.g.   **isosceles triangles**

(a)

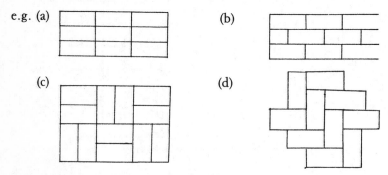

right-angled triangles

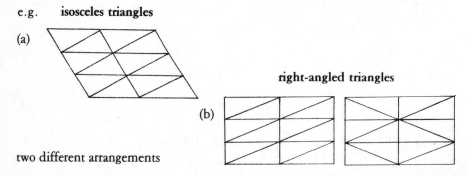

(b)

two different arrangements

162

(c) **Scalene triangles**

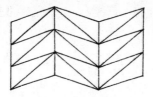

(3) **Rhombuses**

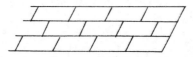

(4) **Parallelograms**

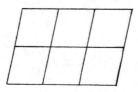

As children sort, tessellate and commit the work to spotted paper, they are becoming aware of the properties of the shapes studied. **Parallel** lines are illustrated in many of these tessellations and children may be introduced to the concept.

As suggested in **2D4** children may arrange these shapes at the intersection of two lines drawn at right angles to strengthen the concept that tessellating shapes fit together to cover the space occupied by four right angles.

e.g. (a)

ab and cd are at right angles to one another.

Scalene triangles are fitted together at intersection **o** so that the sum of the angles is four right angles.

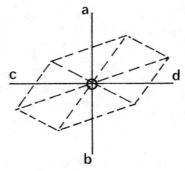

(b)

Parallelograms are fitted at **o** showing that the angles 1, 2, 3, 4 make a total of four right angles.

By drawing round counters, tin lids, coins etc children can produce circular patterns.

e.g.

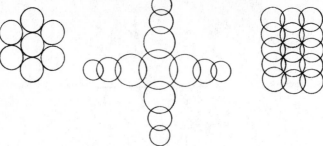

They can also investigate the tessellating properties of circles, to discover that no matter how they arrange them, they do not fit together without spaces, i.e. they do **not** tessellate.

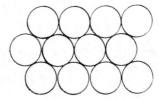

Circles may be folded in half to give semi-circles. Children will discover a variety of ways to fold them as shown on the diagram.

Any of these lines represent folds and each divided the circle in half. Children may be given the names, circumference and diameter at this stage. The centre of the circle is the intersection of the folds. Lines radiate from it like the spokes of a wheel. (Name 'radius' may be appropriate here).

Children should be encouraged to look for circular shapes in the environment and to consider the importance of the discovery of the wheel.

MEASUREMENT

The term 'measurement' may be applied to the remaining six sections:–
Capacity/Volume, Area, Length, Weight, Time and Money. There are
standard units of measurement for each, some of which have changed in
recent years.

The Système International known as **SI**, is a system of measures now
accepted by most countries; it is a modification of the old metric system.
Teachers should acquaint themselves with the new system in order to train
children in the correct usage of it; incorrect or inconsistent 'simplification'
may have to be 'unlearned' later.

All teachers of mathematics should read the booklet, **How to write Metric**,
published by Her Majesty's Stationery Office, London, 1977.

The concept of measurement is formed slowly through varied activities of
comparison, ordering, conservation, measuring with arbitrary units and finally
with standard units. As already stated in the infant section, all measurement
is approximate, but should be as accurate as possible within the limits of the
units of measurement being used.

CAPACITY / VOLUME

C/V 1: HANDLING 3D OBJECTS

In handling a variety of **3D** objects children should experience the two aspects
of the topic:—

(a) the amount of space in a hollow container (capacity)
(b) the amount of space occupied by a solid shape (volume).

(a) **Capacity**
Children need experiences in filling containers with water or sand, comparing
capacities and recording results:—

e.g.

	jug	bowl	jar	mug
cupfuls				
beakerfuls				
cartonfuls				

(b) **Volume**
Solid shapes may be built with cubes and sizes compared.
e.g. How many cubes for the small shape? How many more for the larger
one?

C/V 2: ARRANGING CONTAINERS (ordering)

A variety of containers may be arranged according to their capacity by pouring
water or sand from one to the other. This gives a further opportunity to check

children's ideas of conservation. They will often discover that the large, shallow container holds more than the tall bottle. Children estimate first and then check:—

(a) by filling each container with sand or water using a convenient measure, e.g. cup, eggcup
(b) by filling one container and transferring contents to each in turn
(c) by filling each container in turn and emptying contents into a larger measure which has been graduated with strips indicating the level of eggcupfuls.

C/V 3: CONSERVATION OF VOLUME

By building a variety of shapes with a given number of cubes, children develop the concept of conservation of volume:—

e.g. 36 cubes may be built on the following bases:—
(a) 2×2 (9 layers)
(b) 2×3 (6 layers)
(c) 4×3 (3 layers)
(d) 3×6 (2 layers)

It is a good idea to give children a sheet of cardboard or manilla with the rectangular shapes (indicated above) drawn on it, and ask them to build multi-storey flats on each, in turn and record the number of storeys in each. Irregular shapes, symmetrical shapes etc may also be built.

If children do not readily agree that each shape takes up the same space, i.e. has the same volume, then it is obvious that more time must be spent on similar activities.

C/V 4: USE OF STANDARD MEASURES OF CAPACITY

Through practical activities, children were introduced to the litre and the half litre in the infant section of the guide. Similar activities are necessary, at this stage, to find the capacity of containers to the nearest litre, half litre and quarter litre.

Estimate and then check the following by using the litre jug
(1) How many litres of water will the lemonade bottle hold?
(2) How many litres of water to fill the bucket?
(3) How many litres of water to fill the sink?

Estimate and check using the half litre measure
(1) The capacity of the lemonade bottle to the nearest half litre.
(2) The capacity of the bucket to the nearest half litre.
(3) The capacity of the sink to the nearest half litre.

Half or more than half of the measure, count as one; less than half, disregard.

Activities using a quarter litre jug
(1) How many quarter litres of water to fill the jug?
(2) How many quarter litres of water to fill the tin?
(3) What is the capacity of the milk bottle to the nearest quarter litre?

C/V 5 CALIBRATING A GLASS JAR

In **C/V 2**, children poured sand or water into a measure calibrated in cupfuls. A glass jar of uniform cross section can be calibrated to show ¼ litre, ½ litre, ¾ litre and 1 litre. A strip of paper is stuck vertically on the jar; a ¼ litre jug is filled with water and the contents poured into the jar. The mark ¼ litre is made on the paper at the level of the water. Another ¼ litre is added and ½ litre marked on the paper; another added and ¾ litre marked etc. Children may use this to measure the capacity of various containers by filling them and pouring the contents into the graduated jar. If the level is nearer to ¾ litre than ½ litre, then the capacity is given as ¾ litre (measured to the nearest ¼ litre).

jar of uniform cross section
calibrated in ¼ litres.

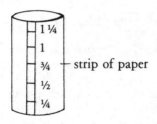

strip of paper

C/V 6: MEASURING CAPACITY IN MILLILITRES

The calibrated measure of **C/V 5** is not a very accurate one, so children need to be introduced to the sub-divisions of a litre, e.g. markings to show 100 millilitres (one tenth of a litre). The contents of various bottles and jars can be poured, in turn, into this and the capacity to the nearest 100 millilitres recorded. Measures calibrated in intervals of 50 millilitres may also be used and the results recorded to the nearest 50 millilitres. Finally children may measure capacity to the nearest 10 millilitres.

It is always advisable to write the word 'litre' in full, as the symbol 'l' may be confused with the digit '1'. The symbol 'ml' may be used instead of the word 'millilitre' or the plural 'millilitres'.

AREA

A1: DEVELOPING THE CONCEPT

The concept of area as the amount of space covered develops slowly through a variety of experiences:—

e.g.

(a) **informally**

    (1) in painting and craft work as children observe the amount of paint required to cover a variety of surfaces.

    (2) in free activity as children place covers on cots, tables etc.

    (3) in needlework as children plan the sizes of dolls' clothes.

(b) **more formally**

    (1) in comparison of two similar shapes when one can be placed on top of the other, e.g. one hand on top of another; one footprint in a larger one; one triangular shape included completely in another.

    (2) in comparison of two shapes when one can be cut to fit completely on the other.

    (3) using arbitrary units of measurement, e.g. sheets of newspaper to cover the floor, cards of uniform size to cover the desks, stamps to cover a page etc.

    (4) using grids made of various shapes which tessellate, e.g. equilateral triangles, hexagons, and finally squares (Demonstrated in 'It's Maths' BBC TV Programme on 'Area').

A2: AREA OF IRREGULAR SHAPES

When children discover that squares are the most suitable units for measuring area, a variety of irregular shapes may be drawn on squared paper, or square grids may be put over the surfaces to be measured. Sheets of transparent squared paper are very useful and can be placed over the irregular shapes, e.g. leaves of different sizes. In considering shapes that are not rectangular it is hoped that children's attention is being focused on the size of the surface and that this is the concept which is being developed **not** the formula length × breadth = area.

The area of an irregular shape may be found by counting whole squares and those whose area is equal to or more than half of a square:—

e.g.

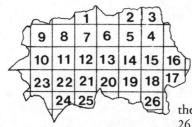

the area is approximately 26 squares

A2: AREA OF IRREGULAR SHAPES (cont'd)

Examples of areas to be measured:—
(1) Sizes of hands (draw round on squared paper).
(2) Sizes of feet (draw round on squared paper).
(3) Sizes of leaves (trace round on squared paper or place sheet of transparent squared paper on top).
(4) Pieces of material (use transparent squared paper).

A3: AREA USING GEOBOARDS

The 9-pin geoboard is illustrated in **2D1** and this may again be used in work on area, though the 16 or 25 pin geoboards give more scope for exploration.

Questions
1. How many different sized squares can you make on the 16-pin geoboard? Record the size of each square on dotted paper.
2. How many different sized rectangular shapes can you make? Draw them on spotted paper and write the area on each, e.g. 2 squares, 3 squares etc.
3. How many shapes had an area of 1 square? 2 squares? 3 squares?
4. What was the area of the largest shape? the smallest? What was the difference in size between them?
5. What area was most difficult to count? Why?

Area of squares and rectangle on 16-pin geoboards

The shapes placed diagonally may be difficult for children to make, and finding the area is not straightforward. The dotted lines indicate how it might be done.

This is a similar activity to that outlined in **A3**, but children can make a greater variety of rectangles and squares on a sheet of squared paper (or square dotted paper). At first a random selection will be made, but gradually children should develop a systematic approach and the following questions might help:—

(1) Draw squares on your paper of different sizes beginning with the smallest (1 square in area).

(2) Draw rectangles with the following areas: 2 squares, 3 squares, 4 squares, 5 squares, 6 squares etc.

(3) How many different shaped rectangles can you make with an area of 12 squares? 24 squares?

(4) Find the areas in two ways:—

    (a) counting the squares.

    (b) counting the rows and the number in each row, e.g.

        An area of 24 squares shown as:—
           2 rows with 12 in each row.
           3 rows with 8 in each row.
           4 rows with 6 in each row.
           6 rows with 4 in each row.

Calculation of area: number of rows × number in each row.

2 rows with 12 in each row.
Total: 24 squares (2 × 12)

4 rows with 6 in each row.
Total: 24 squares (4 × 6)

3 rows with 8 in each row.
Total: 24 squares (3 × 8)

6 rows with 4 in each row.
Total: 24 squares (6 × 4)

Rectangular shapes may be folded and cut so that the relationship between the area of a triangle and a rectangle with the same base and the same height may be investigated:—

e.g. (a)

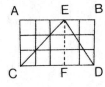

The shape AEFC is a square and if folded about the diagonal CE, the triangle CAE will fit exactly over the triangle CFE. Cut along line DE and fit the triangle EBD over DFE. This demonstrates that the rectangle has been divided equally in two, i.e. the area of the triangle is half the area of the rectangle.

(b)

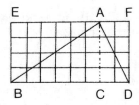

After experiences of folding, cutting and matching the cut out areas over the triangular shape, children are eventually able to calculate the areas of triangles by marking out rectangular divisions as shown in the diagram,

ie $\triangle$ ABC is ½ area of ACBE : 12 squares
$\triangle$ ACD is ½ area of ACDF : 4 squares
Therefore $\triangle$ ABD is the sum of these areas, i.e. 16 squares.

The investigation should lead to the conclusion that the area of $\triangle$ ABD is simply half of $\square$ EFDB.

A6: STANDARD UNITS

All the work in area outlined in the preceding sections is aimed at developing the concept through a variety of practical activities using various measures. When children have had experience in using squares of various sizes to measure areas, the square metre and a square centimetre may be introduced as the standard units. An area of one square metre may be drawn on the playground to give children some idea of its size. When we speak of a square metre, we are **not** referring to **shape** but to an **area** equal to that of a metre square. To help children towards an understanding of this a square metre may be made by sticking sheets of paper together. This could be cut and arranged in a different shape, whose area is still 1 square metre (1m²).

e.g.
square metre.

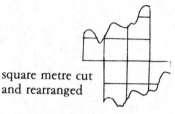

square metre cut
and rearranged

not a 'square' now but constant
area of 1 square metre or 1m².

Paper with centimetre grid may be used for activities in calculating areas. Children now record the area of a rectangle, for example, as 24 cm².

LENGTH

L1: MEASUREMENT USING SPANS ETC.

Some experience of measurement using arbitrary units is necessary to help children appreciate the need for standard units.

A **span** is the distance from the tip of the little finger to the tip of the thumb when the hard is stretched.

e.g.   span

It is difficult for children to measure with hands fully stretched, so it helps if strips of paper or cardboard are cut to the size of the span and these placed end to end to measure objects in the room. Children estimate first and then measure. Results may be tabulated:—

e.g.	Objects to be measured	Estimate in spans	Measurement in spans
	width of desk		
	length of desk		
	length of blackboard		

The width of the **hand** may be marked on a strip of cardboard, several cut out and used as units of measurement. Children measure the same objects and compare results or choose different objects.

The **foot** may also be used as a unit of measurement.

(a) by putting one foot in front of the other to find, e.g. the width of the room.

(b) by drawing round a foot, cutting out a pattern and using it as the unit to measure, e.g. the length of the window sill, the width of the corridor etc. If two patterns are used children can move one and place it in front of the other, making the operation easier.

e.g.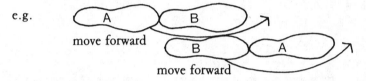

The playground, corridor etc. may be measured in **paces** and results recorded.

pace

As children compare their results when using spans, hands, feet, paces etc. as units of measurement, they realize how inaccurate they are because of the variety of sizes used. The need for a standard unit of measurement becomes apparent and this is introduced as the metre.

L2: ESTIMATION AND MEASUREMENT TO THE NEAREST METRE ETC.

The standard unit of measurement, i.e. the metre is used to measure objects in the school, some of which have already been measured using paces, feet etc.

Metre sticks may be introduced first and used in pairs as illustrated:—

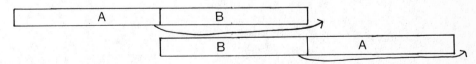

Distances of 2 metres, 3 metres etc. are marked on the playground or corridor and children asked to pace these and count the paces. Heights of door, lengths of rooms, cars etc. may be measured and results tabulated.

L2: ESTIMATION AND MEASUREMENT TO THE NEAREST METRE ETC. (cont'd)

e.g.

	Estimate in metres	Measurement in metres
length of room		
width of room		
height of door		
length of car		

The trundle wheel is a useful tool, provided children have investigated, at a simple level, the relationship between 1 revolution and the linear distance travelled as shown below:—

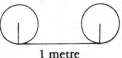

1 metre

It can be used to mark out specified distances, e.g. 5 metres, 8 metres etc. Children should start from a definite mark and move along a straight line (line of tiles, chalk marking etc.), marking the finishing point carefully.

The metre tape may also be used to check measurements already made. Children should work in pairs each checking the results of the other. Measuring to the nearest metre, is only a very rough approximation, so children are introduced to half metres and quarter metres (marked on rods) and measurements made to the nearest ½ metre, nearest quarter metre and, later, nearest tenth of a metre.

L3: MEASURING IN CENTIMETRES

For more accurate measurements, children use metre rods marked in centimetres. Recording is made using one unit **only**, e.g. 1.23 metres or 123 centimetres (Temporary recording of, e.g. 1 metre 23 centimetres may be allowed until children understand decimal fractions). Read 'How to write Metric,' published by Her Majesty's Stationery Office (page 11).

Tapes and rulers marked in centimetres may be used for smaller objects, e.g. length of toy car, length of paint brush, length of book etc. and results tabulated:—

Name of object	Estimate in cm	Measurement in cm	Error
toy car (length)			
paint brush			
book (length)			

L4: PERSONAL MEASUREMENTS

Tape measures marked in centimetres can be used for the following personal measurements: head, neck, ankle, wrist, waist, chest.

Results may be recorded to the nearest centimetre and comparisons made, e.g. Who wears the biggest cap? What is the smallest ankle measurement? etc.

L5: RELATIONSHIPS BETWEEN UNITS OF MEASUREMENT

The relationship between centimetres and metres is shown on most metre rods; there are usually 10 divisions with 10 cm in each, making a total of 100 cm. Children can cut lengths of string, e.g. 10 cm long and find how many stretch along 1 metre rod. Cuisenaire rods of various lengths may be placed on the metre stick and the total length counted; it is easier to cover half the stick first and double the answer. Longs and units from multibase materials may also be used (if cm based). The long represents 10 cm and 10 of them measure the metre stick exactly. Calculations are made using **one unit only**, so until children understand decimal fractions it is best to work in centimetres only, e.g. 1.43 metres expressed as 143 centimetres.

Suggested questions on Measurement
1. Find the total length of:—
    (a) 15 sticks each 3m in length.
    (b) 13 ropes each 5m in length.
    (c) 20 poles each 2m in length.
2. Find the distance right round the playground by measuring with
    (a) a trundle wheel
    (b) a metric tape
    (c) metre sticks (at least two).
Measure each side in turn, record the distance and find the total distance.
3. The sides of a garden are
    as shown on diagram.

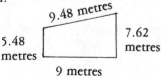

5.48 metres 9.48 metres 7.62 metres 9 metres

Find the length of fencing needed to go right round.
4. The total length of 6 equal rods is 8.16 metres. What is the length of each?
5. The width of my hand is 8 cm. How many hand breadths to measure a desk whose length is 104 cm?
6. If my pace is 62 cm, how far have I walked after 10 paces? Give the answer in metres.

7. The table shows the height of 5 boys:—

James	96 cm
Tom	90 cm
Bill	120 cm
David	115 cm
Peter	106 cm

They stand behind a wall 1 metre high. Name the boys who will be hidden by the wall. If their eyes are 10 cm below the tops of their heads, who will be able to see over the top of the wall? (without standing on tiptoe).

WEIGHT

The development of the concept as outlined in the P1-P3 section should precede the activities described here.

W1: ARRANGING OBJECTS ACCORDING TO WEIGHT

Children arrange a variety of objects, e.g. book, box of chalk, packet of straws, cricket ball etc. in order of weight:—

    (a) by handling and estimating.

    (b) by balancing one against another on scales.

A set of parcels may be prepared to demonstrate that weight is not necessarily related to size, i.e. the large parcel is the lightest of the set while the smallest is the heaviest.

   'Weight shapes' produced by E. J. Arnold, provide a set of 3D shapes from which the following subsets may be selected:—

    (a) identical in shape and size but differing in weight.

    (b) identical in weight but differing in shape and size.

(a) Using Arbitrary Units

The weights of objects may be compared by weighing each against convenient arbitrary units, e.g.

e.g.   Arbitrary units to balance objects

(1)

Objects	Buttons	Lemonade tops	Pegs
key	16	3	11
spool	20	4	16
match box	11	2	8
3 marbles	27	5	19

These are only approximations. The smaller the arbitrary units, the easier it is to achieve a balance point.

The tabulated results marked (1) may be used as data for the following calculations:—

e.g.

	buttons	lemonade tops	pegs
1 key balances	16	3	11
3 keys balance			
1 spool balances	20	4	16
4 spools balance			
1 match box balances	11	2	8
5 match boxes balance			
3 marbles balance	27	5	19
12 marbles balance			
15 marbles balance			

As children use these arbitrary units, they realize that some standard unit of weight is necessary.

(b) Standard units

The kilogram is the standard unit of mass, ('weight' more meaningful at this stage) but, as it is rather heavy for children to handle, submultiples were introduced first (see **W.6** of the infant section). It is possible to give children some idea of how heavy it is by balancing it against e.g. a bag of sugar (1 kg), potatoes, sand, stones etc.

Children should be given opportunities to select objects which weigh approximately 500g and list these as shown:—

e.g.

Object	more than 500g	less than 500g	about 500g
jar of stones	✓		
tin of sand			✓
box of chalks		✓	

Similar activities with appropriate recordings should follow using 200g, 100g, 50g and 10g. It is only by trial and error that children eventually gain enough experience to estimate fairly accurately what unit is nearest in weight to the object being weighed.

Children are invited to weigh a selection of objects and record the results as shown:—

e.g.

Object	Estimated weight	Result by weighing	weights used					
			kilogram	500g	200g	100g	50g	10g
jar of peas				✓			✓	
tin of shells					✓	✓	✓	✓ ✓
golf ball								✓ ✓ ✓ ✓
a pp9 battery					✓ ✓			✓ ✓ ✓

W3: CONTAINERS OF EQUAL SIZE

Identical glass jars with lids are filled with e.g. peas, beans, lentils, rice, sugar, breakfast cereal etc. and weighed in turn on balance scales using the selection of weights suggested in **W2**. Children discover that the weights are all different, though the containers have the same capacity. The jars may be arranged in order of weight and differences noted.

Questions
(1) Which jar is the heaviest?
(2) Which jar is the lightest?

(3) What is the difference in grams between the heaviest and lightest?
(4) How much less than 500g does the jar of cereals weigh?
(5) What is the total weight in grams of the jar of lentils and the jar of beans? etc.

W4: PERSONAL WEIGHTS TO THE NEAREST 100 GRAMS.

When children use personal scales, they are introduced to a new type of weighing device where a pointer moves to indicate a certain reading on the dial. They must be given time to study how it works and to read the weights of members of a group, to the nearest kilogram at first. For a more accurate recording, they read the weights to the nearest half kilogram, and later when decimal fractions are understood, to the nearest tenth of a kilogram (100 grams).

W5: RELATIONSHIPS BETWEEN UNITS OF WEIGHT

As children handle the various weights, they begin to appreciate that they are related to one another and enjoy balancing one against its submultiples:—

e.g. 1 kilogram will balance   2   500 gram weights
                                     5   200 gram weights
                                    10   100 gram weights

From this they can deduce that 1 kilogram balances 1000 grams. As Centi-cube, and unit pieces of some multibase materials each weigh 1g it is possible to count out 1000 in sets of 10 to give children some idea of the relationship between 1g and 1kg.

Calculations
e.g.   (1) If butter costs £1.10 for each kg, find the cost of the following:—
                        ½ kg of butter
                        2 kg of butter
                        2½ kg of butter
       (2) 1 kg of tea costs £3.00. Find the cost of the following:—
                        ¼ kg of tea
                        500g of tea
                        250g of tea
                        750g of tea
       (3) Potatoes cost 26p for 1 kg. Find the cost of the following:—
                        ½ kg of potatoes
                        2 kg of potatoes
                        2½ kg of potatoes
                        5 kg of potatoes.

etc.

TIME

The concept of time is a difficult one to establish. 'Telling the time' and 'timing' are two different ideas; one is simply dial-reading, while the other is concerned with the measurement of the passage of time using arbitrary measures and finally standard units (seconds, minutes, etc.). Both aspects have been considered in the infant section, but need further development here.

T1: USE OF TIMING DEVICES TO SHOW THE LENGTH OF 1 MINUTE, ETC.

Home-made timing devices, e.g. sand and water clocks (tins with holes), pendulums, egg-timers, etc. are useful for comparing the time taken for various activities in the classroom such as counting in twos to 100, running on the spot 50 times, reading a paragraph in a book, etc. Eventually the need for standard units arises and children use instruments which give measurements in seconds, etc.

e.g. (1) A stop-clock with a large sweep seconds hand. Children are able to count out the seconds up to 60 and recognize this as one minute. Activities may now be timed in minutes.

   (b) A pendulum of 25 cm (approximately) swings forwards and backwards in approximately one second; so children can count out 60 complete swings as being approximately one minute. This may be used to time activites.

   (c) Egg-timers measuring 4 minute, 3 minute and one minute intervals may also be used to measure the amount of time spent on classroom activities.

T2: TELLING THE TIME

In **T9** of the infant section, children were introduced to hours, half hours and quarter hours. They now learn to tell the time in 5 minute intervals using the 'PAST' and 'TO' method.

(a)

One half of the clock face is marked 'TO' and the other half 'PAST'.

Children practise counting in 5 minute intervals:—

(a) clockwise: 5, 10, 15, 20, 25 minutes **past** the hour.
(b) anticlockwise: 5, 10, 15, 20, 25 minutes **to** the hour.

If the **minute** hand is in the 'PAST' half, children count clockwise: 5, 10, 15, 20 past 7 (diagram (a)).

(b)   To  Past

If the **minute** hand is in the 'TO' half, children count anticlockwise: 5, 10 minutes to 9 (diagram (b)). Much practice is needed using clocks with movable hands.

T3: MOVEMENT OF HANDS ON CLOCK FACE

It is important that children see the clock not only as an instrument which shows the time, but one which measures the passage of time. Their attention may be drawn to the position of the minute (large) hand and the hour (small) hand at the beginning of a lesson and again at the end:—

e.g.

beginning of lesson   end of lesson

The movement of the minute hand half way round the face indicates that half an hour (30 minutes) has gone. The hour hand has moved half-way between 10 and 11, indicating again that half an hour has passed. It is important that children realize that both hands are moving, measuring the time which has elapsed, one measuring in minute intervals, the other in hours. This is not always obvious when children use clocks with movable hands, as they move the minute hand and forget that the hour hand also moves. Mechanical clocks which no longer keep accurate time, are useful to show the movement of one hand relative to the other, i.e. when the minute hand moves right round the clock face, the hour hand moves from one hour to the next.

It might be profitable at this stage to discuss how many times the minute hand travels round the face in a day, thus focusing attention on the length of a day as 24 hours. When the hour hand travels round once, half of the day (12 hours) has gone. The day is another measure which records the passage of time.

Time may be measured not only by days, hours, minutes, seconds, but also by weeks, months and years. Children are already familiar with the names of the days of the week and months of the year as they daily record the date (see **T6** of the Infant Section).

At this stage they need to become aware that while there is a standard length for weeks, i.e. 7 days, there is no standard length for our calendar months. To establish the length of each, attention may be focused on the following:—

e.g. (a) months when birthdays occur
(b) the month when Christmas comes
(c) the months when we have summer holidays etc.

The old rhyme may also be useful in helping children to differentiate between those that have 30 days and those that have 31 days:—

> 'Thirty days hath September,
> April, June and November,
> All the rest have thirty-one,
> Excepting February alone,
> Which has but twenty-eight days clear
> And twenty-nine in each leap year.'

To familiarize children with the calendar, it is important that they should draw out patterns of some of the months in two ways:—

e.g.

(a)

June						
Sun	Mon	Tues	Wed	Thur	Fri	Sat
				1	2	3
4	5	6	7	8	9	10
11	12	13	14	15	16	17
18	19	20	21	22	23	24
25	26	27	28	29	30	

(b)

June					
Sun		4	11	18	25
Mon		5	12	19	26
Tues		6	13	20	27
Wed		7	14	21	28
Thur	1	8	15	22	29
Fri	2	9	16	23	30
Sat	3	10	17	24	

Questions

1. How many days in the month of June?
2. Tom's birthday is on the 10th of June. What day is this?
3. Which date is 6 days after the 17th June? What day of the week is this?
4. Give the date of the last Monday in June.
5. What is the date of the third Friday in June?
6. Give the dates of all the Thursdays in June.

7. Count **forwards** one week from the following dates:—

8th June	15th June
21st June	11th June

8. Count **backwards** one week from the following dates:—

30th June	16th June
22nd June	20th June

9. How many days:—

from	to	
8th June	22nd June	**counting forwards**
11th June	30th June	
4th June	19th June etc.	

10. How many days:—

from	to	
30th June	11th June	**counting backwards**
23rd June	9th June	
17th June	3rd June	

To summarize this section, children may be asked to complete the following table for the current year, having previously made up their own calendars.

This refers to 1979

Month	No of days	No of Sundays	No of Wednesdays	No of completed weeks
January	31			4
March			5	3
April				
	31			
June				3
July		5		
August				
	30			
			5	
November		4		
December	31			4

Most children are interested to hear how people long ago kept a record of the passing of time. Some of the devices they used have already been mentioned **(T1)**.

(a) Sand clock

These were used for measuring short periods of time and were often found in churches to time the length of the sermon. We sometimes use smaller versions of these as egg-timers.

Children can make sand clocks using two 'Gloy' jars, a cork and a small glass tube:—

e.g.

glass tube
cork —'Gloy' jar

(b) Water clock

As the water trickled out through a small hole at the bottom of the bowl, the level dropped and marks on the inside of the bowl told the hour.

(c) The candle clock

This method may have been invented by King Alfred. The candle was marked to show four equal parts and each took an hour to burn.

To make a candle clock, children need two candles of the same size and shape. Both are put on a tin lid and one is lighted. After half an hour (or other suitable period of time) children put a mark on the unlighted candle. After 1 hour the second mark is made, after 1½ hours the third mark, etc until the unlighted candle is marked in half-hour sections.

This candle clock shows that 1 hour (2 half hours) has gone since it was lighted.

(d) Sun clocks and sundials

Perhaps the earliest method of keeping a rough record of the passing of time was by observing the movement of the stars and the moon. The Red Indians timed events from one full moon to the next. Babylonians, Egyptians, Greeks and Romans measured time by the length of shadows cast by the sun, as illustrated in the following diagrams:—

e.g.

(1) Egyptian sun clock

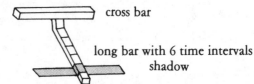

cross bar

long bar with 6 time intervals
shadow

The shadow of the crossbar falling across the long bar indicated the time.

(2) Sundial

The sundial may be seen on the wall of a church, in a garden, etc and usually has twelve time intervals marked on it.

Children can make a simple shadow clock by placing a stick upright in the playground on a sunny day in summer and painting the shadow line each half hour from a given time, e.g. 9.00 am. The numbers 9, 10, 11, 12, etc. may then be marked at the appropriate places.

T6: RECORDING CLOCK TIMES

In **T2** the 'PAST' and 'TO' method was used in teaching children to tell the time. They may now be introduced to the alternative method which uses minutes past only, e.g. twenty minutes to four is really forty minutes past three and may be recorded as 3.40; five minutes to seven may be recorded as 6.55, etc. Children need practice in recording in both methods, but ultimately it is the 'minutes past' method which occurs in timetables, etc. The following table may be completed to show both forms of recording.

20 past 2	2.20
¼ to 6	
	6.45
7 o'clock	
5 to 8	
	6.25
10 to 4	
	11.10

T7: CALCULATIONS

There is no value in working detailed calculations involving hours, minutes, days, etc. unless these have some relevance to the activities in the classroom. They may, for convenience, be divided into two categories:—

(a) related to the clock
(b) related to the calendar.

(a) **The Clock**
As clocks have dials marked in 12-hour intervals, it is necessary to explain the following terms: morning, afternoon, noon, midday, midnight, and perhaps

the abbreviations a.m. (ante meridiem) and p.m. (post meridiem).

Counting forwards and backwards in hours, minutes or a combination of both is a useful activity:—

e.g. (1) What is the time one hour before 11.15?
    (2) Count backwards 2 hours from 1.20?
    (3) What is the time twenty minutes before 8.15?
    (4) The clock shows 11.05, but is 10 minutes fast. What is the right time?
    (5) I leave home at 8.15 am and arrive at school 40 minutes later. At what time do I arrive?
    (6) I put a cake in the oven at 10.20 am and take it out 2½ hours later. What time is this?

It may be necessary at first to provide children with cardboard clocks, so that they can move the hands backwards or forwards to obtain the result.

(7) Complete the following:—

Departure time	Arrival time	Time taken for the journey
5.00 a.m.	Noon	
	11.20 a.m.	1 hour 15 minutes
1.20 p.m.		2 hours 10 minutes
10.40 p.m.	12.15 a.m.	
	4.15 p.m.	5 hours 20 minutes

(b) The Calendar

Suggestions for calculations

(1) How many days are there in the first three months of the year?
(2) Ann goes on holiday on the 2nd July and returns 3 weeks later. What date is this?
(3) Write down the number of days in each month:—
    e.g.   January   31 days
             February
             March   etc.
(4) Add up the days in the first six months. Add up the days in the last six months. How many days altogether in a year?
(5) How many sevens in 365? How many weeks in a year?
(6) January 1st 1978 was a Sunday. What day of the week was 1st January 1979? How did you find out?
(7) The birthdays of some children are given on next page. Give their ages in years and completed months on 1st January, 1979.

		Years	Completed Months
Bert	4. 7.1956		
Betty	12. 6.1960		
Adrian	15.11.1972		
Frances	24. 8.1971		

(8) Arrange the following in order of age, beginning with youngest:—

Name	Date of Birth
Colin	21. 9.1968
Judith	8.11.1970
Niall	14.10.1968
Nicola	5. 8.1970

T8: TIME-TABLES

Children may study school time-tables to extract information, e.g.

Time-Table for P4/P5 (morning)

Period From To	Monday	Tuesday	Wednesday	Thursday	Friday
8.50- 9.00		Morning	Assembly	(in Hall)	
9.00- 9.30	R.E.	R.E.	Oral English	B.B.C. Service (radio)	R.E.
9.30-10.00	TV prog. 'Finding out'	Oral English	Maths	Maths	TV prog. 'Merry Go Round'
10.00-10.15	Oral English	Oral English	Maths	Maths	Oral English
10.15-10.30			BREAK		
10.30-11.00	Maths	Maths	Written English	Oral English	Maths
11.00-11.30	Music (radio)	Maths	Written English	Written English	Maths
11.30-12.00	P.E. (Hall)	Written English	P.E. (Hall)	Music	Oral English

Questions

(These refer to the morning time-table illustrated on the previous page, but may be adapted to suit the one used in class.)

(1) How much time is spent weekly on TV programmes?

(2) How much time is spent weekly on radio programmes?

(3) What is the total amount of time used for Maths lessons?

(4) How much time is used for (a) Oral English?
  (b) Written English?

(5) The time spent on P.E. lessons is .... minutes.

(6) What is the total amount of time spent in the hall each week?

(7) Fill in the following table to show how much time is used **weekly** for each subject.

Less than 1 hour	1 hour	1 ½ hours	2 hours	More than 2 hours

FAVOURITE PROGRAMMES

Children may be asked to fill in the names and times of their favourite programmes using the Radio Times.

Name of Programme		Mon	Tue	Wed	Thur	Fri	Sat	Daily Time Spent	Weekly Time Spent
	Begins Ends								
	Begins Ends								
	Begins Ends								
	Begins Ends								
	Begins Ends								

188

MONEY

Money is included in the 'measurement' section as it is a measure of the exchange value of goods, a concept which develops slowly through many and varied activities.

The use of arbitrary measures to highlight the need for standard measures may serve as an introduction to the topic. Children set up a shop using, e.g. buttons instead of coins. The problem of finding a higher value 'coin' arises when there are not enough buttons left or when the sheer bulk of buttons in one's pocket or purse becomes an embarrassment. Links with history showing the development of our coinage may help towards an understanding of the concept.

M1: PRACTICE IN HANDLING COINS ETC

Most children are familiar with our standard measures of money, i.e. the coins in current use. They do need practice in handling them and giving equivalent values where possible. A game situation may be devised to stimulate interest and provide practice in exchanging coins.

e.g.

Children may work individually or in pairs shaking a die marked (1-6) and selecting suitable coins to represent the values shown. These are placed on the card shown (circles with the values marked is an alternative arrangement). When possible, lower value coins are exchanged for those of higher value, e.g. when a child has covered 5 pence on the board, he should be encouraged to exchange these for a five-pence coin. Selecting and exchanging continue until a child has five 10 pence coins which he exchanges for a fifty-pence coin, thus winning the game. An extended form might show values up to £1.00. It is possible to play the game using a die with faces marked as follows:— 1p,

189

2p, 5p, 10p, 1p, 2p. In this variation, children pick up the coins indicated, exchanging to reach the highest value coin.

The following are examples of work cards which give further practice in handling coins and giving equivalent values:—

e.g.
(1)

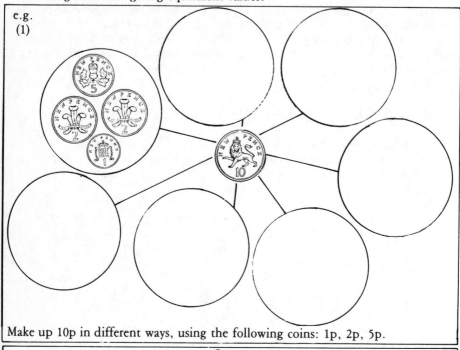

Make up 10p in different ways, using the following coins: 1p, 2p, 5p.

(2) Each row must add up to 50p. Put out coins on the card.

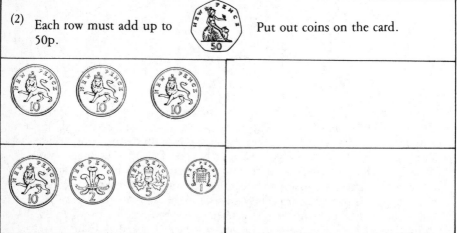

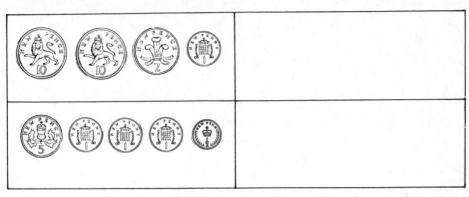

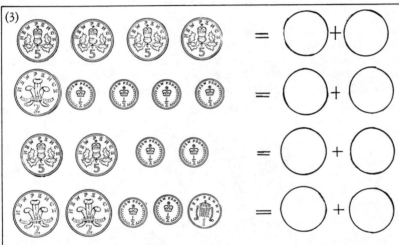

(3)

In each row put out 2 coins making the same amount as the group.

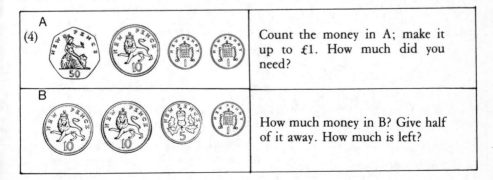

A

(4) Count the money in A; make it up to £1. How much did you need?

B

How much money in B? Give half of it away. How much is left?

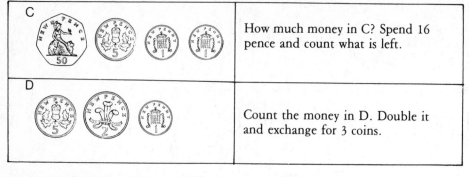

C	How much money in C? Spend 16 pence and count what is left.
D	Count the money in D. Double it and exchange for 3 coins.

M2: SHOPPING AND GIVING CORRECT CHANGE

This may be done as children play 'shop', using real coins and counting change as the shopkeeper does (complementary addition). Work cards may be produced to give practice in a wider range of shopping activities to all children in the class. 'Shopping' stamps produced by Philip and Tacey provide colourful material which may be used in the production of these.

e.g.

(a)

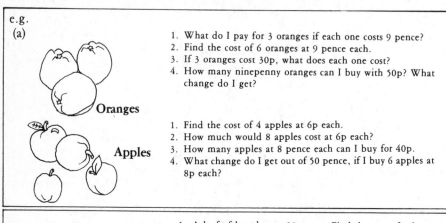

Oranges

1. What do I pay for 3 oranges if each one costs 9 pence?
2. Find the cost of 6 oranges at 9 pence each.
3. If 3 oranges cost 30p, what does each one cost?
4. How many ninepenny oranges can I buy with 50p? What change do I get?

Apples

1. Find the cost of 4 apples at 6p each.
2. How much would 8 apples cost at 6p each?
3. How many apples at 8 pence each can I buy for 40p.
4. What change do I get out of 50 pence, if I buy 6 apples at 8p each?

(b)

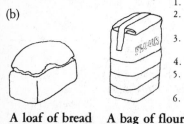

A loaf of bread   A bag of flour

1. A loaf of bread costs 28 pence. Find the cost of 3 loaves.
2. I have 50 pence. How much more do I need to buy 2 loaves?
3. How many loaves can I buy for £1.00? What change do I get?
4. A bag of flour costs 36p. Find the cost of 2 bags.
5. I have £1.00. How much more do I need to buy 3 bags of flour?
6. If I buy a loaf of bread and a bag of flour, how much do I spend? Name the coins given to pay exactly that amount.

(c)

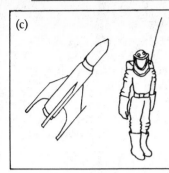

1. A rocket costs 35 pence. What change have I out of £1.00 if I buy two? How much more money would I need to buy three?
2. If a spacemen costs 45p, how many can I buy for £1.00? How much change do I get?
3. How much more do I pay for a spaceman than a rocket? What is the difference in price when I buy two of each?
4. What change do I get out of £1.00 if I buy a rocket and a spaceman?
5. Make up 35 pence in as many ways as you can, using only 10p and 5p coins.

Children may be asked to fill in the following table to show three different ways of paying exactly for the rocket and the spaceman (work card c).

	Coins given				
Toy bought	10p	5p	2p	1p	Total price
The rocket	1				35p
			4		
				3	
The spaceman				1	45p
	2				
		3			

M3: USING THE 100 SQUARE TO SHOW RELATIONSHIPS BETWEEN COINS

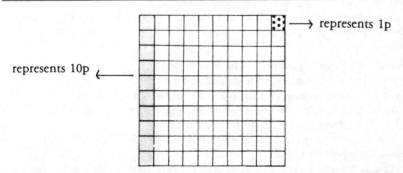

represents 10p

→ represents 1p

If each small square represents 1p, then the large square represents £1.00 or 100 pence. The shaded portion represents the 10p coin ($\frac{1}{10}$ of £1.00). The dotted square represents 1p ($\frac{1}{100}$ of £1.00).

Practical activities help to establish these relationships,

e.g. (a) Colouring in areas representing 24 pence, 36 pence etc. (2 strips of ten and 4 unit pieces; 3 strips of ten and 6 unit pieces).

(b) Placing Cuisenaire rods on the square to represent a sum of money (orange or ten rods first, followed by the colour which represents the unit pieces).

It must be stressed that while this relates to N13, it is not a true decimal system and children can be taught written expressions in money, without an understanding of decimal fractions.

M4: ADDITION, SUBTRACTION, MULTIPLICATION AND DIVISION

The number section deals with these operations in detail; here there is opportunity to practice the skills acquired and to use them in problem solving situations. As the amounts, at first, do not exceed £1.00, calculations are done in pence.

It is very important to check for understanding of the operations, i.e. do children see the link between addition and multiplication; between subtraction and division? Too often the operations are practised in isolation and when children are faced with problem solving situations, they are at a loss to know which one to perform.

M5: IMPORTANCE OF CORRECT NOTATION

Teachers should read some of HMSO publications, e.g. 'Change for a Pound,' 'Decimal Currency' etc. in order to familiarize themselves with the correct approach to the teaching of written and oral expressions in decimal money.

A summary of the important points is included
(1) £ is the symbol for pound and is placed before the amount.
(2) p is the abbreviation for pence and is placed after the amount.
(3) £ and p should **never** appear together and should not be followed by a full stop, except at the end of a sentence.
(4) The decimal point separates pounds from pence; there must always be two digits in the pence columns.
(5) Amounts may be expressed in two forms, e.g. 59p or £0.59. For amounts less than £1.00, the p sign is recommended.
(6) The halfpenny is written as ½p or £0.00½ and **not** £0.005.
(7) Amounts in whole pounds may be written as, e.g. £5 or £5.00.

Children have already been introduced to problem solving situations through work cards etc. Calculations may now include the following: shop bills, cost of dinner tickets, weekly savings, pocket money etc.

(a) Shop Bills

e.g.

½ kg costs 15p   1 kg costs 25p   1 kg costs 16p

1. Find the total cost of ½ kg of onions, 1 kg of carrots and 1 kg of potatoes.
2. What is the cost of 1 kg of onions? 1½ kg?
3. What change have I out of £1 if I buy 3 kg of potatoes?
4. How many kg of carrots can I buy for £1?
5. If 3 kg of onions cost 48p, what is the cost of 1 kg? 5 kg?

(b) Dinner Money

As children handle and count dinner money, they sort the coins into sets whose value is 10p. These are then totalled to make sets of £1. Relevant problems relating to class situations may be devised:—

e.g. Fill in the following table

Class	Number of tickets at 25p each	Number of tickets at 12½p each	Total Value of tickets
P1	20	5	
P2	25	10	
P3		0	£5.00
P4	30		£8.75
P5		5	£4.37½
Totals			

(c) Weekly Savings

Most schools encourage children to develop the habit of saving money regularly. Many and varied calculations may emerge in connection with the money collected.

195

e.g. **Weekly savings for the month of November, 1978**

	Monday 6	Monday 13	Monday 20	Monday 27	Totals
Jane	20p	10p	50p	35p	
Kate	25p		25p	30p	£1.00
Bob		25p	15p	30p	85p
Pat	30p	20p		25p	£1.05

Children may be asked to fill in the blank spaces in the table above.

A series of questions using the completed table may give further practice in counting money.

e.g. (1) What was the total amount saved by the four children?
    (2) Who saved most in the month?
    (3) Who saved the least amount?
    (4) What is the difference between the greatest amount saved and the least amount?
    (5) On which Monday was the greatest amount collected?

(d) Pocket Money

Data relating to the amount of weekly pocket money each child receives can provide further material for computation in money. The results may be recorded graphically as well as in the following tabulated form:—

Amount of pocket money	5p	10p	15p	20p	25p	50p
Numbers of children	3	4			2	
Total amounts			90p	£1.60		£1.50

Children fill in the blank spaces.

Questions similar to those in section C may also be devised for this section.

Section 3

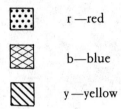

r —red

b—blue

y —yellow

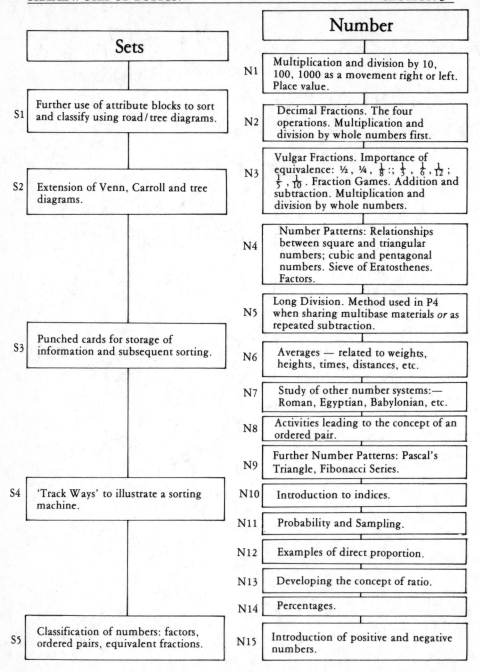

Number

Sets

S1   Further use of attribute blocks to sort and classify using road/tree diagrams.

S2   Extension of Venn, Carroll and tree diagrams.

S3   Punched cards for storage of information and subsequent sorting.

S4   'Track Ways' to illustrate a sorting machine.

S5   Classification of numbers: factors, ordered pairs, equivalent fractions.

N1   Multiplication and division by 10, 100, 1000 as a movement right or left. Place value.

N2   Decimal Fractions. The four operations. Multiplication and division by whole numbers first.

N3   Vulgar Fractions. Importance of equivalence: $\frac{1}{2}$, $\frac{1}{4}$, $\frac{1}{8}$:; $\frac{1}{3}$, $\frac{1}{6}$, $\frac{1}{12}$; $\frac{1}{5}$, $\frac{1}{10}$. Fraction Games. Addition and subtraction. Multiplication and division by whole numbers.

N4   Number Patterns: Relationships between square and triangular numbers; cubic and pentagonal numbers. Sieve of Eratosthenes. Factors.

N5   Long Division. Method used in P4 when sharing multibase materials *or* as repeated subtraction.

N6   Averages — related to weights, heights, times, distances, etc.

N7   Study of other number systems:— Roman, Egyptian, Babylonian, etc.

N8   Activities leading to the concept of an ordered pair.

N9   Further Number Patterns: Pascal's Triangle, Fibonacci Series.

N10   Introduction to indices.

N11   Probability and Sampling.

N12   Examples of direct proportion.

N13   Developing the concept of ratio.

N14   Percentages.

N15   Introduction of positive and negative numbers.

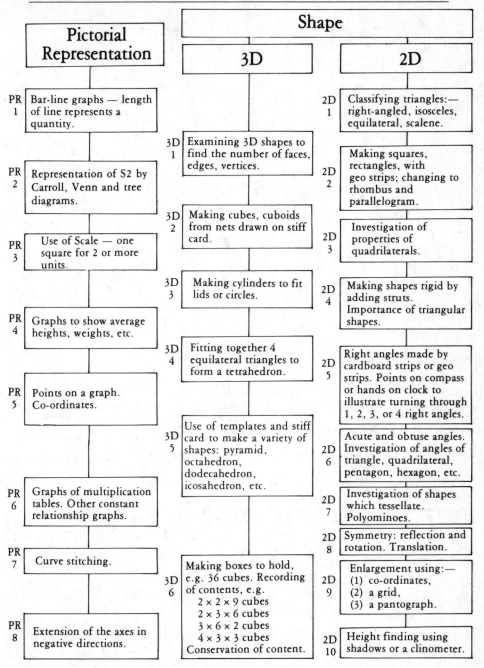

Shape

Pictorial Representation

3D

2D

PR 1	Bar-line graphs — length of line represents a quantity.
PR 2	Representation of S2 by Carroll, Venn and tree diagrams.
PR 3	Use of Scale — one square for 2 or more units.
PR 4	Graphs to show average heights, weights, etc.
PR 5	Points on a graph. Co-ordinates.
PR 6	Graphs of multiplication tables. Other constant relationship graphs.
PR 7	Curve stitching.
PR 8	Extension of the axes in negative directions.

3D 1	Examining 3D shapes to find the number of faces, edges, vertices.
3D 2	Making cubes, cuboids from nets drawn on stiff card.
3D 3	Making cylinders to fit lids or circles.
3D 4	Fitting together 4 equilateral triangles to form a tetrahedron.
3D 5	Use of templates and stiff card to make a variety of shapes: pyramid, octahedron, dodecahedron, icosahedron, etc.
3D 6	Making boxes to hold, e.g. 36 cubes. Recording of contents, e.g. 2 × 2 × 9 cubes 2 × 3 × 6 cubes 3 × 6 × 2 cubes 4 × 3 × 3 cubes Conservation of content.

2D 1	Classifying triangles:— right-angled, isosceles, equilateral, scalene.
2D 2	Making squares, rectangles, with geo strips; changing to rhombus and parallelogram.
2D 3	Investigation of properties of quadrilaterals.
2D 4	Making shapes rigid by adding struts. Importance of triangular shapes.
2D 5	Right angles made by cardboard strips or geo strips. Points on compass or hands on clock to illustrate turning through 1, 2, 3, or 4 right angles.
2D 6	Acute and obtuse angles. Investigation of angles of triangle, quadrilateral, pentagon, hexagon, etc.
2D 7	Investigation of shapes which tessellate. Polyominoes.
2D 8	Symmetry: reflection and rotation. Translation.
2D 9	Enlargement using:— (1) co-ordinates, (2) a grid, (3) a pantograph.
2D 10	Height finding using shadows or a clinometer.

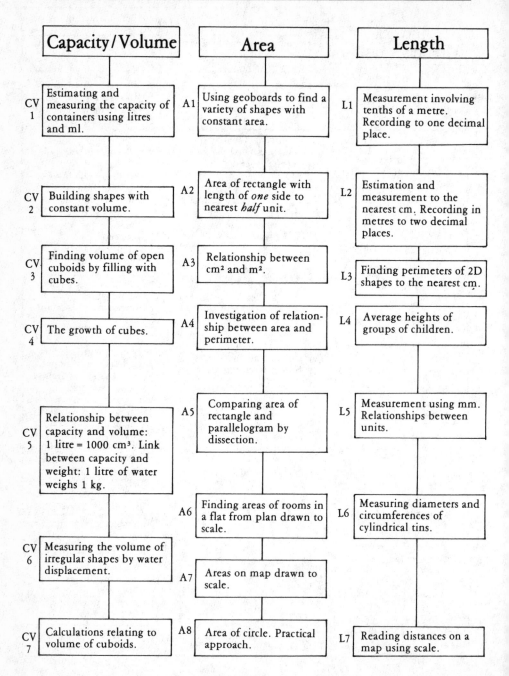

Capacity/Volume

CV 1   Estimating and measuring the capacity of containers using litres and ml.

CV 2   Building shapes with constant volume.

CV 3   Finding volume of open cuboids by filling with cubes.

CV 4   The growth of cubes.

CV 5   Relationship between capacity and volume: 1 litre = 1000 cm³. Link between capacity and weight: 1 litre of water weighs 1 kg.

CV 6   Measuring the volume of irregular shapes by water displacement.

CV 7   Calculations relating to volume of cuboids.

Area

A1   Using geoboards to find a variety of shapes with constant area.

A2   Area of rectangle with length of *one* side to nearest *half* unit.

A3   Relationship between cm² and m².

A4   Investigation of relationship between area and perimeter.

A5   Comparing area of rectangle and parallelogram by dissection.

A6   Finding areas of rooms in a flat from plan drawn to scale.

A7   Areas on map drawn to scale.

A8   Area of circle. Practical approach.

Length

L1   Measurement involving tenths of a metre. Recording to one decimal place.

L2   Estimation and measurement to the nearest cm. Recording in metres to two decimal places.

L3   Finding perimeters of 2D shapes to the nearest cm.

L4   Average heights of groups of children.

L5   Measurement using mm. Relationships between units.

L6   Measuring diameters and circumferences of cylindrical tins.

L7   Reading distances on a map using scale.

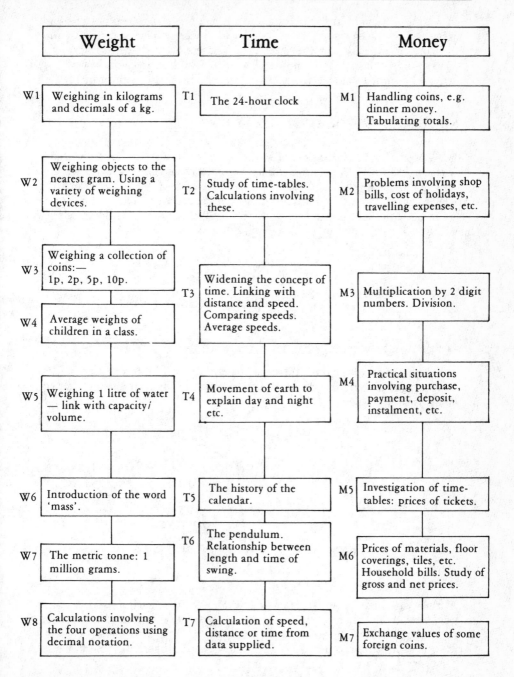

	Weight		Time		Money
W1	Weighing in kilograms and decimals of a kg.	T1	The 24-hour clock	M1	Handling coins, e.g. dinner money. Tabulating totals.
W2	Weighing objects to the nearest gram. Using a variety of weighing devices.	T2	Study of time-tables. Calculations involving these.	M2	Problems involving shop bills, cost of holidays, travelling expenses, etc.
W3	Weighing a collection of coins:— 1p, 2p, 5p, 10p.	T3	Widening the concept of time. Linking with distance and speed. Comparing speeds. Average speeds.	M3	Multiplication by 2 digit numbers. Division.
W4	Average weights of children in a class.				
W5	Weighing 1 litre of water — link with capacity/volume.	T4	Movement of earth to explain day and night etc.	M4	Practical situations involving purchase, payment, deposit, instalment, etc.
W6	Introduction of the word 'mass'.	T5	The history of the calendar.	M5	Investigation of time-tables: prices of tickets.
W7	The metric tonne: 1 million grams.	T6	The pendulum. Relationship between length and time of swing.	M6	Prices of materials, floor coverings, tiles, etc. Household bills. Study of gross and net prices.
W8	Calculations involving the four operations using decimal notation.	T7	Calculation of speed, distance or time from data supplied.	M7	Exchange values of some foreign coins.

SETS

In writing this guide, it was necessary to make a break at the end of section 1 and again at the end of section 2 but ideally there should be continual progression in all sections of the work. Teachers are advised to read again the chapter on sets in section 2 and check that the children are familiar with the activities outlined there. Many of them could be repeated, with profit, before attempting what follows.

S1: FURTHER USE OF ATTRIBUTE BLOCKS

In **S5** of section 2, we considered some 'order' relations, e.g. 'is taller than', 'weights less than', etc., but ordering becomes more complex when we take into account more than one variable. Road/tree diagrams provide frameworks which help children to understand multi-criteria ordering. They are not to be confused with 'decision' trees introduced in **S1** of section 2. Children select a 4x3 system (illustrated in **S7** of section 2).

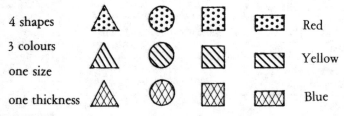

4 shapes   3 colours   one size   one thickness   Red   Yellow   Blue

They are asked to place these pieces at the end of each branch or road so that there is some pattern or order in the arrangement. One of the many arrangements is shown below.

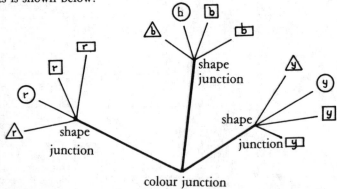

As there are three colours, it is fairly obvious that the first junction is where we decide about colour, and the next junction on each road, where we decide about shape. Whatever order we decide upon at the shape junction on, e.g. the red road, is the order which we follow for the blue and yellow roads.

202

Colour is therefore the first criterion and shape the second. It is possible to interchange the colours and shapes, but a pattern is apparent in each arrangement.

Children select a 3x3 system.

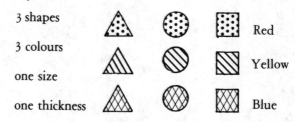

They place these pieces on a diagram like the one illustrated.

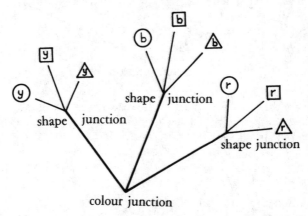

This time children may choose **either** shape **or** colour as the first criterion and the following diagram shows the alternative choice.

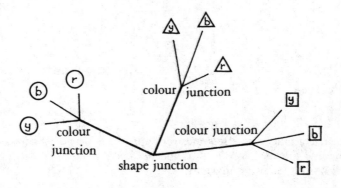

Children may be given all the blocks of one size, e.g. 24 small pieces, and asked to arrange them on a road/tree diagram like the one illustrated below:—

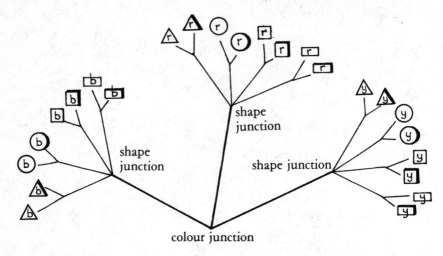

As there are three main sections to the road system, colour is the first criterion; shape is the second; thickness is the third. The arrangement is consistent and takes note of all the attributes of the blocks.

At first junctions, roads lead to   blue
red
yellow

At second junctions, roads lead to

At third junctions, roads lead to   thin   (t)
thick (T)

This may be called a 3 × 4 × 2 system.

An alternative arrangements might have shape as the first criterion, colour as the second and thickness as the third and be described as a 4 × 3 × 2 system, illustrated on the following diagram:—

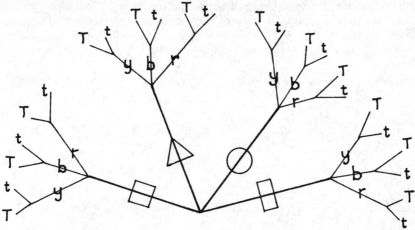

Experiences in multi-criteria ordering using attribute blocks, and road/tree diagrams provide a link with the decision precedure for arranging words in alphabetical order or in deciding which of two numbers is the greater. The procedure for alphabetical order might be written as follows:—

1. Look at the first letters of the words to be considered,
    (a) if letters are different →   decision made,
    (b) if letters are the same →   go on to 2.
2. Look at the second letters,
    (a) if letters are different →   decision made,
    (b) if letters are the same →   go on to 3.
3. Look at the third letters,
    (a) if letters are different →   decision made,
    (b) if letters are the same →   go on to 4, etc.

The decision procedure for deciding which number is greater might be written as follows:—

1. Look at the number of digits,
    (a) if one has a greater number than the other →   decision made,
    (b) if both have the same number →   go on to 2.
2. Look at the first digit in each number,
    (a) if one is greater than the other →   decision made,
    (b) if both are the same →   go on to 3.
3. Look at the second digit in each number,
    (a) if one is greater than the other →   decision made,
    (b) if both are the same →   go on to 4, etc.

S2: EXTENSIONS OF VENN, CARROLL AND TREE DIAGRAMS

In **S1** of section 2 the intersection of two subsets was illustrated by Venn, Carroll and tree diagrams. The sorting process may be extended to include the intersection of three subsets, and children may be asked to put the pieces of a set of attribute blocks in the appropriate places in each of the diagrams illustrated.

Key to the attributes of blocks in each section.

Section	1	2	3	4	5	6	7	8
Large	✓	✓	✓	✓				
Not Large					✓	✓	✓	✓
Yellow	✓		✓		✓		✓	
Not Yellow		✓		✓		✓		✓
Square	✓	✓			✓	✓		
Not Square			✓	✓			✓	✓

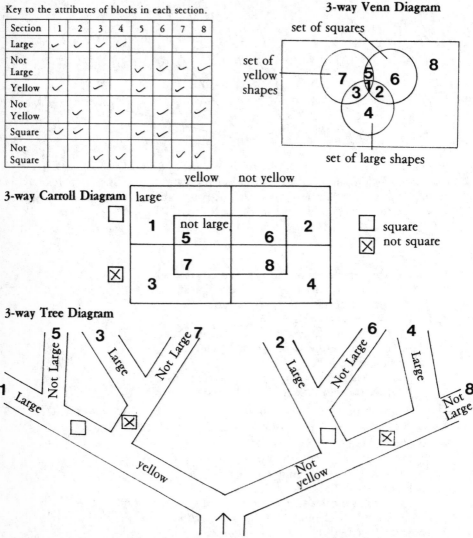

3-way Venn Diagram

3-way Carroll Diagram

3-way Tree Diagram

Reference Book: 'An Introduction to the Dienes Mathematics Programme' by P. L. Seaborne.

S3: PUNCHED CARDS FOR STORAGE OF INFORMATION AND SUBSEQUENT SORTING

In S1 of section 2, sorting activities included the partitioning of a set into two subsets, e.g. red/not red, square/not square etc. The development of this two-way system of sorting may lead to the preparation of a set of punched cards for storage of information leading to sorting activities.

The information stored may relate to a variety of topics within the curriculum, or, as suggested here, to the children in a class. The answers to the following questions provide the necessary data:—

1. Are you a boy?
2. Can you swim?
3. Do you own a bicycle?
4. Can you play a musical instrument?
5. Do you have a telephone at home?
6. Do you have a pet?

Cards, approximately 12 cm x 8 cm are cut and holes, evenly spaced and numbered are punched along one side. The corner of each card is cut off so that the numbers will appear in the proper sequence when cards are assembled for sorting.

Each child has a card like this.

The 'master' card has the question written on it. Any number of questions may be posed and corresponding holes punched.

If a child can answer 'yes' to any question on the 'master' card, he cuts the appropriate hole on his own card:—

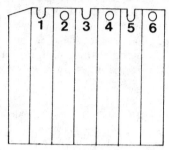

The information given by the preceding card is that a boy in the class owns a bicycle, has a telephone at home, cannot swim or play a musical instrument and does not have a pet.

The following procedure indicates a possible approach to sorting activities:—

1. Assemble all the cards and push a knitting needle through hole 2 and shake. The set of swimmers falls out and the set of non-swimmers is left on the needle.
2. Re-assemble the set of swimmers and insert the knitting needle in hole 3 and shake. The set of children who can swim and who own a bicycle falls out, i.e. the intersection of sets 2 and 3. On the needle is the set who can swim but do not own a bicycle.

Use the set of punched cards to find the following information:—

1. The set of children who can play a musical instrument and own a pet.
2. The set of boys who do not have a telephone at home.
3. The set of children who play a musical instrument, own a bicycle, but do not have a pet.

Reference books:—
'Mathematics in the Later Primary Years' — a Nuffield/British Council handbook for teachers, pages 43, 44.
'Logic' — Nuffield Mathematics Project page 14.
'Computers and Young Children' — Nuffield pages 42-47.
'Towards Mathematics' — J. A. Glenn and D. A. Sturgess pages 181, 182.

S4: 'TRACK WAYS' TO ILLUSTRATE A SORTING MACHINE

In the S3 section we illustrated a two-way system using punched cards. In this section 'track ways' will demonstrate the use of junctions when introducing binary choice. Attribute blocks may be used, but smaller systems selected from the universal set (see S1) are recommended.

Children are asked to move pieces along the track according to the instructions given:—

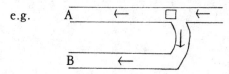

e.g.

At the first junction the square shapes move along the top track to A while all the shapes which are 'not square' are rejected at B.

Another junction may be added and the sorting machine set in motion again.

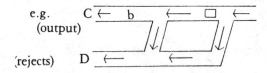

e.g.
(output)

(rejects)

The blocks arriving at C are 'both square and blue' while those arriving at D are 'not square and not blue'. The set of rejects is the complement of the output set.

It is often helpful to place a Carroll diagram at the end of the track to receive the output set. It may be shaded to show the region(s) which are occupied by blocks which have passed along the track.

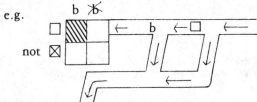

e.g.

Complement set of rejects

There are eight possible arrangements of the blocks, illustrated below as four pairs, each of which produces the same output, showing that 'both square and blue' and 'both blue and square' are commutative statements.

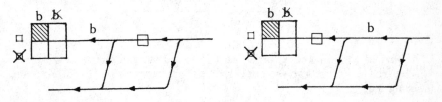

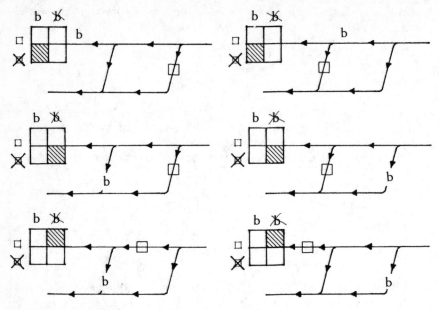

A different arrangement of track is illustrated below:—

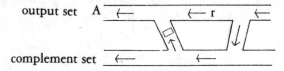

In this sorting machine all red blocks arrive at A, whether or not they are rectangles, but also the rectangles which are not red will arrive at A. The blocks arriving at A are **either** rectangular **or** red. If we put a Carroll diagram at the output the result is shown below:—

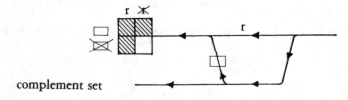

The shaded part illustrates the union of the red set and the rectangular set. Each piece in the union is either (1) red or (2) rectangular or (3) both red and rectangular.

Sometimes a crossed arrangement of track may be used to illustrate negation, e.g.,

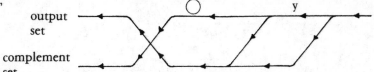

The output set is not both yellow and circular. It is necessary to repeat at this stage that practical activities leading to language development — **not symbolization** — are the objectives we aim to achieve.

Read **An Introduction to the Dienes Mathematics Programme** by Peter L. Seaborne pages 128-137.

S5: CLASSIFICATION OF NUMBERS

Factors

Number	Factors	Number of Factors
1	1	1
2	1, 2	2
3	1, 3	2
4	1, 2, 4	3
5	1, 5	2
6	1, 2, 3, 6	4
7	1, 7	2
8	1, 2, 4, 8	4
9	1, 3, 9	3
10	1, 2, 5, 10	4
11	1, 11	2
12	1, 2, 3, 4, 6, 12	6
13	1, 13	2
14	1, 2, 7, 14	4
15	1, 3, 5, 15	4
16	1, 2, 4, 8, 16	5

From this tabulation the set of **prime numbers** (those with only two factors) may be isolated — 2, 3, 5, 7, 11, 13, etc. The numbers with an **odd** number of factors form the set of **square numbers** — 1, 4, 9, 16, etc. Children might be encouraged to continue the investigation.

ORDERED PAIRS
(a)

	pork	beef	lamb	ham
peas	(peas (pork	(peas (beef	(peas (lamb	(peas (ham
carrots	(carrots (pork	(carrots (beef	(carrots (lamb	(carrots (ham
beans	(beans (pork	(beans (beef	(beans (lamb	(beans (ham

The diagram (a) shows all the possible pairs which can be selected when given the choices indicated.

(b)

	2	4	6	8
1	(1, 2)	(1, 4)	(1, 6)	(1, 8)
2	(2, 2)	(2, 4)	(2, 6)	(2, 8)
3	(3, 2)	(3, 4)	(3, 6)	(3, 8)
4	(4, 2)	(4, 4)	(4, 6)	(4, 8)

Diagram (b) illustrates a set of ordered pairs formed by linking each member of set A, (1, 2, 3, 4), with every member of set B, (2, 4, 6, 8). An interesting subset C is formed by the pairs which lie along the diagonal from top left to bottom right [(1, 2), (2, 4), (3, 6), (4, 8)].

Diagrams (a) and (b) are sometimes referred to as Cartesian products, in honour of the seventeenth century Mathematician.

EQUIVALENT FRACTIONS
The set of ordered pairs [(1, 3), (2, 6), (3, 9) . . . .] might be labelled as the equivalence set of $\frac{1}{3}$.

The fraction $\frac{2}{3}$ may be used to describe the set of ordered pairs [(2, 3), (4, 6), (6, 9)].

Equivalence classes of ordered pairs, e.g. [(3, 4), (6, 8), (9, 12) . . . . .] may be illustrated using thread or rubber bands and a piece of stiff cardboard. Nicks are cut and numbered as shown in the diagram. Threads or bands joining ordered pairs belonging to the same equivalence class all intersect at the same point.

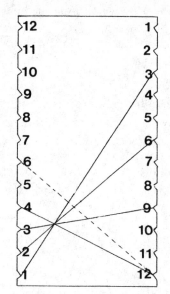

The equivalence set
[(1, 3), (2, 6), (3, 9), (4, 12)..]
is illustrated.

The ordered pair (6, 12) does not belong to this set.

The same information may be transferred to a graph as illustrated below.

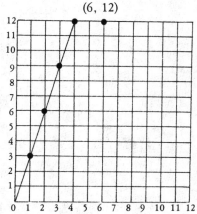

All the points lie on a straight line which goes through the point of origin.

The ordered pair (6, 12) does not lie on the line and is not a member of the set.

EQUIVALENT FRACTIONS (continued)

A fraction is a member of a family of equivalent fractions which represent a rational number, i.e., a number written as a ratio, e.g. $\frac{1}{3}$. When we write $\frac{2}{3} = \frac{4}{6}$ we mean that the rational number represented by $\frac{2}{3}$ is the same as the rational number represented by $\frac{4}{6}$.

We may adopt the 'cross-product' rule as a test for equivalent fractions $\frac{2}{3} = \frac{8}{12}$ if $2 \times 12 = 3 \times 8$. In any one class there is an unlimited number of equivalent fractions which may be built up as follows:—

$$\frac{2}{3}, \quad \frac{2 \times 2}{3 \times 2}, \quad \frac{2 \times 3}{3 \times 3}, \quad \frac{2 \times 4}{3 \times 4}, \quad \frac{2 \times 5}{3 \times 5} \quad \text{etc.}$$

or $$\frac{2}{3}, \quad \frac{4}{6}, \quad \frac{6}{9}, \quad \frac{8}{12}, \quad \frac{10}{15}$$

In each case the 'cross-product' test can be applied.

The following activities might prove useful at this stage:—

(1) examining sets of fractions testing for equivalence,
(2) supplying missing fractions in equivalent sets,
(3) generating sets of equivalent fractions.

Examples of (2) illustrated below.

Complete the following sets:

(a) $\quad [\dfrac{3}{5}, \quad \dfrac{6}{10}, \quad \dfrac{\Box}{\Box}, \quad \dfrac{12}{20}, \quad \dfrac{\Box}{\Box}, \quad \dfrac{\Box}{\Box}]$

(b) $\quad [\dfrac{3}{4}, \quad \dfrac{\Box}{\Box}, \quad \dfrac{9}{12}, \quad \dfrac{\Box}{\Box}, \quad \dfrac{45}{60}]$

NUMBER

N1: MULTIPLICATION AND DIVISION BY 10, 100, 1000

Much of the work of this section depends on a thorough understanding of place value and the development of this in **N2** of the P4-P5 section should be studied.

In **N11** of section 2 practical activities using multibase materials were used to demonstrate that multiplication by 10 was a movement of digits one place to the left; division by 10 was a movement of digits one place to the right. It is essential that children should experience this movement and thus be prevented from accepting the prevailing notion that multiplying by 10 means adding zero.

Activities on an abacus board demonstrate the movement right or left of counters which are used to represent numbers.

e.g.

1000	100	10	1		$\frac{1}{10}$	$\frac{1}{100}$
		O O O O	O O			
O O O O	O O					
					O O O O	O O

42×100 ↘ (left column)

$\leftarrow 42 \div 100$ (right)

Children put out counters to represent 42. They move each group two places to the left and discover that the counters represent the number 4200, i.e. 42×100. The counters are returned to their original position and then moved two places to the right, representing 0.42, i.e. $42 \div 100$. Movement right and left of the counters and recording of the operations performed helps to develop the idea that digits move and **not** the decimal point.

Multiplication and division by 1000 may also be demonstrated as shown on the following diagram:-

e.g.

10 000	1000	100	10	1		$\frac{1}{10}$	$\frac{1}{100}$	$\frac{1}{1000}$
			OOO OO	O				
							OOO OO	O
OOO OO	O							

51×1000 ↘ (left)

$51 \div 1000$ ↙ (right)

These activities stress again the importance of place value and help to strengthen and develop the concept.

N2: DECIMAL FRACTIONS

N12 of section 2 introduces decimal fractions and a revision of the work suggested there might be beneficial. Performing operations with decimal fractions should present little difficulty if, as suggested, they are regarded as an extension of the place value system of notation, i.e. in base ten, each digit with the same symbol, is $\frac{1}{10}$ of the one immediately to the left and ten times greater than the one on the right.

e.g.   2 2 2 . 2 2 2
        a b c   d e f

f is $\frac{1}{10}$ of e; e is $\frac{1}{10}$ of d; d is $\frac{1}{10}$ of c; etc and a is 10 times b; b is 10 times c; c is 10 times d; etc.

Addition and subtraction of decimal fractions were introduced in **N12** of section 2. Further examples involving these operations are appropriate at this stage.

Problems involving multiplication and division introduce these operations in a practical way, e.g. what is the total length of 8 pieces of ribbon each measuring 22.3 cm?

e.g.

(a)   22.3   8 times three tenths gives 24 tenths or 2.4. The 4 tenths are
     $\underline{\times 8}$ recorded and the 20 tenths (2 units) added to the 16 (8 × 2) etc
     178.4

(b)   If I cut a piece of string 15.6 cm long into 6 equal parts, what is the length of each part?

$$\begin{array}{r} 2.6 \\ \hline 6\,|\,15.6 \end{array}$$

When children record 2 in the quotient, there are 3 units left. These changed to tenths give $30+6$ (already there) giving a total of 36. These share among 6 giving 6 tenths to be recorded.

Multiplication and division by 20, 30 etc. is regarded as a movement of digits (left or right) and then multiplication or division by 2, 3, etc.

e.g.

(1)	56.36×20	(2)	43.52×30
$\times 10 \longrightarrow$	563.6	$\times 10 \longrightarrow$	435.2
$\times 2 \longrightarrow$	1127.2	$\times 3 \longrightarrow$	1305.6
(3)	$246.4 \div 20$	(4)	$342.6 \div 30$
$\div 10 \longrightarrow$	24.64	$\div 10 \longrightarrow$	34.26
$\div 2 \longrightarrow$	12.32	$\div 3 \longrightarrow$	11.42

These examples show a movement of digits (not the decimal point). When the example 26.4×3.2 is considered, it is best to regard these as whole numbers, e.g. 264×32 and adjust the answer accordingly.

$$\begin{array}{r} 264 \\ \underline{\times 32} \\ 7920 \\ \underline{528} \\ 8448 \end{array}$$

26.4 was multiplied by 10 to make it a whole number. 3.2 was also multiplied by 10. The product of the two whole numbers is therefore 100 times greater than the required product and so the answer 8448 must be divided by 100, giving 84.48.

Division problems may be tackled by multiplying the divisor by 10, 100, etc. in order to produce a whole number. The dividend is multiplied by the same number.

e.g.

(a) $8.64 \div 3.6$

becomes $86.4 \div 36$ (each multiplied by 10)

(b) $28 \div 0.08$

becomes $2800 \div 8$ (each multiplied by 100)

N3: VULGAR FRACTIONS

A revision of the work and activities outlined in **N13** of section 2 is necessary before attempting any formal work in operations with fractions. Much of the work that was formerly done in addition, subtraction, etc is out of date, but **equivalence** of fractions is still essential. In reaching this understanding children need experience, over a period of time, of many examples of fractions. Some of these examples will arise incidentally and be discussed; others will develop through sharing, folding, cutting, etc.

Generating families or sets of fractions is an activity which helps to establish equivalence.

e.g.

the 'half family'

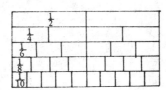

The 'half' family was produced by dividing the half into two equal parts, then 3, 4, 5, etc.

The recorded result reads $\frac{1}{2} = \frac{2}{4} = \frac{3}{6} = \frac{4}{8} = \frac{5}{10}$, etc.

Families of fifths may be generated in a similar way:—

e.g.

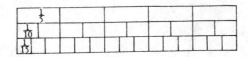

The family of fifths was produced by dividing the fifth into two equal parts and then three, etc.

The recorded result reads $\frac{1}{5} = \frac{2}{10} = \frac{3}{15}$ etc.

Strips of card may be prepared and marked off to show halves, quarters, thirds, fifths, sixths, eighths, tenths, etc. Children can use these to find relationships.

e.g.

(a) 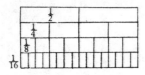 (b)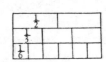

(a) This diagram gives sets of equivalent fractions.

e.g.　or　　$\frac{1}{2} = \frac{2}{4} = \frac{4}{8} = \frac{8}{16}$

　　　or　　$\frac{6}{8} = \frac{3}{4} = \frac{12}{16}$

　　　or　　$\frac{3}{8} = \frac{6}{16}$

(b) Here we demonstrate $\frac{1}{2} = \frac{3}{6}$ and $\frac{1}{3} = \frac{2}{6}$; $\frac{2}{3} = \frac{4}{6}$ but show that the family of thirds is not related to the family of halves.

Squares drawn on spotted cm paper and divided into fractional parts, provide a means of testing the understanding of fractions. Children are asked to label each fraction shown. They are labelled here for the convenience of the teacher.

e.g.

(a) 　(b) 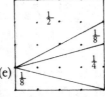　(c)

(d)　(e) 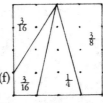　(f)

In labelling these correctly, children are engaged in an exercise on area as the size of each part must be given in relation to the whole square. They are also introduced to addition (and subtraction) of fractions in a practical way.

e.g.　in (a) $\frac{1}{3} + \frac{2}{3} = 1$

　　　in (b) and (c) $\frac{1}{3} + \frac{1}{2} + \frac{1}{6} = 1$ or $\frac{1}{3} + \frac{1}{6} = \frac{1}{2}$

　　　in (d) $\frac{1}{4} + \frac{3}{8} + \frac{3}{8} = 1$ ($\frac{1}{4}$ may be thought of as $\frac{4}{16}$ or $\frac{2}{8}$)

　　　in (e) $\frac{1}{2} + \frac{1}{4} + \frac{1}{8} + \frac{1}{8} = 1$ (the halves and quarters are thought of in terms of eights)

　　　in (f) $\frac{3}{16} + \frac{3}{16} + \frac{1}{4} + \frac{3}{8} = 1$ (here the sections might well be marked in sixteenths)

Some children might arrive at the answers by mental calculations involving both addition and subtraction of fractions.

If children have (through many practical activities) been led to an understanding of equivalence, they will see, e.g. ¼ as belonging to the family of $(¼, \frac{2}{8}, \frac{3}{12}, \frac{4}{16} \ldots \ldots)$ and so (d) might read $\frac{2}{8} + \frac{3}{8} + \frac{3}{8} = \frac{8}{8} = 1$.

More formal work in addition and subtraction of fractions will be made easier if children understand the concept of equivalence, e.g. $\frac{1}{3}$, ¼, $\frac{1}{12}$ may be added if children have a mental picture of the families to which each belongs:—

e.g. $\frac{1}{3}$ belongs to $(\frac{1}{3}, \frac{2}{6}, \frac{3}{9}, \frac{4}{12} \ldots \ldots \ldots .)$

       ¼ belongs to $(¼, \frac{2}{8}, \frac{3}{12}, \frac{4}{16} \ldots \ldots .)$

       $\frac{1}{12}$ belongs to $(\frac{1}{12}, \frac{2}{24}, \frac{3}{36}, \frac{4}{48} \ldots \ldots .)$

Twelfths are common to all three, so the addition would appear as:—

$$\frac{4}{12} + \frac{3}{12} + \frac{1}{12}$$
$$= \frac{8}{12}$$
$$= \frac{2}{3} \quad (\frac{4}{12} + \frac{4}{12} = \frac{1}{3} + \frac{1}{3} = \frac{2}{3} \text{ if reference is made to the family of}$$
$$\text{thirds)}$$

At first it is essential that children use the extended form for addition and subtraction. Examples are best restricted to simple fractions which are in common use.

The name 'denominator' may be introduced as the one which gives the family name to the set of fractions and indicates the number of portions into which the unit has been divided. The name 'numerator' tells how many of these have been selected.

The concept of a fraction as **part of a unit** needs to be developed; a fraction as part of a group or collection must also be established.

e.g.

$$\begin{matrix} ●OO \\ ●OO \\ ●OO \\ ●OO \end{matrix} \quad \begin{matrix} \frac{1}{3} \text{ of } 12 = 4 \\ \text{or} \\ 4 = \frac{1}{3} \text{ of } 12 \end{matrix} \quad \begin{matrix} ●●● \\ OOO \\ OOO \end{matrix} \quad \begin{matrix} \frac{1}{3} \text{ of } 9 = 3 \\ \text{or} \\ 3 = \frac{1}{3} \text{ of } 9 \end{matrix} \quad \begin{matrix} ●●● \\ ●●● \\ OOO \end{matrix} \quad \begin{matrix} \frac{2}{3} \text{ of } 9 = 6 \\ \text{or} \\ 6 = \frac{2}{3} \text{ of } 9 \end{matrix}$$

More difficult examples may follow, e.g. $\frac{3}{8}$ of 24; $\frac{2}{5}$ of 30; $\frac{4}{5}$ of 20, etc.

It is often necessary to multiply fractions by whole numbers, e.g. $5 \times \frac{3}{4}$ and this can be illustrated by using the number line

e.g.

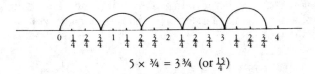

$$5 \times ¾ = 3¾ \text{ (or } \tfrac{15}{4})$$

Multiplication of fractions by whole numbers is probably all that is required of primary school children but sometimes it may be necessary to demonstrate the meaning of e.g. ¼ of ⅓. This may be illustrated by a square divided into thirds and then each third divided into four equal parts.

e.g.

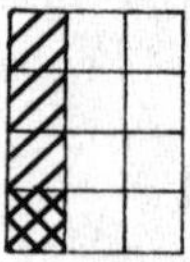

The shaded part illustrates ¼ of ⅓ as being equal to 1/12.

⅓ of ¼ could also be illustrated on the same diagram.

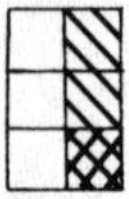

In diagram (b) the square was divided in half and then ⅓ of ½ shaded giving ⅙.

Division of fractions, e.g. 3 ÷ ¾ may be illustrated using the number line and reads: 'How many ¾ lengths in 3 units?'

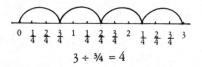

$$3 ÷ ¾ = 4$$

Remembering that multiplication is the inverse of division this may be written as 4 × ¾ = 3.

Cuisenaire rods may be used to develop the **ratio** aspect of fractions. They are made up of rods measuring 1-10 cm in the following colours:—

1 - white	4 - pink	7 - black	9 - blue
2 - red	5 - yellow	8 - brown	10 - orange
3 - light green	6 - dark green		

Halves may be shown in a variety of ways:—

e.g.

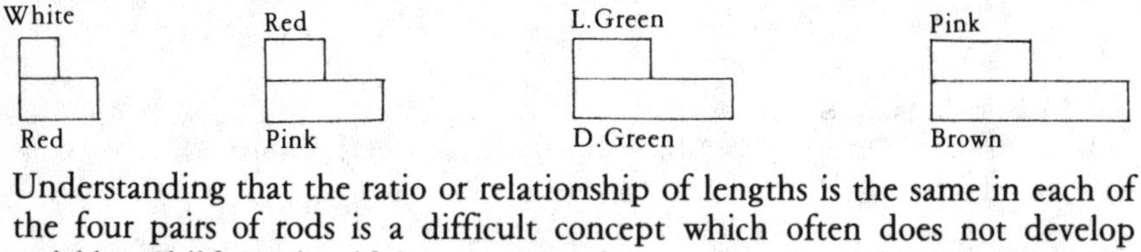

Understanding that the ratio or relationship of lengths is the same in each of the four pairs of rods is a difficult concept which often does not develop quickly. Children should be encouraged to make comparisons not only in terms of **difference** but also in terms of **ratio** and many examples can be found using the rods:—

e.g.

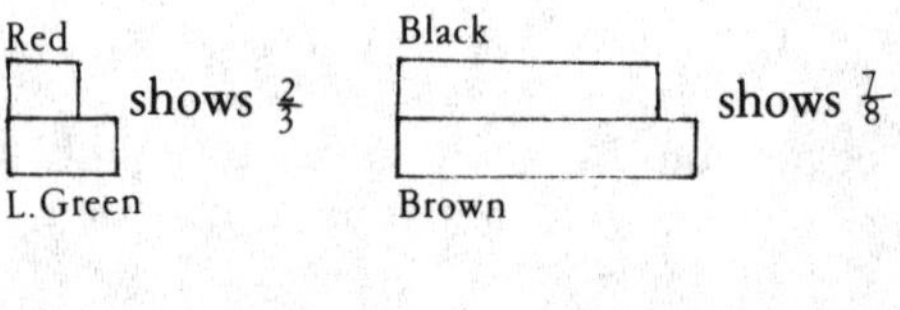

In each case the difference is 1 but the fraction represented is quite different. The **ratio** aspect is illustrated in diagrams (a) and (b) (below).

(a)

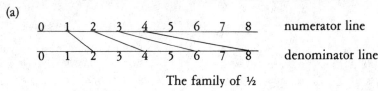

The family of ½

(b)

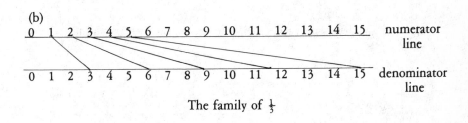

The family of ⅓

N4: NUMBER PATTERNS

A description of square and triangular numbers was given in **N7** of the P4-P5 section. It is interesting to study not only their growth but also relationships existing between them.

Square numbers:　　　　　1, 4, 9, 16, 25, 36 ......
Triangular numbers:　　　1, 3, 6, 10, 15 ....

Two triangular numbers adjacent to each other produce a square number when added together.

e.g.　　　$1 + 3 = 4$　　　　$3 + 6 = 9$　　　　$6 + 10 = 16$
　　　　　　　$= 2 \times 2$　　　　　$= 3 \times 3$　　　　　$= 4 \times 4$
　　　　　　　$= 2^2$　　　　　　$= 3^2$　　　　　　$= 4^2$

Pentagonal Numbers

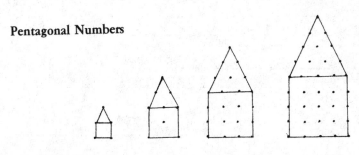

The pentagonal numbers are made up of square and triangular numbers, e.g.

Completing the following table helps to assess the understanding of the patterns.

Square Numbers	4	9	16		36		64	
Triangular Numbers	1	3	6	10		21		36	
Pentagonal Numbers	5	12	22					

Finding the rule for the 12th pentagonal number might be a useful investigation.

The Growth of Cubes

Children may investigate the growth of cubes by building up small cubes to make larger ones. Multibase cubes are useful here and children discover that in order to turn each cube into the next larger one, they must add 3 flats (squares), 3 longs and a unit cube.

It is possible to tabulate the growth of cubes and to use the table to build up the cubes of larger numbers.

Side of Cube	1	2	3	4	5	6	7	8
Number of unit cubes	1	8	27	64	125	216	343	512
Number added		7	19	37	61	91	127	169
How many more added than last time			12	18	24	30	36	42

The Sieve of Eratosthenes

A number which has no factors other than 1 and itself is called a prime number. Eratosthenes, in the third century, used the sieving method to isolate the prime numbers.

1	②	③	4	⑤	6	⑦	8	9	10
⑪	12	⑬	14	15	16	⑰	18	⑲	20
21	22	㉓	24	25	26	27	28	㉙	30
㉛	32	33	34	35	36	㊲	38	39	40
㊶	42	㊸	44	45	46	㊼	48	49	50
51	52	㉝	54	55	56	57	58	㊾	60
㊽	62	63	64	65	66	㊿	68	69	70
㊹	72	⑬	74	75	76	77	78	㊴	80
81	82	⑧③	84	85	86	87	88	⑧⑨	90
91	92	93	94	95	96	⑨⑦	98	99	100

On the 100 square above, the numbers which are circled are prime numbers and were obtained by the following method:—

1. Eliminate all multiples of 2 except 2
2. Eliminate all multiples of 3 except 3
3. Eliminate all multiples of 5 except 5
4. Eliminate all multiples of 7 except 7
5. Cross out 1 (it is generally accepted that 1 is **not** a prime number).

A study of these prime numbers may lead to the following discoveries:—
(a) All prime numbers except 2 are odd.
(b) There are 'twin' primes, e.g.   11, 13
$$41, 43$$
137, 139 (Extending beyond the
149, 151   100 square)
(c) Prime numbers, with the exception of 2, 3, precede or follow a multiple of 6.
(d) Every prime number is flanked by two even numbers, one of which must be divisible by 3 (except 2, 3).
(e) Some prime numbers are the sum of two square numbers,

e.g. $\quad 5 = 2^2 + 1^2 \qquad 53 = 7^2 + 2^2$
$29 = 5^2 + 2^2 \qquad 73 = 8^2 + 3^2$
$37 = 6^2 + 1^2 \qquad 97 = 9^2 + 4^2$

(f) Prime numbers are **not** rectangular numbers, i.e. 7×1 is not a rectangle.

Further investigations might be carried out, e.g. to find 2, 3 or 4 primes which have a total of 78.

7	2	37
19	53	41
23	23	78
29	78	
78		

Repeat for other suitable totals, e.g.52.

Factors

Factors and products were introduced in a game situation in P5 (Ref. **N9** of section 2). Children were given practice in multiplication facts, e.g. $4 \times 6 = 24$ etc.; they were also required to answer, e.g. 'What are the factors of 24?' To discover all the factors of 24, children may arrange 24 blocks in as many ways as possible, e.g.

1 set of 24	2 sets of 12	6 sets of 4	8 sets of 3
24 sets of 1	12 sets of 2	4 sets of 6	3 sets of 8

Patterns on the multiplication square (Ref. **N4** P4-P5 section) draw attention to factors and products. When children colour in the pattern of, e.g. 4, they are in fact saying that 4 is a factor of all the numbers that are coloured.

Prime numbers were isolated using the sieve of Eratosthenes; **prime factors** may be shown using the 'family tree'.

e.g.

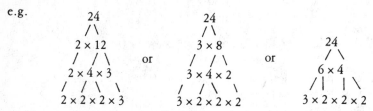

The 'trees' may be built up using cubes, buttons or counters. All prime factors are also prime numbers.

It is sometimes helpful if children have discovered rules for divisibility by 2, 4, 8; 5, 10; 3, 6, 9; as they can quickly recognise whether, e.g. 9 is a factor of certain numbers. A further stage of investigation might be to find the factors common to several numbers, i.e. the H.C.F. (the highest common factor).

N5: LONG DIVISION

Teachers should read carefully sections **N6**, **N9** and **N11** of section 2. Children who were introduced to recorded division using multibase materials and the long division pattern, have few problems in recording division by 20, 30,

40; 21, 31, 41, and later 29, 39... 19.

In the early stages it is essential to think in terms of material to be shared,

e.g.

```
        F  L  U
           2  4              23           23
   23 |5   6  3             × 5          × 4
       -4   6  +            ───          ───
          ───              115           92
          1  0  3
          -  9  2
             ───
             1  1
```

There are not enough flats, but they may be exchanged for longs giving 56 to be shared. Each person gets 2, and 10 are left over. These are exchanged for units and added to the 3 already there, giving 103 to be shared. Trial sums may be worked at the side to determine whether 4 or 5 are given to each and the result recorded. The labels might eventually be HTU as these are relevant to the work in base 10. As was suggested earlier, it is good to think of multiplication as the inverse process to division and so a check up may be used by multiplying 24 by 23 and adding remainder 11.

The repeated subtraction method was illustrated in **N6** of section 2 and may be the method preferred by some teachers.

```
e.g.          24
          23 | 563
             - 230      10 times ⎫
             ─────               ⎪
               333              ⎪
             - 230      10 times ⎬  total of 24 recorded above
             ─────               ⎪
               103              ⎪
                92       4 times ⎭
             ─────
                11               remainder is 11
```

N6: AVERAGES

Children's first idea of an average may arise when several, with unequal numbers of marbles wish to re-distribute so that each has the same amount to play a game. This leads to the method of adding up all the separate unequal amounts and sharing equally among the number of children.

The scores of the game might be recorded in graphical form
e.g.

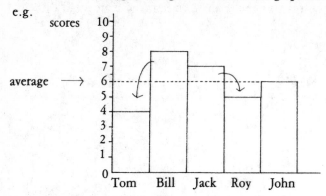

Children are invited to investigate the situation and arrive at an average score. Obviously it must lie somewhere between 4 and 8, so 6 might be considered. On the diagram above it is not difficult to see how the scores were re-arranged so that each is alike.

To find the average length of six pieces of ribbon, they may be placed end to end on a metre stick and the total length recorded. To find the average, the total length is divided by 6. When children grasp what an average means, then more difficult examples may be worked, but a practical approach is necessary in the early stages.

N7: STUDY OF OTHER NUMBER SYSTEMS

A study of some ancient number systems may give children a greater appreciation of their own and again draw attention to the 'place value' feature which is missing from many of them.

(a) Roman

Most children have met numbers written in Roman numerals, e.g. on clock faces, on old tombstones and in some Bibles. The Romans counted in powers of ten, but had no 'place value' system.

$$X = 10$$
$$C = 10 \times 10$$
$$M = 10 \times 10 \times 10$$

A special feature of the Roman notation was a symbol for the five of each grouping,

e.g. $V = 5$
$$L = 50$$
$$D = 500$$

Groupings were recorded by repeating symbols,

    e.g. CCXXXII = 232

A number of lesser value placed before another was subtracted, while one placed after, was added,

    e.g. IV = 4
            VI = 6

    or   XL = 40
            LX = 60

(b) Egyptian

The Egyptian system also counted in tens and numbers were usually written from right to left with the singles' digit on the extreme left.

    $\cap$ = 10

    9 = 10 × 10

    $\stackrel{\circ}{\lambda}$ = 10 × 10 × 10

The number 1342 was written:—

    II ∩∩∩∩ 999 $\stackrel{\circ}{\lambda}$

The general plan of the notation was to have special symbols for powers of 10 and to repeat these as necessary.

(c) Babylonian

Around Babylon, clay was abundant, and the people impressed their symbols in the damp clay tablets, and then baked the tablets in the sun or in a kiln, thus forming documents practically as permanent as stone. Since the pressure of the stylus gave a wedge-shaped symbol, the writings are known as cuneiform.

    The symbols were $\blacktriangledown$ = one (also 60, 60², etc.)

                        $\blacktriangleleft$ = 10 (also 10 × 60)

The Babylonians developed a positional system with base 60. With such a large base it would be awkward to have unrelated names for the digits, 0, 1, ... 59, so a simple grouping system to base 10 was used for these numbers,

e.g.

    $\blacktriangledown\blacktriangledown\blacktriangleleft\blacktriangleleft\blacktriangleleft\blacktriangledown$

        $\blacktriangleleft\blacktriangleleft$ = 60 + 60 + 10 + 10 + 10 + 10 + 10 + 1 = 171

Performing the operations of addition, subtraction, multiplication and division, using any of these cumbersome systems, is extremely tedious as children who experiment with them soon discover. None of them had a symbol for zero.

(d) The Mayan System

In the course of early Spanish expeditions into Yucatan, it was discovered that the Mayans had a well-developed positional system, complete with zero. The base was 20, but the digits 1-19 were grouped to the base 5.

⬭	= 0	══	= 10
•	= 1	··⸱══	= 12
──	= 5	═══	= 15
···══	= 8	····═══	= 19

The Mayan numerals appear to have been used for writing numbers rather than for calculation.

Our own number system, a combination of the work of the Arabs and Hindus, has three important features:—

(a) the positional principle (place value)
(b) the symbol zero
(c) grouping to the base 10.

The devising of a scheme whereby any number may be represented by means of 9 symbols and zero is one of the most important achievements of human intellect. 'The idea is so simple', wrote the 18-19th century mathematician Pierre-Simon, 'that this very simplicity is the reason for our not being sufficiently aware how much admiration it deserves'.

N8: ACTIVITIES LEADING TO THE CONCEPT OF AN ORDERED PAIR

Fixing the position of desks in a classroom by using numbers and letters is perhaps the easiest way to introduce children to the idea of an ordered pair or co-ordinates.

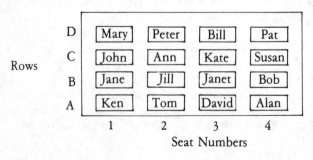

Seat Numbers

John's position may be recorded as 1C
Pat's position may be recorded as 4D
Janet's position may be recorded as 3B
Tom's position may be recorded as 2A

If we use numbers 1, 2, 3, 4 instead of letters A, B, C, D the positions would now read:—

John   (1, 3)   Janet   (3, 2)
Pat   (4, 4)   Tom   (2, 1)

An order has been established, i.e. the horizontal number precedes the vertical and practice in plotting co-ordinates must be given so that children quickly find positions on a grid.

Games may be devised to give practice in marking positions, e.g. two dice of different colours are chosen, red to represent the horizontal position and blue, the vertical. When these are thrown two numbers appear, e.g. red 4 and blue 5. This position is marked by placing a small counter on the grid in the appropriate place.

e.g.

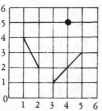

The dice are thrown by the partner in the game, and his position recorded with a different coloured counter. The aim may be to get any one of the following:—

(1) 3 counters in a row
(2) points at the corners of a square
(3) points at the corners of a rectangle.

Ladders may be added so that children may move along these if they arrive at either end. The game may also be played on a pegboard.

Exercises in plotting co-ordinates to give familiar shapes adds interest to the activity.

e.g.

(a)

Children are asked to plot the following:—

(1, 1), (4, 1), (1, 3),
(4, 3), (2, 4), (3, 4),
(2, 5), (3, 5)

(b)

(c)

Children may be asked to plot the points which give shapes (b) and (c) or to draw shapes of their own and write down the co-ordinates.

The following star constellations may also be plotted:—

(a) Orion (10, 4), (13, 6), (12, 9), (14, 10), (16, 11), (18, 14), (16, 4), (12, 16).
(b) Casseopaeia (5, 7), (8, 9), (9, 5), (12, 4), (13, 6).
(c) The Plough (48, 15), (51, 23), (44, 28), (51, 7), (9, 23), (48, 19), (48, 29).

The following activities with pegs on pegboards provide areas of investigation:—

(a) Put pegs to represent the four corners of a square. Add 2 to the horizontal co-ordinate and 3 to the vertical co-ordinate.
(b) Double both co-ordinates of each corner of the square.
(c) Put pegs at (1, 2), (2, 4), (3, 6), (4, 8). What did you notice?
(d) Put the pegs at (1, 3), (2, 6), (3, 9), (4, 12), etc. Comment.

N9: FURTHER NUMBER PATTERNS

Pascal's Triangle

An activity leading to the pattern described as Pascal's Triangle might follow.

e.g.

Children are invited to travel from A to every point on the grid restricting their movements to two directions, e.g. down and to the right. From A to B the routes might be described as follows:—

(1) 2 right and 1 down;
(2) 1 down and 2 right;
(3) 1 right, 1 down and 1 right.

If the number of routes from A to each point on the grid is marked, the following pattern emerges:—

```
starting ──────→  A   1   1   1
point             1   2   3   4
                  1   3   6   10
                  1   4   10  20
                                B
```

Rotate the square
through 45° to this position.

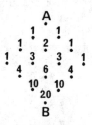

A pattern of numbers emerges and is part of the series known as Pascal's Triangle, shown below in three forms A, B, C.

These show how the patterns may be extended.

e.g.

```
                                    1
                            1               1         X
                      1           2               1
              A           1           3       3       1
                    1           4       6       4       1
                1       5       10      10      5       1
            1       6       15      10      15      6       1
        1       7       21      35      35      21      7       1
    1       8       28      56      70      56      28      8       1
                    Y
```

```
B
1
1 1     X
1 2 1
1 3 3 1
1 4 6 4 1
1 5 10 10 5 1
1 6 15 20 15 6 1
1 7 21 35 35 21 7 1
1 8 28 56 70 56 28 8 1
      Y
```

```
              X
C
1 1 1 1 1 1 1 1 1
1 2 3 4 5 6 7 8
1 3 6 10 15 21 28
1 4 10 20 35 56
1 5 15 35 70
1 6 21 56
1 7 28
1 8   Y
1
```

231

Many interesting patterns may be found by using these, e.g.

1. The binary system (base 2) may be found by adding the totals of the lines in A and in B.
2. Triangular numbers on lines X Y in forms A, B and C.
3. In form C each row is made up of the running totals of the row immediately above. The fifth row, e.g. has:—

$$5(1 + 4), \ 15(1 + 4 + 10), \ 35(1 + 4 + 10 + 20), \text{ etc.}$$

A pattern of numbers in the form of Pascal's triangle occurs in the study of probability. If 4 coins are tossed into the air together, they may land showing all 4 heads, or they may land showing all 4 tails. They may also land showing some combination of heads and tails. A table listing all possibilities is shown below.

4 Heads	3 Heads + 1 Tail	2 Heads + 2 Tails	1 Head + 3 Tails	4 Tails
H H H H	H H H T	H H T T	H T T T	T T T T
	T H H H	T T H H	T T T H	
	H H T H	H T T H	T H T T	
	H T H H	H T H T	T T H T	
		T H T H		
		T H H T		

An investigation using Cuisenaire rods may also lead to a pattern of numbers in the form of Pascal's Triangle.

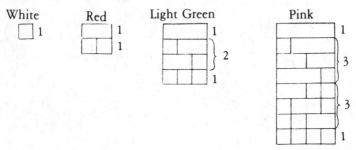

For example, the pink rod is matched by 2 rods in 3 different ways, by 3 rods in 3 different ways and by 4 rods in 1 way. The number of patterns obtained by beginning with the pink rod is $1 + 3 + 3 + 1$. From the diagram it can be seen that the numbers of patterns obtained by beginning with a white, a red, a green and a pink rod are in the form of Pascal's Triangle.

$$(1), \ (1, 1), \ (1, 2, 1), \ (1, 3, 3, 1), \text{ etc.}$$

Further investigations with other rods are required to determine whether or not the pattern is continued. An investigation of the cross-link between the numbers 11^{0}, 11^{1}, 11^{2}, 11^{3}, 11^{4}, and the rows in Pascal's Triangle might also be of interest.

```
      1
     1  1
    1  2  1
   1  3  3  1
  1  4  6  4  1
 1  5  10  10  5  1
1  6  15  20  15  6  1
```

The totals obtained by adding diagonally gives another series of numbers 1, 1, 2, 3, 5, 8, 13, 21, etc. To continue the sequence, add the two preceding terms. This series was developed by Leonardo of Pisa, nicknamed **Fibonacci**.

Rectangles drawn below are based on **Fibonacci** numbers.

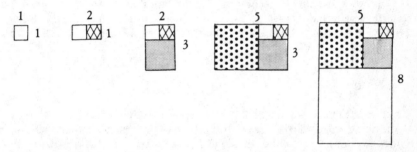

At each stage, the length of the new rectangle is equal to the sum of the length and breadth of the last rectangle. These are good approximations to a 'golden rectangle', the ratio of whose sides, the 'golden ratio', has often been thought to form the basis of an ideal system of proportion. This ratio seems to appear both in shapes and in numbers, and examples may be found in nature, in painting and in architecture. A postcard 5 × 3 or a sheet of foolscap, 13 × 8, are good approximations of the 'golden ratio'.

N10: INTRODUCTION TO INDICES

This activity might introduce the topic.

1. Fold a strip of paper (30 cm × 5 cm) in half.
2. Open it out. How many rectangles? How many creases?
3. Fold the paper as before, and then fold in half again.

4. How many rectangles? How many creases?
5. Refold the paper as it was, and then fold in half again.
6. How many rectangles? How many creases?
7. Record your results.

Number of times folded	Number of rectangles	Number of creases
1	2	1
2	4	3
3	8	7

The centre column may be re-written like this:

$$2 = 2$$
$$4 = 2 \times 2$$
$$8 = 2 \times 2 \times 2$$

The numbers in the first column tell the number of twos in the second column. For 6 folds we would expect to find 6 twos in the second column or $2 \times 2 \times 2 \times 2 \times 2 \times 2$. A shorthand way of writing all the 2's in the middle column is

$$2 = 2^1$$
$$2 \times 2 = 2^2$$
$$2 \times 2 \times 2 = 2^3 \text{ etc.}$$

When a number is written as 2^3, it is called 2 to the power 3.

Multibase material in a variety of bases may be used to demonstrate index notation. A number may be written as 1 1 1 1 (base five) and is made up of the following:—

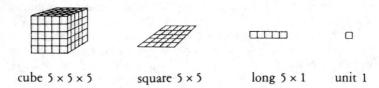

cube 5 × 5 × 5　　　square 5 × 5　　　long 5 × 1　　　unit 1

The cube is made up of five layers each containing 25 (5 × 5) units. The square is made up of 25 (5 × 5) units and the long 5 × 1 units. In index notation the recording would be:—

$$5 \times 5 \times 5 = 5^3 \text{ (cube)}$$
$$5 \times 5 = 5^2 \text{ (square)}$$
$$5 = 5^1 \text{ (long)}$$
$$1 = 5^0 \text{ (unit)} \text{ — usually arrived at by}$$
$$\text{deduction following the pattern}$$

Powers of 2 may be built up using Cuisenaire rods.

e.g.

$$2^0 = 1$$ □

$$2^1 = 2$$ ▭

$$2^2 = 4$$ ▭

$$2^3 = 8$$ ▭

A table of indices might be built up:—

e.g.

2^0	$= 1$	3^0	$= 1$
2^1	$= 2$	3^1	$= 3$
2^2	$= 4$	3^2	$= 9$
2^3	$= 8$	3^3	$= 27$
2^4	$= 16$	3^4	$= 81$
2^5	$= 32$	3^5	$= 243$
2^6	$= 64$	3^6	$= 729$
2^7	$= 128$	3^7	$= 2187$
2^8	$= 256$	3^8	$= 6561$
2^9	$= 512$	3^9	$= 19683$
2^{10}	$= 1024$	3^{10}	$= 59049$

Calculations, using this information, are simplified,

e.g. $64 \times 16 = 2^6 \times 2^4$

$\qquad = 2 \times 2 \times 2 \times 2 \times 2 \times 2 \times 2 \times 2 \times 2 \times 2$

$\qquad = 2^{10}$

$\qquad = 1024$ (using the table).

or $\quad 2187 \times 27 = 3^{10}$ (or multiplied by 3, ten times).

$\qquad = 59049$

Children soon realise that for multiplication, indices are added and the answer found by reference to the table.

For division, the indices are subtracted,

e.g. $1024 \div 256 = 2^{10} \div 2^8$

$\qquad = 2^2$

$\qquad = 4$ (may be proved by dividing 1024 by 256 or by multiplying 256 by 4).

Using indices, it is possible to record very large numbers:—

e.g. $\quad 10^5 = 10 \times 10 \times 10 \times 10 \times 10$

$\qquad = 10\ 000$

or $10^5 \times 10^8 = 10\ 000\ 000\ 000\ 000$

Interesting patterns may be produced from a table of powers, if we reduce each number to one digit, called the digital root:—

e.g. $27 \rightarrow 2+7 \rightarrow 9$

e.g. $256 \rightarrow 2+5+6 \rightarrow 13 \rightarrow 1+3 \rightarrow 4$

   $3125 \rightarrow 3+1+2+5 \rightarrow 11 \rightarrow 1+1 \rightarrow 2$

Digital roots are printed in large type

Powers

Numbers \ Powers	1	2	3	4	5	6	7
1	1 **1**	1 **1**	1 **1**	1 **1**	1 **1**	1 **1**	1 **1**
2	2 **2**	4 **4**	8 **8**	16 **7**	32 **5**	64 **1**	128 **2**
3	3 **3**	9 **9**	27 **9**	81 **9**	243 **9**	729 **9**	2187 **9**
4	4 **4**	16 **7**	64 **1**	256 **4**	1024 **7**	4096 **1**	16384 **4**
5	5 **5**	25 **7**	125 **8**	625 **4**	3125 **2**	15625 **1**	78125 **5**
6	6 **6**	36 **9**	216 **9**	1296 **9**	7776 **9**	46656 **9**	279936 **9**
7	7 **7**	49 **4**	343 **1**	2401 **7**	16807 **4**	117649 **1**	823543 **7**

Children may discover the pattern of 7 to be a reversal of the pattern of 4 and the pattern of 5 to be a reversal of the pattern of 2.

The activity provides plenty of practice in multiplication and is self-checking when children discover the pattern. If they are sufficiently interested to continue the pattern, a calculator might be used to speed up the work. Investigation of patterns formed by the digital roots in the following series might be appropriate here:—

e.g.

Add 3

$1 \longrightarrow 4 \longrightarrow 7 \longrightarrow \overset{10}{1} \longrightarrow \overset{13}{4} \longrightarrow \overset{16}{7} \longrightarrow \overset{19}{1}$ etc.

Add 4

$1 \longrightarrow 5 \longrightarrow 9 \longrightarrow \overset{13}{4} \longrightarrow \overset{17}{8} \longrightarrow \overset{21}{3} \longrightarrow \overset{25}{7}$

$\longrightarrow \overset{29}{2} \longrightarrow \overset{33}{6} \longrightarrow \overset{37}{1} \longrightarrow \overset{41}{5} \longrightarrow \overset{45}{9} \longrightarrow \overset{49}{4}$ etc.

Add 5

$1 \longrightarrow 6 \longrightarrow \overset{11}{2} \longrightarrow \overset{16}{7} \longrightarrow \overset{21}{3} \longrightarrow \overset{26}{8} \longrightarrow \overset{31}{4}$

$\longrightarrow \overset{36}{9} \longrightarrow \overset{41}{5} \longrightarrow \overset{46}{1} \longrightarrow \overset{51}{6} \longrightarrow \overset{56}{2} \longrightarrow \overset{61}{7} \longrightarrow \overset{66}{3}$ etc.

Add 6

$1 \longrightarrow 7 \longrightarrow \overset{13}{4} \longrightarrow \overset{19}{1} \longrightarrow \overset{25}{7} \longrightarrow \overset{31}{4} \longrightarrow \overset{37}{1}$ etc.

Add 7

$$1 \longrightarrow 8 \longrightarrow 6^{15} \longrightarrow 4^{22} \longrightarrow 2^{29} \longrightarrow 9^{36} \longrightarrow 7^{43}$$
$$\longrightarrow 5^{50} \longrightarrow 3^{57} \longrightarrow 1^{64} \longrightarrow 8^{71} \longrightarrow 6^{78} \longrightarrow 4^{85} \quad \text{etc.}$$

Children investigating the structures may discover:—

e.g.　　Add 6 is a reversal of add 3
　　　　Add 5 is a reversal of add 4.

They may wish to continue the investigation to find other relationships.

N11: PROBABILITY AND SAMPLING

The study of probability is a suitable topic for children at the upper end of primary schools, if it emerges from practical activities which involve only simple calculations. The developed concept is a difficult one; the aim at primary level should be to introduce the topic in such a way as to stimulate further investigation.

Tossing a coin 50 times and recording scores as 'heads' or 'tails' is a simple activity. Comparing results of several children in a group may reveal that heads appeared as frequently as tails, i.e. the probability of throwing heads was 1 out of 2 or ½.

Many and varied activities are necessary before children arrive at anything approaching an 'occurrence ratio', though, gradually, they will come to see this as:　$\dfrac{\text{occurrence of event}}{\text{total number of trials.}}$

An excellent probability kit, produced by Geoffrey Giles as part of the 'Dime' project, and marketed by Oliver and Boyd, gives children an interesting selection of experiments, a few of which are listed below:—

(1) Tube containing a die. Children shake 50 times each and record a win

   (a) if a six is on top
   (b) if a two is on top
   (c) if top number is odd.

(2) Tube containing two dice. Shake 50 times and record a win

   (a) if sum is even
   (b) if product is even
   (c) if sum is a prime number.

(3) Tube containing 2 copper coins and 1 silver one. Shake 50 times and record a win

   (a) if both copper coins are heads
   (b) if both copper coins are tails.

(4) Tube containing a red die and a blue die. Shake 50 times and record a win if both dice show the same number.

(5) Tube containing 2 yellow cubes and 1 red cube each with a hole through

the middle. A win is recorded if the red cube does not have a hole on its top face.

Other interesting games may be found in 'Probability and Statistics', part of the Nuffield Mathematics Project.

e.g. (1)

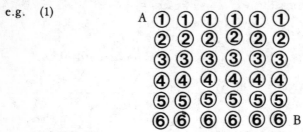

The game is played by 2 players, using a board with 36 lattice points, each marked with a numbered circle.

One player places a counter at A and the other at B. Each throws the die in turn, making a move only when a number adjacent to his own appears on the die, i.e. **A** moves if he throws a 1 or a 2; **B** moves if he throws a 5 or a 6. The player to arrive first at the opposite corner is the winner.

In **N9** the total number of routes from A to each point on the grid was traced and was part of the series of numbers known as Pascal's Triangle.

(2) Choose a partner. Each player has 12 counters. Play for these with 3 dice. When 11 is the total for one throw (by either partner) A gives a counter to B. When 14 is the total at one throw (by either) B gives a counter to A. The player who first wins all the counters wins the game. Which player (A or B) is most likely to win and why?

Many children will simply perform the experiments and record the results; others, with the help of the teacher, will estimate or predict what the result should be. Collecting data, recording it accurately and perhaps working out $\dfrac{\text{the number of wins}}{\text{the total number of throws}}$ as a decimal fraction, is all that is required of children at this stage.

Sampling

Sampling is a special branch of statistics — a method by which some property is investigated by testing a fraction of it. As it is often impossible to test a large number of items, a sample is selected and used as being typical of the complete set. Choosing samples so that resulting information will be reliable, is a difficult problem, and not one which most primary school children will handle expertly. Engaging in sampling activities, however, does provide a base from which future work in this field might grow.

e.g. (1) 5 containers having a certain ratio of black marbles to red ones:—

      (a) 45 red, 5 black   )
      (b) 40 red, 10 black)   children are given the containers without
      (c) 35 red, 15 black)   labels and by sampling try to attach them
      (d) 30 red, 20 black)   correctly.
      (e) 25 red, 25 black)

(a)   Choose a container. Take a sample of one marble, 5 times, replacing it each time and recording the colours selected. Guess which label is needed.

(b)   Repeat using 10, 20, 30, 40, 50 samples and guess. After 50 samples, it is more likely that the choice is correct.

(2)   A bag of marbles containing 200 white and 800 black

      (a) Take samples of one, five times, and record the number of white marbles.

      (b) Take samples of 20, 50... 100 and record.

The large samples give a truer estimate of the proportion of white marbles to black ones.

Other examples of sampling may be found in:—

(1) 'Statistics and Probability' by P. A. Caine, published by Chatto and Windus.

(2) Core Unit 24 of 'Towards Mathematics' by J. A. Glenn and D. A. Sturgess, published by Schofield and Sims Ltd.

N12: EXAMPLES OF DIRECT PROPORTION

The concept of proportion is a difficult one, but children will meet examples of **direct** proportion when they buy a number of items, e.g. bars of chocolate, ice-cream cones, lollipops, etc. and tabulate the result:—

e.g. (a)

Number of lollipops	1	2	3	4	5	10	20
Cost in pence	2	4	6	8	10	20	40

When the number of items is doubled, the cost is doubled; 2 cost 4p and 4 cost 8p.

    When the number of lollipops is halved, the cost is halved; 20 cost 40p and 10 cost 20p.

The information may be represented in graphical form:—

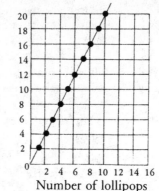

Cost in pence

Number of lollipops

The cost of 7, 8, 9, etc. may be read from the graph.

(b) Further examples of direct proportion are illustrated below. In each case the ratio of L to P is the same.

Length of side of square (L)	1	2	4	5	10	20
Perimeter of square (P)	4	8	16	20	40	80

Children might be given a table to complete where there are two variables in direct proportion to each other:—

(c)

Number of packets	1	2	3			6	
Cost at 15p per pkt.				60	75		105

N13: DEVELOPING THE CONCEPT OF RATIO

In **N3**, Cuisenaire rods were used to illustrate the ratio aspect of fractions, e.g.

red
green

gives the ratio of red to green as 2/3; of green to red as 3/2.

green
crimson

gives the ratio (of green to crimson as 3/4)
(of crimson to green as 4/3)

The ratio of black pegs to white is 3/9 or 1/3.
The ratio of white pegs to black is 9/3 or 3/1.

The ratio of houses to trees is 3/5.
The ratio of trees to houses is 5/3.

The following activities might help to develop the concept.

(a) Measuring lengths of ribbon A, B, C in centimetres and recording the following ratios:—

A to B →   B to A →   C to A →
A to C →   B to C →   C to B →

(b) Weighing objects A, B, C and recording their weights in grams. Expressing the ratios of A to B; A to C; B to A, B to C; C to A and C to B.

(c) Finding the ratios between the following quantities, remembering that each pair must be measured in the same unit before a ratio can be expressed:—

10 grams	: 1 kilogram
10 seconds	: 2 minutes
10 centimetres	: 5 metres
10 pence	: £3

N14: PERCENTAGES

Percentages are really ratios whose denominator is 100. The meaning of a percentage is much more important at this stage than the performance of calculations involving percentages. The chief use is for comparison; hence the choice of a fixed denominator.

A tray, holding 100 blocks, may be used to demonstrate the meaning of percentages. 20 blocks are removed, i.e. $\frac{20}{100}$, called 20 per cent and written as 20%. 80 blocks remain, i.e. $\frac{80}{100}$ called 80 per cent and written as 80%.

In **N3**, children had experience in generating families of fractions and should be able to relate $\frac{50}{100}$ as being equivalent to ½; $\frac{25}{100}$ as being equivalent to ¼; $\frac{75}{100}$ as being equivalent to ¾.

There are many practical activities which help to establish the idea of percentages a few of which are included here.

e.g. (a)

Give children squared paper (10 × 10) and ask them to colour in patterns using 4 different symbols. Record the total number of squares for each symbol in three different ways:—

e.g.

	Number	Fraction	Percentage
O	24	$\frac{24}{100}$	24%
X	40	$\frac{40}{100}$	40%
⣿	20	$\frac{20}{100}$	20%
☐	16	$\frac{16}{100}$	16%

(b) Make a pattern on a '100' square using the following symbols as indicated:—

(1) ⣿ 15% (3) ☐ 50%

(2) X 25% (4) O 10%

(c) A set of dominoes marked with percentages, decimal fractions and vulgar fractions, help children to see the relationships in the set.

e.g. CUT →

$\frac{1}{10}$	20%
$\frac{1}{5}$	0.25
$\frac{1}{4}$	80%
$\frac{8}{10}$	$\frac{3}{4}$
75%	50%
$\frac{1}{2}$	$\frac{3}{10}$
30%	0.15
15%	10%

A set may contain any number of cards, but the last one links up with the first, e.g. 10% = $\frac{1}{10}$.

(d) Tables may be prepared for children to complete.

e.g.
(1)

Fraction	$\frac{1}{10}$		$\frac{1}{100}$		$\frac{7}{100}$	
Decimal fraction	0.1	0.75		0.25		0.3
Percentage	10		5			

(2)

Ratio	$\frac{1}{5}$		$\frac{4}{5}$		$\frac{1}{4}$	
Percentage	20%	40%		70%		60%

(3)

Area of shape A in squares	40	30		3	18	
Area of shape B in squares	80		100	12	24	20
A as a percentage of B	50%	50%	10%			20%

For further examples refer to Core Unit 22 of 'Towards Mathematics' by J. A. Glenn and D. A. Sturgess, published by Schofield and Sims Ltd. and 'Maths Adventure' Books 4 and 5 by Jan Stanfield, published by Evan Bros. Ltd.

N15: INTRODUCTION OF POSITIVE AND NEGATIVE NUMBERS

These may be introduced as an extension of the number line left of zero with symbols to denote negative and positive values, e.g. $^-7$ to be read as negative, 7 and $^+7$ as positive 7. These symbols are quite distinct from plus and minus which are used to indicate the operations of addition and subtraction. Positive and negative numbers may be referred to as directed numbers or signed integers.

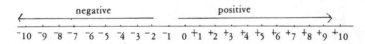

A forward count of 5 is written as $^+5$ while a backward count is written as $^-5$.

A game may be played using a black die and a white one. The number on the white die indicates how many steps forwards (to the right of zero) are to be taken; the black die tells how many steps backwards (to the left of zero) are to be taken. If white shows 6 and black shows 4, take 6 steps to the right, beginning at zero, then 4 to the left, arriving at $^+2$. Alternatively, the backward move of 4 may be made first, followed by the forward move of 6. In each case the result is the same as shown on diagrams (a) and (b).

(a)

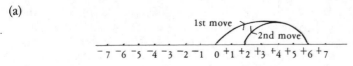

(b)

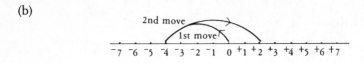

The game may be played in pairs, the winner being the person who moves off the line (at either end) first.

Positive and negative numbers have been used to show movement right and left of zero. They may also be used to show movement up or down:—

e.g. (1) a lift moving above or below ground level
(2) the mercury in a thermometer moving above or below zero
(3) the diver moving from a diving board above sea level, into the water, below sea level.

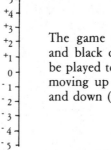

The game using the white and black dice might again be played to give practice in moving up (positive values) and down (negative values).

The horizontal and vertical positions may be combined as shown in the diagram below and the grid used to play a game, described below.

first position of partner marked in a different colour or simply using 'X'

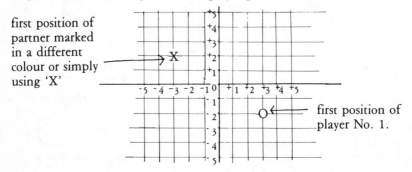

first position of player No. 1.

To play a game on the grid, mark a blue die and a red one with the following integers: ⁻1, ⁻2, ⁻3, ⁺1, ⁺2, ⁺3. When the dice are thrown, two of these are uppermost, e.g. ⁺3 (red) and ⁻2 (blue). The integer shown on the red die is taken to represent a movement on the horizontal line, while the integer shown on the blue die indicates a movement on the vertical line, i.e. move along 3 to the right of zero and 2 down, drawing a small circle to mark the spot. If the first throw by the partner shows, e.g. ⁻3 (red) and ⁺2 (blue) move 3 to the left of zero and 2 up, drawing a circle to mark the spot. Remember the move in the horizontal direction comes first, followed by a move in the vertical direction. When the dice are thrown the second time, the horizontal and vertical movements are made from the first small circle; when they are thrown the third time, the movements begin at the second circle and son on; it is not necessary to return to zero each time. The game continues until one player has 3 circles in a row horizontally, vertically or diagonally. The partner's position is marked with a different coloured circle or different symbol, e.g. a cross (X).

Variations may be suggested by the children, e.g. a circle with its centre at 0 may be drawn. The winner is the person who moves outside first.

The games suggested here are useful in the introductory stages to give the idea of movement on a number line. It is also necessary to convey the idea of e.g. ⁻2 as a debt of 2, which may be cancelled by a gift of 2 or by ⁺2. This introduces children to the additive inverse which helps in the understanding of subtraction of integers at a later stage.

A game to give practice in pairing off numbers to cancel debts (i.e. to add together to give zero) may be devised.

Cards marked, e.g.

| Gift of £5 | Debt of £5 | etc. |
| ⁺5 | ⁻5 | |

are prepared in pairs so that the 'gifts' may be matched with corresponding 'debts'. The cards are placed face down on the table and children take turns to lift them in pairs. If two cards show gifts and debts of the same amount, they are kept as a pair by the person who lifted them. If the two cards show different amounts, they are put down again. The person who collects most pairs is the winner.

Counters in two colours, e.g. black and white may be used to illustrate the integers, black representing negative quantities and white, positive ones. Each of the following represents a surplus of two black counters and is therefore equivalent to ⁻2:—

(a) ● ● ● ○

(b) ● ● ● ● ● ○ ○ ○

(c) ● ●

Addition may be demonstrated as the putting together of two sets:—

e.g.

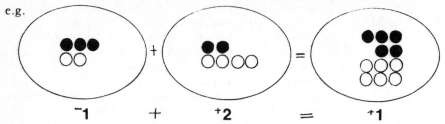

Later, subtraction may be explained as a taking away process.

e.g.

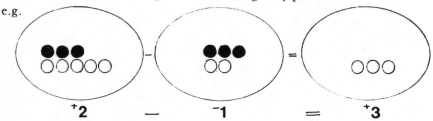

Further information may be found in the following:—
(1) Core Unit 25 of **Towards Mathematics** by J.A. Glenn, and D.A. Sturgess, published by Schofield and Sims Ltd.
(2) **Maths Adventure** Books 4 and 5 by Jan Stanfield, published by Evans.
(3) **Mathematics in the Later Primary Years** — Nuffield/British Council handbook for teachers, published by W. and R. Chambers.
(4) 'Mathshow' — (BBC Television) — Teachers' Notes for Spring 1976.

PICTORIAL REPRESENTATION

PR1: BAR-LINE GRAPHS

In section 2, bar or column graphs were illustrated. Sometimes the columns in a bar chart are replaced by straight lines to display information more effectively.

e.g.

(1) **Number of absentees in P7**

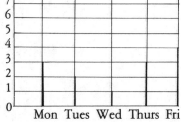

Questions
(1) On which day were there fewest children absent? Can you suggest a reason?
(2) On which day was the attendance smallest?
(3) How many children were absent on Monday? Tuesday?
(4) What is the total number of absentees for the week?

(b) **Makes of cars parked in the school playground**

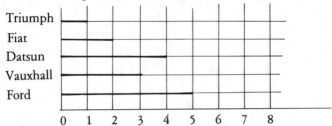

Questions
(1) What was the most popular make of car?
(2) How many Datsun cars were parked in the playground?
(3) Name the make of car which appeared once?
(4) How many cars were there altogether?
(5) Place the makes of cars in order of popularity.

PR2: CARROLL, VENN AND TREE DIAGRAMS

These three ways of representing the sorting process were illustrated in **S2**. Again, it needs to be stressed, that the practical activity is of primary importance; the visual representation is only of secondary importance.

Further examples for the children to interpret:—

(a) **CARROLL DIAGRAM**

boys   not boys

go home for dinner	1 5 **don't**	2 6 **wear**
	glasses	
don't go home for dinner	7	8
	3	4

Universal Set:—
Children in a class

Children are asked to describe the occupants of each section: they are listed here for the teacher's benefit.

1. Boys who wear glasses and go home for dinner.

2. Girls who wear glasses and go home for dinner.
3. Boys who wear glasses and don't go home for dinner.
4. Girls who wear glasses and don't go home for dinner.
5. Boys who don't wear glasses and go home for dinner.
6. Girls who don't wear glasses and go home for dinner.
7. Boys who don't wear glasses and don't go home for dinner.
8. Girls who don't wear glasses and don't go home for dinner.

(b) **VENN DIAGRAM**

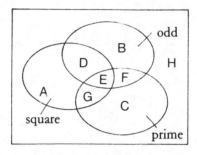

Universal Set:—
Numbers 1-24

Again children are asked to interpret the diagram by completing the following sections:—

A ——— ....
B ——— ....
C ——— ....
D ——— ....
E ——— ....
F ——— ....
G ——— ....
H ——— ....

(c) **TREE DIAGRAM**

Universal Set: Children in a class

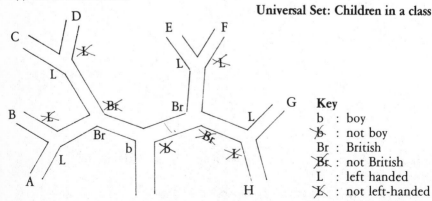

Key

b : boy
b̷ : not boy
Br : British
B̷r̷ : not British
L : left handed
L̷ : not left-handed

PR2: CARROLL, VENN AND TREE DIAGRAMS (cont'd)

To interpret the graph children are asked to describe the subsets at the following sections. Answers are listed for the teacher's benefit.

A. Left-handed British boys.
B. British boys who are not left-handed
C. Left-handed boys who are not British.
D. Boys who are not British and are not left-handed.
E. Left-handed British girls.
F. British girls who are not left-handed.
G. Left-handed girls who are not British.
H. Girls who are not British and are not left-handed.

PR3: USE OF SCALE

When children begin to use large numbers in their graphical work, they find that the page will not accommodate the drawing, so discussion arises as to what can be done. There are at least two possible solutions:—

(a) use paper with smaller grid (½ cm);
(b) let 1 square represent 2, 3, 5, 10, etc. on the cm grid.

e.g. (b) **Number of meals served to each class on a particular day**

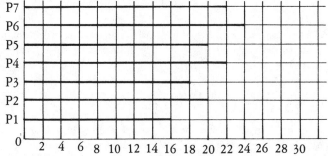

The scale here is one square representing 2 units.

PR4: GRAPHS TO SHOW AVERAGE HEIGHTS, ETC.

In **N6**, practical methods of obtaining averages were illustrated. Finding the average height of the class or of a group of children provides another opportunity for a practical approach. Children cut strips of paper the same length as their height and pin these vertically side by side to form a graph. The representation of the graph on paper calls for some scaling down as mentioned in **PR3**. Children may fold their paper in half, in half again until the strip fits into a page. In this way one graph may be drawn to scale. The average height may be found in a similar way to the method shown in **N6** or by finding the total length of the strips and dividing by the number of strips.

Average weights of various groups may also be found and the results shown on a graph.

e.g. **Finding the average weight of a group of children**

Bob weighed 27 kilograms
Sue weighed 25 kilograms
Jack weighed 29 kilograms
Ann weighed 21 kilograms
John weighed 28 kilograms

   Total   130

Average weight 26 kg

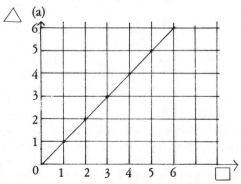

The diagram shows how the pieces above the dotted line were transferred to fill up the spaces underneath the line to make each column the same height, thus giving some meaning to the term 'average'.

PR5: POINTS ON A GRAPH. CO-ORDINATES

In **N8**, children were introduced to the idea of an ordered pair and several games were played to help in plotting points correctly. The points (1,1), (2,2), (3,3), (4,4), (5,5), (6,6) lie in a straight line as the diagram (a) shows.

250

If we label the horizontal axis ☐ and the vertical axis △ we could write the statement ☐ = △ because all values given to ☐ are the same for △.

The points (1,2), (2,4), (3,6), (4,8), (5,10) also lie in a straight line as diagram (b) shows.

(b)

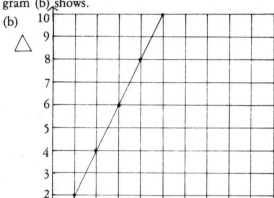

Table of ordered pairs

☐	△
1	2
2	4
3	6
4	8
5	10

This time we could write 2 × ☐ = △

The diagram is called the graph of the relation 2 × ☐ = △

Graphs of other relations may be drawn, children first compiling a table of ordered pairs:—

e.g.

☐	△
2	1
3	2
4	3
5	4
6	5

This set of ordered pairs produces the graph of the relation ☐ = △ + 1 illustrated on diagram (c).

When the points are plotted the result appears as shown below:—

(c)

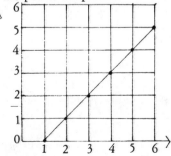

This is a graph of the relation ☐ = △ + 1

When the graph of a relation is a straight line, we call it a **linear** relationship.

From tables of ordered pairs children may be able to write down what the graph of the relation would be in terms of □ and △

e.g.

□	△
1	3
2	4
3	5
4	6

graph of
the relation
□ = △ −2

□	△
1	3
2	6
3	9
4	12

graph of
the relation
□ = △ ÷ 3

□	△
0	1
1	2
2	3
3	4

graph of
the relation
□ = △ −1

Sometimes the graph of a relation is a curve as shown in diagram (d).

(d) **How squares grow**

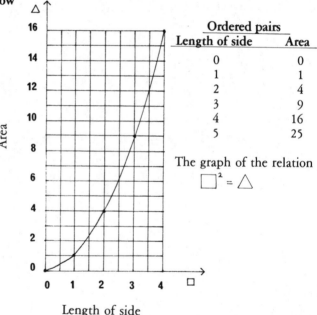

Ordered pairs

Length of side	Area
0	0
1	1
2	4
3	9
4	16
5	25

The graph of the relation

$$□^2 = △$$

Length of side

For further information read:—

(1) **Relations and Graphs** by P. A. Caine, published by Chatto and Windus.
(2) Core Unit 13 of **Towards Mathematics** by J. A. Glenn and D. A. Sturgess, published by Schofield and Sims Ltd.
(3) **Graphs Leading to Algebra**, Nuffield Mathematics Teaching Project.

A graph which shows proportionate increases is a straight line and is sometimes referred to as a constant relationship (ratio) graph. The quantities shown on a straight line graph vary continuously and intermediate points have meaning. Multiplication tables are examples of this linear relationship. The graphs illustrated below demonstrate this:—

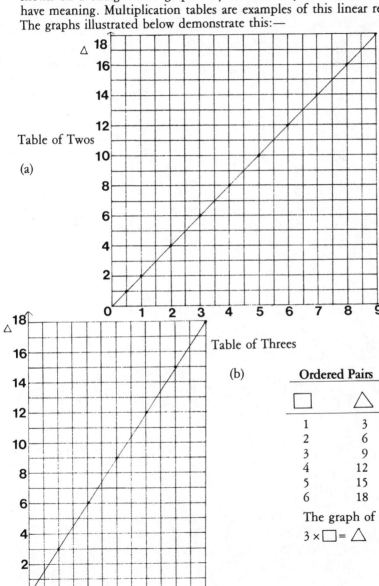

Table of Twos

(a)

Table of Threes

(b)

Ordered Pairs

□	△
1	3
2	6
3	9
4	12
5	15
6	18

The graph of the relation

$3 \times □ = △$

Graphs of fractions are also examples of constant relationships. The fraction ½ can be expressed as the ordered pair (1,2); the fraction ⅓ as (1,3); the fraction ¾ as (3,4). These points can be marked on squared paper, but for fractions, the numerator is marked along the vertical axis and the denominator on the horizontal axis, shown in diagram (c).

Graphs of fractions

(c)

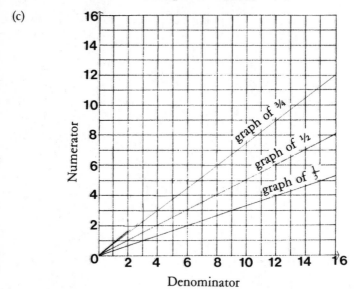

Ordered pairs for ½			Ordered pairs for ⅓	
Numerator	Denominator		Numerator	Denominator
1	2		1	3
2	4		2	6
3	6		3	9
4	8		4	12 etc.
5	10 etc.			

Ordered pairs for ¾	
Numerator	Denominator
3	4
6	8
9	12
12	16 etc.

The graph showing the relationship between the side of a square and the perimeter is another example of a constant relationship graph.

e.g.

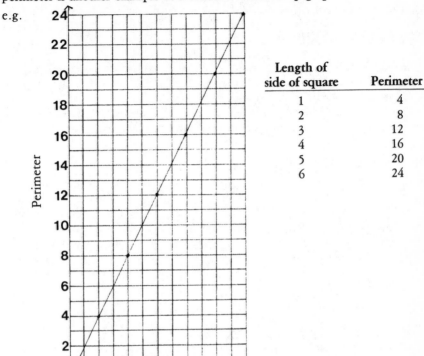

Length of side of square	Perimeter
1	4
2	8
3	12
4	16
5	20
6	24

The constant ratio graphs already described are examples of direct proportion and link up with **N12**.

The following are also examples:—

(a) Ready reckoner type: price related to weight
price related to number of articles bought
conversion of miles to kilometres
conversion of English money to foreign currency.

(b) Circumference of circle and its diameter.

(c) Volume of water and its weight.

(d) The height of the first bounce of a ball and the height of the first drop.

(e) Number of sides of polygon and number of struts to make it rigid.

For further information read:—

(1) **Using Graphs Book 2** by A. L. Griffiths published by Oliver and Boyd.

(2) **Primary Mathematics Today** (p.303-305) by E. M. Williams and Hilary Shuard published by Longman.

(3) Curriculum Bulletin No. 1 — The Schools Council — Chapter 6.

PR7: CURVE STITCHING

At primary level, the main purpose of curve stitching is its aesthetic value, though it may link with the earlier work on relationships (**PR5**). It may also lead into a mathematical investigation of curves.

Points are marked out at regular intervals on different cardboard shapes and joined with coloured threads to form patterns of curves.

e.g.

(a) Circular shapes

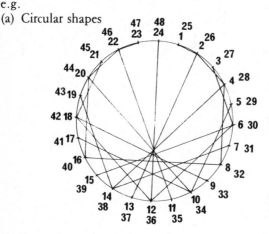

A circle is drawn on cardboard and the circumference marked off as shown. The points which map the two time tables are joined

$$1 \longrightarrow 2$$
$$2 \longrightarrow 4$$
$$3 \longrightarrow 6$$
$$4 \longrightarrow 8 \text{ etc.}$$

This may be linked with **PR5** and called the graph of the relation $2 \times \square = \triangle$

(b)

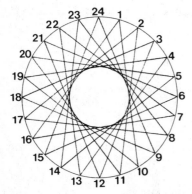

In this diagram 1 is joined to 9; 2 to 10, etc. or by adding 8. This may be linked with **PR5** and called the graph of the relation

$$\square + 8 = \triangle$$

The paths traced by the following are parabolic curves:—

  (a) a shell fired from a gun
  (b) a ball thrown in the air
  (c) a jet of water from a hose pipe.

Children may be introduced to these curves through patterns produced by curve stitching.

e.g.

(a)

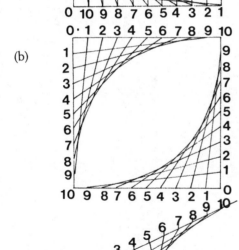

Two lines are drawn at right angles and the axes numbered as shown. Lines are drawn from 1 to 1; 2 to 2, etc. and the curved formed is an example of a parabola.

(b)

Two curves may be produced by numbering the sides of a square as shown and joining the numbers as on (a).

(c)

This time the angle between the two lines has been altered, but the curve produced is another example of a parabola.

A curve made from straight lines is called the 'envelope' of the straight lines.

For further information read:—
(1) **Curves** by Stuart E. Bell, published by Longman (**Maths in the Making No. 5**).
(2) **Starting Patterns with Thread** by D. Neville Wood, published by Studio Vista, a division of Cassell and Collier.
(3) **Mathematics and Curve Stitching** by David S. Fielker **Mathematics Teaching** No. 64.

PR8: EXTENSION OF THE AXES IN NEGATIVE DIRECTIONS

In **N15**, children were introduced to negative numbers by various activities designed to give practice in movements left and right; up and down. The grid used for the game, played with red and blue dice, showed the axes extended in negative directions, horizontally and vertically. Children may be asked to draw shapes on a similar grid from co-ordinates given, or alternatively, draw shapes and write down the co-ordinates.

e.g.

(a)

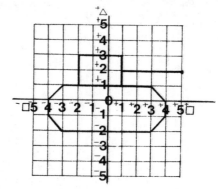

(b)

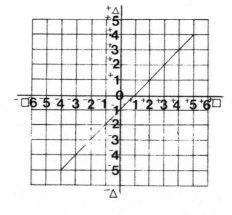

If the graph of the relation $\square = \triangle + 1$ (see **PR5**) is extended, another set of ordered pairs may be added to the table which children have already compiled.

e.g.

	$\square$	$\triangle$
This set		
illustrated in	5	4
PR5	4	3
	3	2
	2	1
	1	0

This demonstrates that the difference between $^-1$ and 0 is $^-1$

	$\square$	$\triangle$
Now extended	$^-1$	0
to include	$^-2$	$^-1$
negative	$^-3$	$^-2$
numbers	$^-4$	$^-3$

between $^-2$ and $^-1$ is $^-1$, etc.
or $^-2$ minus $^-1 = ^-1$
$^-3$ minus $^-2 = ^-1$ etc.

In other words, we might say that subtracting a negative number has the same effect as adding its inverse.

(c)

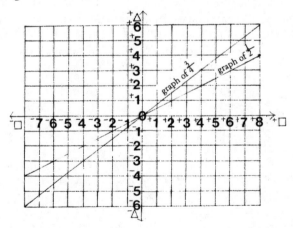

If the graphs of ¾ and ½ are extended we have a set of integers as shown:—

$\square$	$\triangle$
4	3
8	6
$^-4$	$^-3$
$^-8$	$^-6$

$\frac{3}{4} = \frac{^-3}{^-4}$

and $\frac{6}{8} = \frac{^-6}{^-8}$

This indicates that when we divide a negative number by a negative number the result is positive.

For further information read:—

(1) **Graphs Leading to Algebra**, Nuffield Mathematics Teaching Project.
(2) **The Schools Mathematics Project**, Book C, published by Cambridge University Press.
(3) Core Unit 25 of **Towards Mathematics** by J. A. Glenn and D. A. Sturgess published by Schofield and Sims Ltd.

SHAPE — THREE DIMENSIONAL

3D1: EXAMINING 3D SHAPES

The work outlined in **3D5** and **3D6** of section 2 may be repeated at this stage:—

(a) construction of 3D shapes using card to draw attention to the number of faces.
(b) construction of 3D shapes using pipe cleaners and straws to draw attention to the number of edges and the number of vertices.

The selection of shapes provided for children to examine should include the five regular solids, i.e. solids with all faces alike.

e.g.

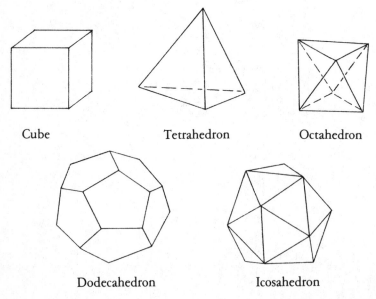

Cube   Tetrahedron   Octahedron

Dodecahedron   Icosahedron

3D1: EXAMINING 3D SHAPES (cont'd)

The results of the investigation may be tabulated in the following form:—

Name of shape	Number of faces	Number of vertices	Number of edges
cube	6	8	12
tetrahedron	4	4	6
octahedron	8	6	12
dodecahedron	12	20	30
icosahedron	20	12	30
cuboid	6	8	12
pyramid (square base)	5	5	8
prism (△)	5	6	9
prism (⬡)	8	12	18

The information is recorded for the teacher's benefit.

Children will notice that the number of edges is always greater than the number of faces or vertices and some may arrive at the formula faces + vertices = edges + 2.

3D2: MAKING CUBES AND CUBOIDS FROM NETS DRAWN ON STIFF CARD

In **3D5** of section 2 children used card to make cubes and cuboids. Now they might be invited to plan their own 'nets,' and a variety of these will emerge. Children should try to discover as many as possible of the eleven different patterns of nets for cubes, (see **2D7**). Two examples are shown here:—

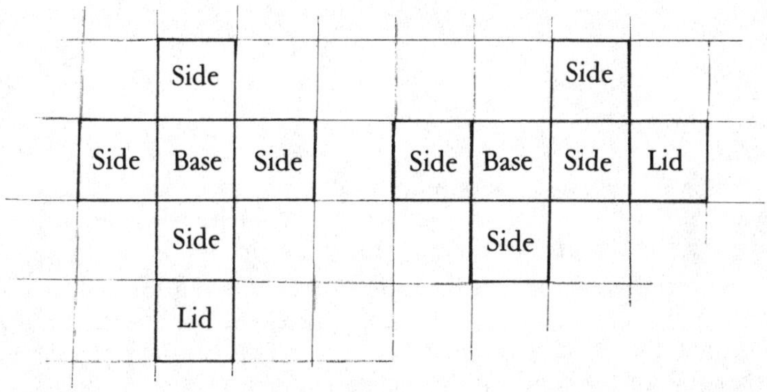

The patterns may be extended for **cuboids**. Two are illustrated below.

				End	Base	End
	Side					
End	Base	End			Side	
	Side				Lid	
	Lid				Side	

When children have planned their nets on squared paper, they draw them on stiff card, cut them out and stick them together with sellotape. Alternatively, they may add flaps so that the shapes may be held together with glue.

3D3: MAKING CYLINDERS TO FIT LIDS OR CIRCLES

In opening various 3D shapes (see **3D4** of section 2) children discover that a cylinder may be made from two circular shapes and a rectangular one. They are now invited to make cylinders to fit lids or circles, using their own initiative to solve the problem. Children's own attempts, however imperfect, are much more valuable than more perfect solutions obtained by following closely directed step-by-step instructions.

Having exhausted their own ideas, however, they are ready for a more systematic development as illustrated in the following sections.

e.g. Children may use a lid to cut out two circles from thick card.

The rectangle to complete the cylinder must be wide enough to wrap round the lid, i.e. it must be the same length as the circumference of the circle. The following instructions give one way of obtaining this:—

Make a spot on the edge of the lid and put this on a dot marked 'A' on the thick card. Roll the lid along a straight line until the spot touches the paper again and mark it 'B'. The distance between the dots is the circumference of the circle and also the width of the rectangular net.

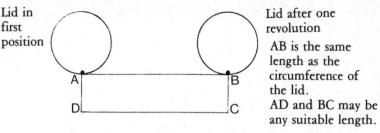

Lid in
first
position

Lid after one
revolution

AB is the same
length as the
circumference of
the lid.
AD and BC may be
any suitable length.

Children may now complete the cylinder using one circle for the top and one
for the bottom.

3D4: FITTING TOGETHER FOUR EQUILATERAL TRIANGLES

A tetrahedron may be made by joining together four equilateral triangles; an
easier way is to draw nets like those illustrated:—

(a)

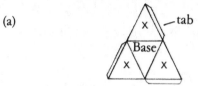

Draw the net on thick card, and bend up the three triangles marked X until
they touch.

(b) This is another way of drawing a net of a tetrahedron.

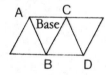

Folds are made along the lines AB, BC and CD to complete the solid.

3D5: MAKING A VARIETY OF SHAPES

(a) **Pyramid**
A net with a square in the middle and an equilateral triangle on each side can
be used to make a pyramid.

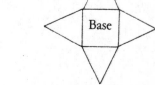

One with isolsceles triangles may also be used.

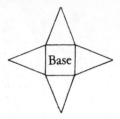

(b) Octahedron

The octahedron is a regular solid made with 8 equilateral triangles or from a net like the one illustrated.

Folds are made to bring together like markings.

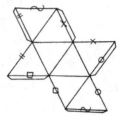

(c) The Dodecahedron

This is another regular solid made up of 12 faces, all of which are regular pentagons.

Draw a large regular pentagon from a template and join alternate corners. This produces a smaller pentagon in the centre.

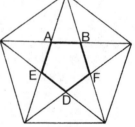

half the net of the dodecahedron

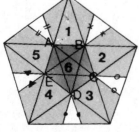

Now join alternate corners of the small pentagon and continue the lines until they meet the outer pentagon. These 6 pentagons form half the net of the dodecahedron. The edges are linked as shown. The second half is exactly the same and when each half is made into a cup shape, they are linked to form a solid shape.

(d) The Icosahedron

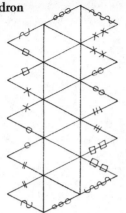

Like the tetrahedron and the octahedron, the icosahedron is also made from equilateral triangles — 20 in all.

This net shows one way of linking the triangles to make a solid shape. Fold along the lines shown and link **like symbols** together.

Like the previous model, two distinct halves emerge and when each is completely joined, the final link 000 to 000 can be made.

Books to read

1. **Looking at Solids** (Mathematics in the Making, Book 3) by Stuart E. Bell, published by Longman.
2. **Solid Geometry** (Patterns in Mathematics) by P. A. Caine, published by Chatto and Windus.
3. **Understanding Shapes and Solids** (New Mathematics) by L. Lackie, published by Nelson.
4. Core Unit 15 of **Towards Mathematics** by J. A. Glenn and D. A. Sturgess, published by Schofield & Sims.

3D6: MAKING BOXES

Planning boxes to hold, e.g. thirty-six cubes, links solid geometry with volume and capacity **C/V6**. It is a good idea to encourage children to see in how many different ways the cubes may be arranged, e.g.

(1)   4 cubes on base $2 \times 2 \times 9$ cubes
     9 rows

(2)   6 cubes on base $2 \times 3 \times 6$ cubes
     6 rows

(3)   18 cubes on base $3 \times 6 \times 2$ cubes
     2 rows

(4)   12 cubes on base $3 \times 4 \times 3$ cubes
     3 rows

When planning the nets for the boxes to hold the various arrangements, children realize that a little extra space must be left for manipulation.

e.g.
(1)

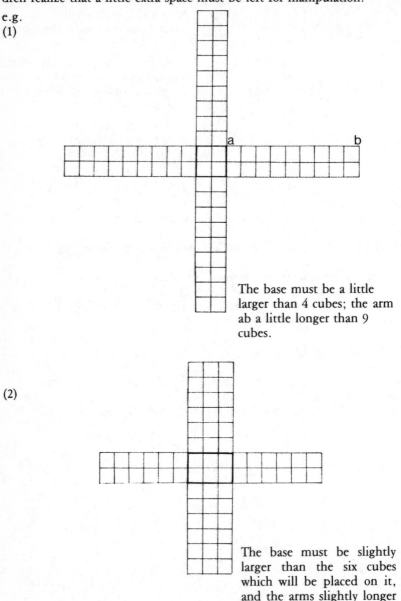

The base must be a little larger than 4 cubes; the arm ab a little longer than 9 cubes.

(2)

The base must be slightly larger than the six cubes which will be placed on it, and the arms slightly longer than six cubes.

(3)

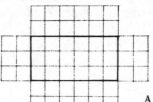

A net of a different shaped box. Children need to be reminded to allow space for manipulation.

(4)

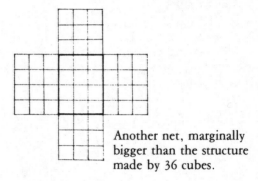

Another net, marginally bigger than the structure made by 36 cubes.

SHAPE — TWO DIMENSIONAL

2D1: CLASSIFYING TRIANGLES

If children are given a collection of triangles of different shapes and sizes, they can sort them according to their properties.

(a) Triangles with all three sides the same length. (equilateral)
(b) Triangles with two sides the same length. (isolsceles)
(c) Triangles with all three sides of different lengths. (scalene)
(d) Triangles having one right-angle. (right-angled).

Some triangles belong to set (b) and also to set (d); some belong to set (c) and also to set (d) as illustrated on the following diagrams:—

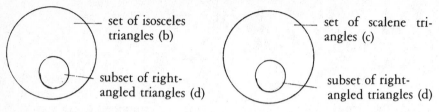

Right-angled triangles belong either to the set of isosceles triangles or to the set of scalene triangles.

Children are asked to make a variety of triangles on geoboards, transfer the shapes to dotted paper and classify as indicated above — a, b, c or d. They will soon discover that it is impossible to make an equilateral triangle on the 9-pin geoboard or the 16-pin board but quite easy on the isometric one.

Equilateral triangles

Children might be asked to find how many of each size can be made on an isometric geoboard bounded by 4 pins on one side and 3 on the other. Recording results on spotted paper helps in classifying these.

The triangles illustrated may be called similar triangles, i.e. they differ in size only.

(b) Isosceles triangles
Children are invited to make as many different-sized isosceles triangles as possible on a 16-pin geoboard and may produce the following:—

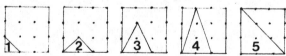

They are then asked to record the number of each size it is possible to make on the board, e.g.

size 1 → 36
    2 → 24   (These figures are recorded
    3 → 16   for the teacher's benefit).
    4 → 8
    5 → 4

Numbers 1, 2, 5 are right-angled isosceles triangles and belong in (d) also.

(c) **Scalene triangles** (Those illustrated are not right-angled).

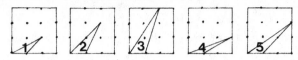

Questions:
(1) How many different sized scalene triangles can you make on your 16-pin geoboard? Transfer the shapes to spotted paper.
(2) Take each shape in turn and see how many you can make in different positions on the board. Rotate the board to help you. Record the results.

(d) **Right-angled triangles**
Children are asked to make as many different sized right-angled triangles as possible on a 16-pin geoboard. Some are illustrated below.

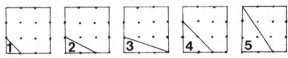

Questions:
(1) How many times can you make shape 5 on the board? Record.
(2) Make each shape in as many positions as possible and record your results on spotted paper.

Numbers 2, 3 and 5 are scalene and 1 and 4 are isosceles.

2D2: MAKING SQUARES AND RECTANGLES WITH GEOSTRIPS

Geo strips are strips of plastic in varying lengths with holes at each end
Pieces may be linked together with metal fasteners to make two-dimensional shapes.

Children are given four strips of equal length (or four strips of card) and asked to make a square. When invited to change its shape they produce a rhombus.

e.g.

1st shape

A ▪———▪ B
│   │
D ▪———▪ C

A
D ◇ B
C

2nd shape

Questions:
(1) Is the first shape the same as the second?
(2) Are the sides the same?
(3) Are the angles the same?
(4) How many right angles in 1st shape?

2D2: MAKING SQUARES AND RECTANGLES WITH GEO-STRIPS (cont'd)

(5) Which angles in the second shape are bigger than a right angle? Which are smaller?

(6) What is the new shape called?

Children are now given four strips to make a rectangle and asked to change its shape.

e.g.

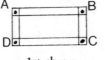

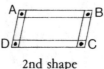

1st shape   2nd shape

Questions:

(1) What has changed? Sides? Angles?

(2) Which angles are greater than a right angle? (If in doubt make a right-angle tester — **2D3** of section 2). Which angles are less than a right angle?

(3) What is the new shape called?

Both figures give examples of parallel lines, i.e. lines which never meet. Children can make sets of parallel lines on geoboards, dotted paper etc. Gradually they are developing an awareness of the properties of the shapes studied.

2D3: INVESTIGATION OF PROPERTIES OF QUADRILATERALS

Work similar to that outlined in **2D2** of section 2, is a suitable introduction to classification activities. Squares and rectangles were considered as quadrilaterals having certain distinguishing features; rhombuses, parallelograms and trapezia may now be included and their properties investigated.

(a) **Rhombuses**

Different sized rhombuses may be made on an **isometric** geoboard as illustrated above. Each shape here is shown on a separate board, but children may use coloured bands and fit all on one board.

Questions:

(1) How many shapes exactly the same as No. 1 can you make? Encourage a systematic approach, e.g. How many on the bottom row? How many on the next? etc.

(2) Is 1(a) the same size as No. 1? How many of these can you make? Record the results on spotted paper.

(3) How many of size 2 can you make? Rotate the board to help you. Record your results on spotted paper.

(4) Make shapes the same size as No. 3 and count. Record your results.

(5) How many shapes the same size as No. 4 can you make? Draw these on spotted paper.

(b) **Parallelograms**

A   C   E   B   D

Questions:

(1) How many different parallelograms can you make on a 16-pin geo board?

(2) How many parallelograms exactly the same as A can you make?

(3) Find how many there are similar to B.

(4) Investigate how many of C, D, and E can be made. The dotted lines indicate how the investigation may proceed.

(c) **Trapezia**

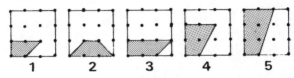

1   2   3   4   5

The shapes illustrated show trapezia in a variety of sizes. Questions similar to those used in sections (a) or (b) help to stimulate an investigation as to how many of each may be made. Rotating the geo board through 1, 2, or 3 angles, helps children to see the shapes in different positions.

As children make these quadrilaterals in different positions they are developing a better understanding of their properties and may conclude the investigation by tabulating the results as shown in the following table:—

	Opposite sides equal	One pair of parallel sides	Opposite angles equal	All sides equal	All angles right angles	Diagonals always at right angles	Diagonals always equal
□	Yes	Yes	Yes	Yes	Yes	Yes	Yes
▭	Yes	Yes	Yes	No	Yes	No	Yes
◇	Yes	Yes	Yes	Yes	No	Yes	No
▱	Yes	Yes	Yes	No	No	No	No
◺	No	Yes	No	No	No	No	No

Information recorded for teacher's benefit.

In **2D2** children were able to change a square into a rhombus and a rectangle into a parallelogram. The question might be asked:— 'How can we make these shapes rigid? They may arrive at the correct solution, i.e. adding a strut.

e.g.

(a)   The square is now rigid.   (b)   The rectangle is now rigid.

Children make a variety of shapes and add struts to make them rigid. In doing this they are made aware of the importance of triangular shapes which are rigid. Many examples of these may be found in the environment (school, street, buildings, bridges etc.)

There are several ways of making a shape rigid, but the aim is to use the least number of struts.

e.g. (a)   (b)

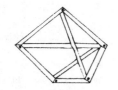   

Both shapes (a) and (b) are rigid but in (b) only two struts were used and three triangular shapes emerge.

The results of the investigation might be tabulated as shown in the following diagram.

Number of sides in shape	Number of struts needed to make it rigid	Number of triangles formed when the shape is rigid
3	0	1
4	1	2
5	2	3
6	3	4
7	4	5

Information recorded for teacher's benefit.

Questions:—

How many struts must be added to make the following figures rigid:—

twenty-sided? twenty-four sided? one-hundred-sided?

How many triangles are formed in each of these?

In **2D3** of section 2, the concept of angles was introduced as:—

    (a) a static measure as seen in the corners of objects in the environment.

    (b) a measure of the amount of turning, illustrated by paper rotating about a pin.

Experience of both aspects is necessary to develop the concept.

    Right angles may now be made using cardboard strips or geo strips, the size checked on the folds of the right-angle tester (**2D3** of section 2).

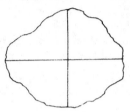

The movement of the **minute** hand of a clock draws attention to the (b) aspect,

e.g. (1) Movement from 12 o'clock to 3 o'clock shows a right angle as a quarter turn.

    (2) Movement from 12 o'clock to 6 o'clock is half a turn, or two right angles.

    (3) Movement from 12 o'clock to 9 o'clock is three quarters of a turn, or three right angles.

    (4) Movement from 12 o'clock to starting point — a complete turn or revolution — 4 right angles.

Points on a compass may also be used to show movement through 1, 2, 3 or 4 right angles.

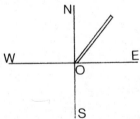

Paper is folded as shown and the points marked. A movable arm is fastened at O and rotated through 1, 2, 3, 4 right angles.

Questions:

Name the angles made by the following rotations (clockwise):—

(1) from North to East

(2) East to South

(3) North to South

(4) North to West

(5) North, back to North again, etc.

The length of the arm may be shortened and the same questions asked again, in order that children may realize that it is the amount of turning and not the length of the arms which decides the size of the angle.

e.g.
(a)  (b)

(a) is greater than (b) because the amount of turning is greater. The longer arms of (b) do not make the angle greater.

If a smaller angle is required, then the folded right angle (**2D3** of section 2) can be halved, giving half a right angle or an eighth of a turn. This will give eight points of the compass.

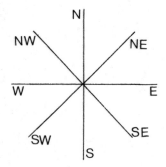

If the revolution is thought of in terms of steps — 360 in all, the word degrees may be introduced and a right angle called 90 degrees. The sizes of the angles made by the following rotations could be recorded:—

    (1) North to South East
    (2) North East to South West
    (3) South West to North West etc.

2D6: ACUTE AND OBTUSE ANGLES ETC.

Cardboard strips or geo strips fastened together may be used to demonstrate angles of various sizes. The two strips may be held together and then gradually opened to produce angles which are smaller than right angles, i.e. acute angles.

They may be extended to produce angles greater than a right angle but smaller than two right angles. These are called obtuse angles.

Angles of a triangle

(a)

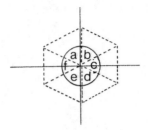

This diagram shows six equilateral triangles tessellating at 0 (Refer to **2D4** of section 2). Six angles (a + b + c + d + e + f) are equal to four right angles, i.e. 6 equal angles amount to 360°: 1 angle is equal to 60°.

The equilateral triangles will tessellate, no matter how each is turned, so we can ssume that 60° is the size of any angle of an equilateral triangle.

(b)

The angles of an equilateral triangle may be cut out and fitted together as shown in (b) to make a straight line or two right angles, i.e. 180°. As each is equal, we can again state that an equilateral triangle has three angles each measuring 60°.

The tessellation of scalene triangles illustrated below, shows that two sets of three angles (a + b + c) together amount to 360°, so that one set (the angles of a scalene triangle,(a + b + c) adds up to 180°.

e.g.

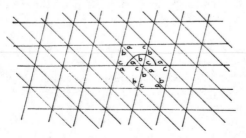

The angles of **any** triangle may be fitted together to make two right angles, i.e. 180°.

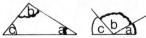

Angles of a quadrilateral

Children will readily agree that a square and a rectangle each have four right angles. They may be encouraged to investigate the angles of any quadrilateral. The idea of tessellating shapes to meet at the intersection O of the following diagram, has already been explored in **2D6** of section 2.

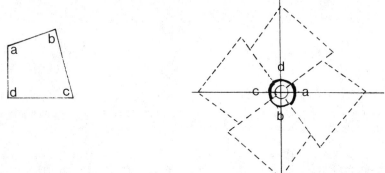

The angles a, b, c, d of the quadrilateral fit completely over four right angles. The diagram shows the shape arranged in different positions and is the beginning of a tessellation.

The corners may be torn off and arranged as shown.

When fitted together they made a complete revolution or 360° (4 right angles).

Investigations with any quadrilateral will show that the sum of the angles is 360°.

Angles of a regular pentagon

In **2D6** of section 2, the investigation showed that regular pentagons did not tessellate. Fitting them together on the paper marked with four right angles will not help us to find the size of the angles, as there is a gap of unknown size (at the moment).

e.g.
(a)

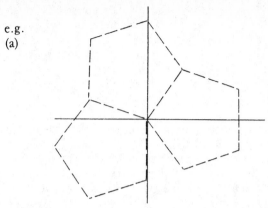

Children could cut out a regular pentagon and fold as shown in (b) to find the centre. They can join vertices to the centre to produce five isosceles triangles.

(b)

Fold along the dotted lines to find the centre.

2D6 illustrated the sum of the angles of any triangle as 180° so we can state that the sum of the angles in triangles a, b, c, d, e is 900° or ten right angles. If we subtract the angles at the centre (360°) we are left with 540° to be divided equally in 5, thus giving 108° as the angle of a regular pentagon.

Angles of a regular hexagon

The figure is divided into six equilateral triangles the sum of whose angles is (6 × 2 right angles) 1080°

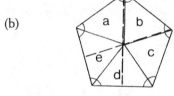

If we subtract the angles at the centre, we are left with 720° to be divided equally in six, giving 120° as the angle of a regular hexagon.

Alternative methods for arriving at the results are illustrated on the following diagrams:—

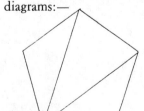

The regular pentagon is divided into three triangles the sum of whose angles is 3 × 180°.
The size of each angle of the regular pentagon is

$$\frac{3 \times 180}{5} \quad \text{degrees}$$

i.e. 108°

277

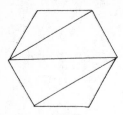

The regular hexagon is divided into four triangles the sum of whose angles is $4 \times 180°$.

The size of each angle of the regular hexagon is

$$\frac{4 \times \overset{30}{\cancel{180}}}{\cancel{6}} \text{ degrees}$$

i.e. 120°

In similar ways we could find the angles of a regular octagon, nonagon (nin-sided figure), decagon (10-sided) etc.

It must be stressed that not many children will participate in the total investigation, but may be content with the section which demonstrates the size in relation to right angles, e.g. triangles and quadrilaterals.

2D7: INVESTIGATION OF SHAPES WHICH TESSELLATE

In **2D4** and **2D6** of section 2 tessellations of regular and non-regular shapes were investigated. The investigation may be extended to shapes not already included:—

e.g. (a) **quadrilaterals (irregular)**.

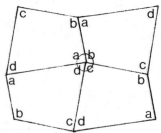

If these are fitted as shown in the diagram the block of four forms a tessellating unit.

(b) **Isosceles trapezia**

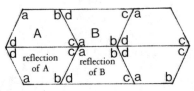

These may be fitted together in various ways. Attention should be focused on the reason why shapes tessellate (fit together at point so that the sum of the angles is four right angles). Refer to **2D6** of section 2.

(c) **Right-angled trapezia**

These are fitted together so that the right angles come together, producing isosceles trapezia.

(d) Kites

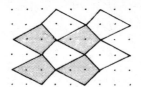

These may be tessellated as shown opposite.

(e) Tessellation of letters of alphabet:—

e.g. (1)

(2)

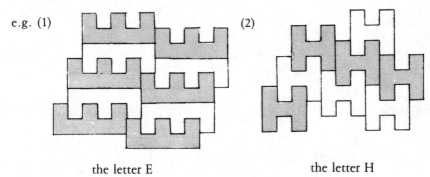

the letter E   the letter H

(f) Semi-regular Tessellations

Two or more sets of regular polygons may be fitted together to form a tessellation:—

e.g.

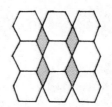

(1) regular octagons and squares.

(2) regular hexagons and rhombuses.

(g) Tessellations may be built up by adding to and taking from other shapes:—

e.g. (a) Squares

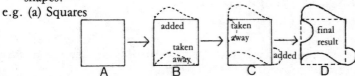

By adding the same shape as was taken away in diagrams B and C, the final result is shown in D — a shape which will tessellate as illustrated below:—

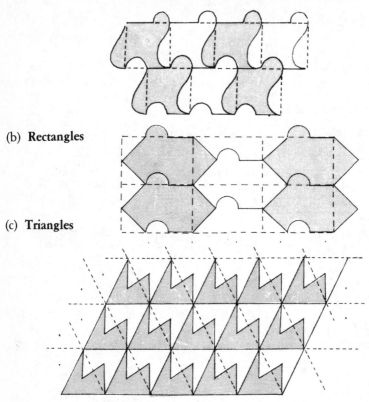

(b) **Rectangles**

(c) **Triangles**

Polyominoes

These are shapes made by fitting squares together so that they make a unit which can be cut out without falling apart.

e.g. Domino: made from two squares

Tromino: made from three squares   or

Tetromino: made from four squares

Pentomino: made from five squares

Hexomino: made from six squares

Children may be given some plastic squares and asked to make as many different patterns as possible using three, four, five then six squares. Results should be recorded on squared or spotted paper.

The arrangement of four squares is shown below.

The five tetrominoes

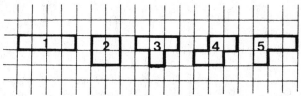

These shapes will tessellate and children should be encouraged to attempt this on squared paper. The rectangle and square have already been done, so 3, 4, 5 might be tessellated, as illustrated. These are **not** the only arrangements and a variety of patterns should be produced.

3

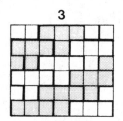

4

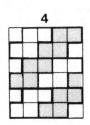

5

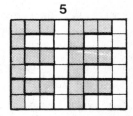

Pentominoes

The investigation of pentominoes should lead to the discovery of twelve different arrangements of five squares. Again children cut out a selection of each and try fitting them together in a repeating pattern.

The set of twelve pentominoes.

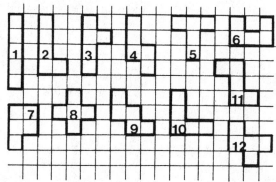

When drawing these children may produce duplicates. By cutting out, rotating or reflecting, they can check which are the same and which are different. Sets of these are commercially produced in plastic and provide many and varied activities.

Some tessellations using pentominoes

No. 7   No. 8   No. 9

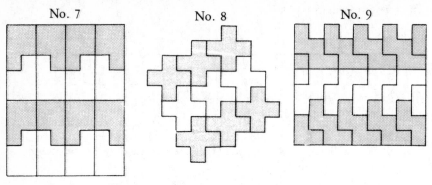

Rectangular arrangements in the following sizes may be made:—

3 × 5   5 × 5   7 × 5   9 × 5
4 × 5   6 × 5   8 × 5   10 × 5

Two sets may be arranged on a square (11 × 11) to cover all except one square. These are illustrated for the teacher's benefit.

Rectangular arrangements of pentominoes

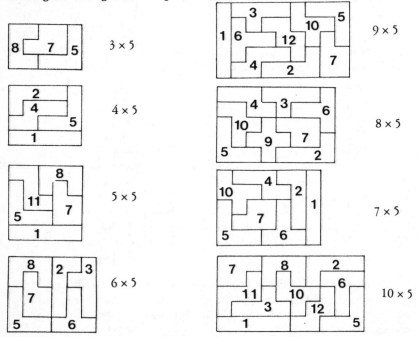

Two sets of pentominoes used to make a square (11 × 11). Black square is vacant.

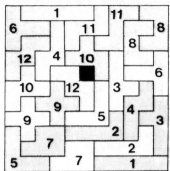

Hexominoes

These are different arrangements of six squares. As there are thirty-five different hexominoes, a class investigation is likely to be a lengthy one, but if interest is sustained, it will be profitable.

At first children make random arrangements and check with partners for duplicates etc. Gradually a more systematic method begins to emerge as children explore all the possibilities, perhaps in the following way:—

(1) the arrangement of 6

(2) the arrangements which might be described as 5 + 1.

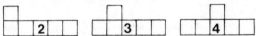

(3) The arrangements which might be described as 4 + 2.

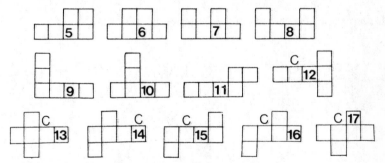

(4) The arrangements of 3 + 3.

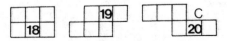

(4) The arrangements of 2 + 2 + 2.

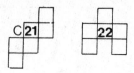

(5) The arrangements of 1 + 2 + 3 (or 3 + 2 + 1 or 1 + 3 + 2).

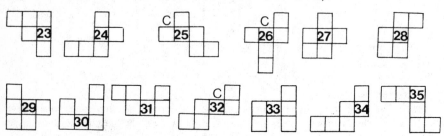

Some of these shapes when cut out will fold to make cubes and children could be set the task of finding these. They are marked with 'C' for the convenience of the teacher.

Each of the thirty-five shapes can be used to form tessellating patterns. Children may draw these on squared paper after they have fitted together several of the cut-out shapes. Each child in the class could experiment with a different shape.

Some of the tessellations are illustrated, but there may be alternative ways of making the patterns.

Examples of Tessellations of hexominoes

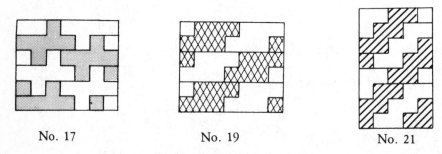

No. 17   No. 19   No. 21

In tessellations 17, 19, 21, parts of the shapes had to be added to fill the rectangle.

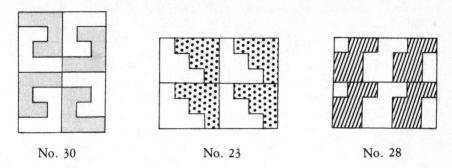

No. 30   No. 23   No. 28

Polyiamonds

These are made in a similar way to polyominoes using equilateral triangles instead of squares.

When two are joined we have a shape sometimes called a **diamond**; it is this which leads to the use of the word polyiamond. The diamond is the only shape we can make by joining equilateral triangles. Mathematicians give the name 'rhombus' to the shape (**2D2**).

A **triamond** is formed by joining together three equilateral triangles.

Only one arrangement is possible.

This shape is usually called a trapezium.

Tetriamonds are arrangements of four equilateral triangles.

There are three different tetriamonds in the set.

Pentiamonds are arrangements of five equilateral triangles.

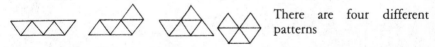

There are four different patterns

Hexiamonds are arrangements of six equilateral triangles.

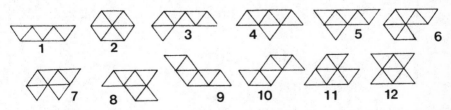

There are twelve different arrangements

From the set of hexiamonds, children might select sets of shapes bounded by four, five, six or seven sides.

The only **regular** six-sided figure is the hexagon; other six-sided figures are irregular hexagons. There are examples of irregular pentagons, heptagons etc.

Several of each shape may be cut out and investigated for tessellating properties. The results could be recorded as illustrated below. Dotted isometric paper is recommended for this work.

Selections of tessellations using hexiamonds
The numbers refer to the arrangements illustrated on previous page.

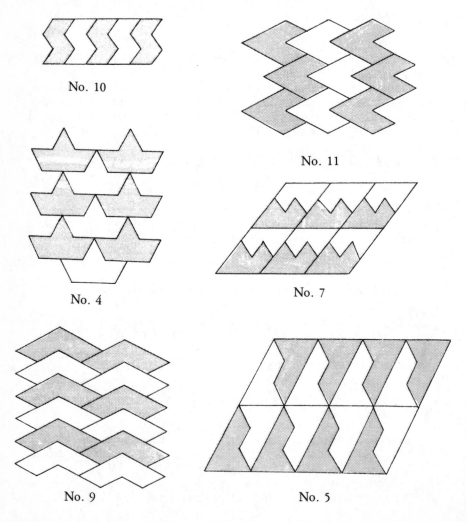

No. 10

No. 11

No. 4

No. 7

No. 9

No. 5

In **2D5** of section 2 symmetry by **reflection** was illustrated in a variety of ways. Attention may now be focused on the symmetry of mathematical shapes already handled.

e.g. Squares, cut out of paper, are folded in as many ways as possible:

Children discover that there are four ways of doing this; we can state that a square has four lines of symmetry.

Repeat with a rectangle:—

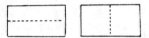

Children discover that when folded diagonally, one half does **not** coincide with the other; a rectangle has only two lines of symmetry. By folding the following shapes as indicated by the dotted lines, children discover how many lines of symmetry each has:—

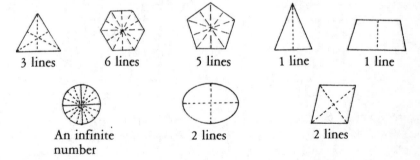

| 3 lines | 6 lines | 5 lines | 1 line | 1 line |

| An infinite number | 2 lines | 2 lines |

Some letters of the alphabet are symmetrical and children may look for lines of symmetry in them:—

e.g.

All these show symmetry by **reflection.**

Rotational symmetry may be demonstrated by cutting out a square and rotating to see how many ways it may be fitted into the hole. If the right hand corner is marked X children will know when it has returned to the starting point.

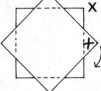

This exercise may be repeated with equilateral triangles, hexagons, rectangles, pentagons, isosceles triangles, parallelograms etc. and the number of rotational symmetries noted.

The hole fitting activities help children to become familiar with the properties of the shapes handled, e.g. the fact that the parallelogram can be given a half turn to fit into the hole, shows that the opposite sides are of equal length (because they change places), that the opposite angles are equal (for the same reason) and that the diagonals bisect each other (because the two parts of each diagonal change places).

Shapes drawn on squared paper may be rotated clockwise or anti-clockwise through one, two, three or four right angles.

e.g.
(a)   (b)

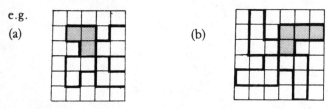

The resultant shapes, therefore, are examples of rotational symmetry.

Shapes may be reflected in a line or rotated about a point. They may also be translated in any direction, e.g. horizontally, vertically or diagonally as illustrated in the following diagrams:—

Translation

(a)   (b)   (c)

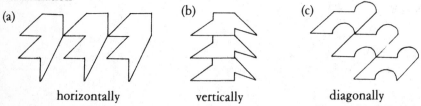

horizontally   vertically   diagonally

Examples of reflection, rotation and translation may be found in **2D7** in the tessellation of a variety of shapes. Pentominoes, for example, may be classified according to the symmetry they possess:—

e.g. (1) no symmetry

(2) line symmetry

(3) rotational symmetry

(4) both line and rotational symmetry.

Many of the tessellations were produced by **translation** of the shapes.

When children have carried out activities involving reflection, rotation and translation, they may wish to investigate patterns which use a combination of two or more of these:—

(a)

This shows translation of shape A.

(b)

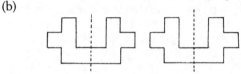

This shows reflection and translation.

(c)

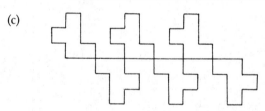

Rotation through 180° and translation.

2D9: ENLARGEMENT

When shapes are enlarged they are **similar** in all respects to the original; the only thing that changes is the size.

(1) This may be done using **co-ordinates**

e.g.

The co-ordinates for figure A are:—
(1,1), (1,2), (2,0), (2,3).
By doubling each we produce the following set:— (2,2), (2,4), (4,0), (4,6) which enlarges the figure to four times its original size, shown in B.

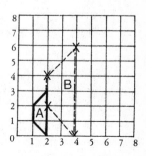

(b) If we enlarge in one direction only, e.g. horizontal, we produce another set of co-ordinates:—

(2,1), (2,2), (4,0), (4,3) — shown in diagram C.

The figure is still an isosceles trapezium, which has grown in width but not in height.

Caricatures are produced when the multiplying factor is used in one direction only.

(2) Using a grid

A simple method of enlarging a drawing is to cover it with a sheet of tracing paper marked off in, e.g. half centimetre squares or by drawing squares lightly on the picture. The drawing may be transferred to paper marked in cm squares by carefully copying the picture square by square, noticing where the lines of the picture cross the lines of the grid.

'A' was drawn on ½ cm paper.

The enlargement 'B' was drawn on cm paper.

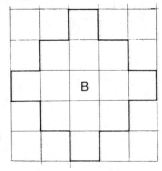

If the areas of the figures are compared, 'B' is four times the area of 'A'.

Drawing to scale is the reverse of the activity, i.e. large squares are marked on the original drawing which is then transferred to smaller grid paper step by step.

(3) Using a pantograph

A pantograph is a simple mechanical device for enlarging irregular shapes.

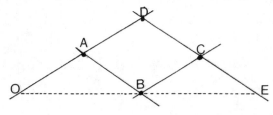

It may be made from geo strips or strips of stout card. In the previous diagram, ABCD is a parallelogram and O, B and E are in a straight line. O is fixed to the paper when an enlargement is being made. As B is moved to trace the outline of the figure, E copies the figure on a larger scale. It may also be used for diminishing the size of a drawing.

A simple device is an 'elastic pantograph'. Two (or more) elastic bands of the same size are knotted together. A drawing pin in the loop of one of the bands acts as the enlarging centre. A pencil in the loop of the other will now draw the enlargement if the knot is made to follow the outline of a figure.

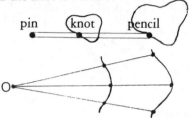

Read **Notes on Mathematics in Primary Schools** published by Cambridge University Press (Pages 154-156).

2D10: HEIGHT FINDING

(1) Using shadows

Before children are involved in height finding activities, much preliminary work involving shadows is necessary, e.g. when shadows are longest, shortest etc. Using sticks of known length, e.g. ½ metre, 1 metre, 2 metres, children measure the length of the shadows cast by them. They discover that the shadow cast by the 2 metre stick is twice as long as that cast by the 1 metre stick; the shadow of the 1 metre stick is double that of the ½ metre one. This knowledge can be used in reverse to determine the height of a pole using scale drawing on squared paper.

e.g.

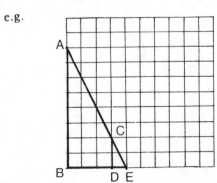

AB represents the pole.
CD represents a metre stick.
BE is the shadow cast by AB.
DE is the shadow cast by CD.
The shadow BE is four times as long as shadow DE.
The height AB must be four times CD, i.e. 4 metres high.

This is an example of direct proportion and links with **N12**.

Using a clinometer
A simple clinometer may be made from a square of cardboard cut in half diagonally.

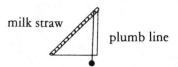

A milk straw is attached as a 'sighter' and a plumb line is added (piece of thread and a small weight).

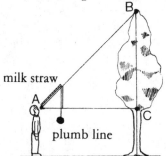

milk straw   plumb line

Holding the triangle with AQ **horizontal**, a child moves to a position where he can sight the top of the tree along AP as shown in the diagram.

The distance AC is measured and the height of the boy (to eye level). The height of the tree is the sum of these two measurements since AC = CB (two sides of square).

Commercially made clinometers are available but they involve measurement of angles other than 45° and the subsequent calculations are probably too involved for most children in the primary school.

CAPACITY/VOLUME

It is essential to read the development of this topic in the previous sections of the book to ensure that children have had experience in comparison, ordering, conservation and measuring with arbitrary and standard units. The work in this section is simply an extension of what has previously been done.

C/V1: CAPACITY OF CONTAINERS

Children collect various containers, fill with water in turn and pour the contents into the litre measure (graduated to measure to the nearest 10 millilitres). The record might appear as shown below.

e.g.

Container	Estimated capacity in ml	Actual capacity to nearest 10 ml	Actual capacity expressed in litres
cup	200	180	0.18
small vase			
milk bottle			
egg cup			
tumbler			

The discussion that follows is most important and the following questions might help to develop the topic further:—

1. Which container holds most? least?
2. Express in litres and decimal fractions of a litre(to the nearest $\frac{1}{100}$ of a litre) the difference in capacity between the milk bottle and the cup.
3. What is the total volume represented by all the containers?
4. Find the average volume of all containers in litres and decimal fractions of a litre (to the nearest $\frac{1}{100}$).
5. Calculate how many cupfuls would be needed to fill two litre jugs.

C/V2: BUILDING SHAPES WITH CONSTANT VOLUME

To establish the idea of conservation of volume children experiment with a number of cubes, e.g. forty-eight and see how many different arrangements, both regular and irregular may be made. Attention should be drawn to the regular shapes and children encouraged to count the number of cubes in each layer and the number of layers. This eventually leads to the standard formula for finding the volume:—

e.g.

Number of cubes to form length of layer	Number of cubes to form breadth of layer	Number of layers in the shape	Total number of cubes used
6	4	2	48
8	3	2	48
6	2	4	48
4	2	6	48

The experience gained here may be applied to a problem solving situation where children are asked to make boxes which hold a given number of cubes. See **3D6** for a development of this.

C/V3: FINDING VOLUME OF OPEN CUBOIDS BY FILLING WITH CUBES

Children fill open cuboid shapes with cubes and record the number required for each. The smaller the measuring unit, the more accurate will be the result, so centimetre cubes are perhaps the most suitable at this stage. Children should be encouraged to complete the bottom layer first and then build layer by layer, until the cuboid is filled. Later, children build along the length of the shape, the breadth of the shape and finally the height, quickly calculating the total number required.

e.g.

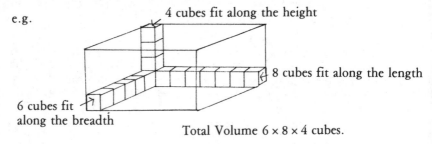

4 cubes fit along the height

8 cubes fit along the length

6 cubes fit along the breadth

Total Volume 6 × 8 × 4 cubes.

C/V4: THE GROWTH OF CUBES

Using a box of centimetre cubes (Centicubes are appropriate here) children build cubes of varying sizes and record the total number of unit cubes needed for each.

e.g.

Number of cubes along each edge	Total number of cubes used
1	1
2	8
3	27
4	64
5	125

etc.

See **N4** for the development of the number pattern associated with their growth.

C/V5: RELATIONSHIPS

An open plastic cube measuring 10 cm × 10 cm × 10 cm may be filled with centimetre cubes and children record the volume as 10 layers with 100 cubes in each making a total of 1000 cubes. When the cubes are removed children are asked to fill the open cube with water and measure the capacity using a graduated litre measure. The discovery that 1 litre of water has the same volume (capacity) as 1000 cubes (cm), is a very important one. Sand may also be used to demonstrate that the quantity required to fill the open cube, will also fill the litre jug.

The litre jug is weighed and the weight recorded. The jug is filled with water and weighed again. When the weight of the jug is subtracted from the total weight of water and jug, the result shows that 1 litre of water weighs 1 kilogram.

Recording   e.g.   Weight of 1 litre measure is... 0.075 kg
Weight of 1 litre measure plus water is 1.075 kg
Therefore the weight of 1 litre of water is... 1 kg.

Questions
1. What is the weight of 500 millilitres of water?
2. 100 grams is the weight of ..... millilitres of water.
3. What is the weight of 250 millilitres of water?
4. The capacity of a cylindrical tin is 840 millilitres. Express this in cubic centimetres.

C/V 6: VOLUME OF IRREGULAR SHAPES

The link between volume and capacity may again be demonstrated by water displacement. Stones of various sizes may be immersed in a graduated container holding water and the rise of levels noted. The volume of water displaced is equivalent to the volume of the stone. A displacement can may be used instead, and the displaced water measured in a calibrated container.

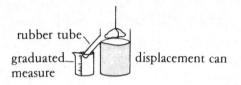

rubber tube

graduated measure   displacement can

C/V 7: CALCULATIONS

In **C/V 2** children recorded the volume of various regular cuboids

(a) counting the number of cubes to form the **length** of a layer
(b) counting the number of cubes to form the **breadth** of a layer
(c) counting the number of layers (or **height**) of the layers.

The total number of cubes used was shown as the product of all three. From building with cubes, children now progress to measuring the length, breadth and height of the objects and calculate the volume by finding the product of the three measurements.

As the measurement of objects may include lengths in metres, it is necessary to give children some idea of the space occupied by a cubic metre. Teachers may use metre rods and corner junctions to make the framework of an open cube.

e.g.  corner junction

metre rod

Alternatively they may purchase a commercially produced metre kit. (See **Six to Twelve** Catalogue). If the blocks of Tillich's Multibase materials are fitted along one edge, children will discover that ten of them are needed. They will then be able to calculate ten rows of 10 or 100 blocks as the number required for the bottom layer. As 10 layers are needed to fill the cube, a further calculation gives the volume as 1000 blocks (or large cubes). Each large cube is equivalent to 1000 cm³, so the total volume of the cubic metre is (1000×1000) cubic centimetres (1 million cm³).

We may state that 1 cubic metre = 1 million cubic centimetres.

Calculations of volumes from given data
Teachers should relate all such calculations to realistic, practical situations.

length	breadth	height	volume
7 cm	4 cm	3 cm	...... cm³
10 cm	5 cm	4 cm	...... cm³
7 m	1.6 m	5 m	...... m³
4 m	1.25 m	4 m	...... m³

Complete the following table:—

length	breadth	height	volume
8 cm		5 cm	200 cm³
	5 cm	7 cm	280 cm³
6.5 m	2.5 m	7 m	
15 m	4 m		162 m³

AREA

A1: USING GEOBOARDS

Before commencing this section, teachers should read the development of area in the preceding sections. It is essential that some activities in covering surfaces with arbitrary and then standard units should be included in the programme.

On 16-pin or 25-pin geoboards children make shapes with constant area, e.g. two squares, three squares etc.

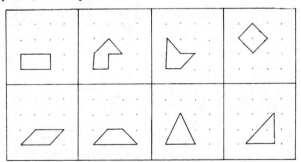

The shapes are transferred to dotted paper.

The work on polyominoes in **2D7** is linked with this as each shape in the set has a constant area.

The Chinese Tangram puzzle is an interesting and effective way of demonstrating conservation of area. The pieces can be cut out of thick card and rearranged to form a great variety of shapes. Plastic sets may be purchased at a reasonable price.

Chinese Tangram

The seven pieces of the puzzle may be used to construct geometrical shapes, e.g. triangle, trapezium, parallelogram etc., or representational figures, e.g. human figures moving, fish swimming, cats or pigs lying down, bridges, shops, houses etc. For illustrations of other possible arrangements consult **Tangram** by Joost Elffers published by Penguin.

geometrical shapes

rectangle

parallelogram

trapezium

triangle

representational figures

house

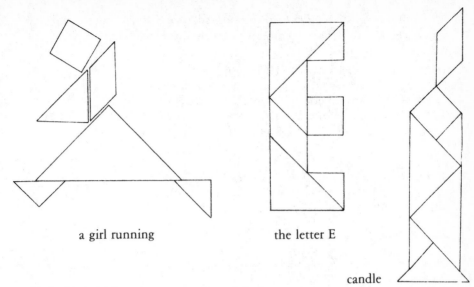

a girl running   the letter E

candle

Each shape is the same area as the original square.

A2: AREA OF A RECTANGLE USING HALF UNITS

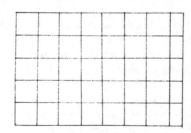

The area may be found by counting squares, or as shown below.

The length of the rectangle is 7½ cm (to the nearest half cm). The breadth is 5 cm. Each row contains 7½ or 7.5 cm. There are five rows, so the area is 7.5 × 5 cm², i.e. 37.2 cm². Children might complete the following:—

	Length	breadth	area
Areas	13.5 cm	7 cm	
of		5 cm	47.5 cm²
rectangles	11.5 cm	9 cm	
	15.5 cm		124 cm²

In **A6** of section 2 children were introduced to the square metre and the square centimetre. The relationship between these may be investigated as follows:—

1. Draw a square, 1 metre by 1 metre on the floor.
2. Using centimetre squared paper, cut out squares 25 cm by 25 cm.
3. Cover the square metre with these — 16 in all.
4. Calculate the area of 1 sheet — then the area of 16, i.e. one sheet measures 25 × 25 cm² : 16 sheets measure 25 × 25 × 16 cm² or 10 000 cm².

1 square metre is equal to 10 000 square centimetres i.e.

1m² = 10 000 cm²

A4: AREA AND PERIMETER

At this stage, children will probably understand the meaning of perimeter, but some may still confuse it with area. Shapes with equal areas, but different perimeters may be made on geoboards etc. and children's attention drawn to the **constant areas** but **changing perimeters.**

e.g.

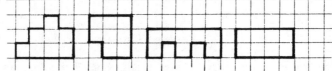

These shapes have equal areas, but different perimeters.

Shapes with equal perimeters, but different areas may also help children to differentiate between the two concepts.

e.g.

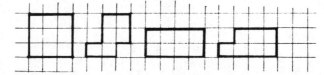

The perimeter of each is 12 cm, but the areas are all different.

Finding the rectangle which encloses most space is a useful activity. Children draw rectangles (or make them on geo boards) with perimeters each 24 cm and record areas as shown:—

Width	Length	Area
1 cm	11 cm	11 cm²
2 cm	10 cm	20 cm²
3 cm	9 cm	27 cm²
4 cm	8 cm	32 cm²
5 cm	7 cm	35 cm²
6 cm	6 cm	36 cm²

The rectangle 6 cm by 6 cm (a square) is the one which encloses most space.

The investigation may be carried a stage further by asking the question: 'Is the square the shape which encloses the largest **possible** area?'

Children cut out lengths of cord, e.g. 16 cm and make loops

e.g.  joined with sellotape

Each loop in turn is made into one of the shapes illustrated and fastened with pins or stuck with sellotape on to a sheet of squared paper. The area of each is recorded as shown:—

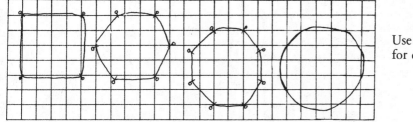

Use sellotape for circle

Children discover that as the number of sides increases, the area increases. Eventually the circle emerges as the shape enclosing the greatest area.

A5: AREA OF PARALLELOGRAM

The areas of rectangles and parallelograms may be demonstrated by dissection as illustrated:

The triangle 'a' is cut off and attached as shown, thus forming a rectangle whose area may be calculated (a) by counting the squares; (b) by multiplying the length by the breadth.

A variety of parallelograms may be drawn on squared paper and children given practice in cutting and reassembling these to form rectangles.

e.g.

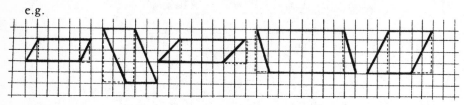

The area of any parallelogram may be found by changing it into a rectangle of equal area.

A6: AREAS OF ROOMS

Drawing to scale is the reverse of enlargement (see **2D9**). Plans of bungalows, flats etc may be drawn on cm grid paper, the scale given as, e.g. 1 cm represents 1 m, i.e. 1 : 100 and calculation of areas of rooms made.

e.g.

```
┌──────────────┬──────────────┐
│   kitchen    │    lounge     │
│              │               │
│  bathroom    │               │
│         hall │               │
│              │               │
│ bedroom  1   │  bedroom  2   │
└──────────────┴──────────────┘
```

Complete the following table:

Name of room	Area on plan	Actual area
Kitchen	12 cm²	12 m²
Bathroom	8 cm²	8 m²
Bedroom 1	12 cm²	12 m²
Bedroom 2	13.5 cm²	13.5 m²
Hall	7.5 cm²	7.5 m²
Lounge	27 cm²	27 m²

The total area of the flat is 10×8 m² $= 80$ m².

It is also the total of all the areas recorded above, i.e. 80 m².

Plans using different scales may also be drawn and areas calculated, e.g.

(1) 2 cm represent 1 m, i.e. 1:50

(2) 5 cm represent 1 m, i.e. 1:20

A7: AREAS ON MAP DRAWN TO SCALE

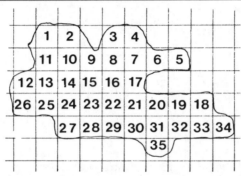

The diagram illustrates an island whose area is 35 squares (approximately). If the scale is 1 cm represents 1 kilometre, i'e 1:100 000 then the area may be expressed as 35km². If the scale is 1:2500 000 each cm represents 25 km and each cm² represents 625 km².

To find the area of any section of a map, a transparent grid may be placed on the map, the number of squares counted and the calculation made according to the scale given.

A8: AREA OF CIRCLE

The area of a circle was found in **A4** by counting the squares. Another method is to cut out a circle and fold it into eighths as shown in the diagram.

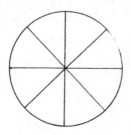

Cut along the folds and rearrange the pieces to make a parallelogram (approximately) with one side equal to the radius of the circle and the other equal to half the circumference of the circle.

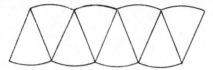

Gradually increase the number of divisions, until the area of the circle has been rearranged in the form of a rectangle whose length is **half the circumference of the circle**, and whose breadth is the **radius**.

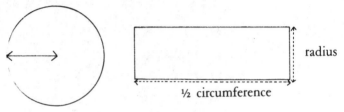

radius

½ circumference

This is a suitable formula for the area of a circle at this stage, as it reminds children of the thought processes involved in arriving at the result.

LENGTH

L1: MEASUREMENT TO THE NEAREST TENTH OF A METRE

Using metre rods marked in **tenths**, children measure a variety of objects to the nearest tenth of a metre. The recording is in **one unit** only:—

Object measured	Estimated length	Actual length
teacher's desk	2m	2.2 m
trolley	1 m	1.5 m
display board	2.5 m	2.3 m
child's desk	0.5 m	0.7 m

m is the **symbol** for metre or metres. It is **not** an abbreviation and does not need a full stop.

In writing numbers less than 1, the digit 0 is placed before the decimal point.

A set of tapes of various sizes may be measured to the nearest tenth of a metre and lengths recorded, e.g. 0.7 m, 0.3 m etc.

Questions
(1) What is the length of the shortest tape? the longest?
(2) What is the difference in length between the shortest and longest tapes?
(3) What is the total length of all the tapes?
(4) Find the average length (see **N6**).

L2: ESTIMATION AND MEASUREMENT TO THE NEAREST CENTI-METRE

Metre rods or tapes marked in centimetres are used to measure, more accurately, objects already measured to the nearest ½, ¼, $\frac{1}{10}$ of a metre. This time measurement is to the nearest centimetre and recording is made to two decimal places.

The **symbol** for centimetre or centimetres is cm and does not require a full stop.

e.g.

Object measured	Estimated length	Actual length
trolley	1.12 m	1.54 m
display board	2.55 m	2.33 m
child's desk	0.53 m	0.72 m

Children may be given a box of assorted tapes and asked to measure each one as accurately as possible, to the nearest centimetre. They can measure a set of lines of different lengths, or draw lines to given dimensions, e.g. 0.03 m, 0.15 m, 0.07 m etc.

L3: FINDING PERIMETERS OF 2D SHAPES TO THE NEAREST CM

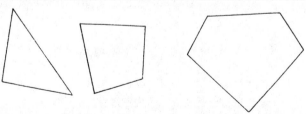

To find the perimeters of 2D shapes children are given a selection of these and a ruler or tape measure marked in cm. They measure each side, record and add up the totals to find the distance right round. With regular figures, they should discover that it is only necessary to measure one side and multiply

L3: FINDING PERIMETERS OF 2D SHAPES TO THE NEAREST CM (cont'd)

by the number of sides. Measurement for these shapes is taken to the nearest centimetre.

L4: AVERAGE HEIGHTS OF GROUPS OF CHILDREN

A height-measure may be a strip of thin card fastened to the wall, with markings in centimetres and metres. Children are in groups working in pairs. One child stands against the wall while the other one places a ruler on his head and reads off the marking on the height-measure, e.g. 156 centimetres. This can also be recorded as 1.56 metres. Commercially produced measures are available, but are rather expensive.

A graph of the heights may be drawn (see **PR4**). This may be a random arrangement at first, but could eventually show the heights in order beginning with the smallest. The average height may be found in a practical way (see **N6** and **PR4**) or by calculation.

L5: MEASUREMENT USING MILLIMETRES

The millimetre is the recognized submultiple of the metre and may be introduced at this stage. Rulers marked in cm and mm can be used to measure lines drawn on a page,

e.g.

                                             4.2 cm or 42 mm
                                             6.5 cm or 65 mm
                                             9.3 cm or 93 mm

Children may draw lines to given lengths, but must have pencils with sharp points in order to measure accurately.

The relationship between millimetres and centimetres is easily seen on rulers or tapes showing divisions in both submultiples, i.e. 1 cm = 10 mm.

The relationship 100 = 1 metre was established in **L5** of section 2; we can extend this to include the millimetre, i.e. 10×100 mm = 1 metre or 1000 mm = 1 metre.

The following table may be completed:—

Expressed in millimetres	Expressed in centimetres	Expressed in metres
956	95.6	0.956
1432	143.2	1.432
2573	257.3	2.573
74	7.4	0.074

L6: MEASURING DIAMETERS AND CIRCUMFERENCES OF CYLINDRICAL TINS

Circular shapes were explored in **2D7** of section 2 and children were introduced to the concept of diameter and circumference. They are now invited to measure the circumference and diameter of a variety of cylindrical tins and record their findings. The tins can be placed between two blocks as shown; the distance between is the diameter.

diameter

The circumference may be measured in several ways:—

e.g.

(1) Wrap a tape measure carefully round and read the measurement where the overlap crosses the mark at the beginning of the tape.

(2) Put a mark on the rim of a tin and place this beside a mark on a strip of paper. Roll the tin until the mark touches the paper again and make a second mark. The distance between the two marks is the circumference of the tin.

Circumference

(3) Wrap a strip of paper round a tin until it overlaps. Stick a pin through the overlap. Open out the strip and measure the distance between the pin marks to find the circumference of the tin.

Record results as follows:—

Cylindrical tins	Circumference	Diameter
Number 1		
Number 2		
Number 3		
Number 4		

The results could be illustrated on a graph (**PR6**). Children should eventually discover that there is a constant relationship between the two and it is slightly greater than 3:1.

307

L7: READING DISTANCES ON A MAP USING SCALE

Measurement of an irregular line, e.g. a route on a map, may be done by dividing it into short intervals each regarded as being straight.

e.g.

The distance from A to B is approximately 11 cm.

A piece of cotton or thin cord can be used to follow the path of a river, railway etc. and the length measured. Before the actual distance can be determined, children must have some understanding of scale (see **A6**). If the scale is 1:100 000, each centimetre on the map will represent 1 kilometre; if it is 1:5 000 000, each cm will represent 50 kilometres.

A map-measuring wheel is a useful tool for finding distances on maps.

WEIGHT

W1: WEIGHING IN KILOGRAMS AND DECIMALS OF A KILOGRAM

The relationships between the various units of weight were established in **W5** of section 2. Weighing activities using tenths of a kilogram, i.e. 100 gram weights are apropriate here.

Children weight, e.g. 200 grams of sand, pebbles, marbles etc.
400 grams of sand, pebbles, marbles etc.
600 grams of sand, pebbles, marbles etc.

and record as follows:—

$$200g \longrightarrow 0.2 \text{ kg}$$
$$400g \longrightarrow 0.4 \text{ kg}$$
$$600g \longrightarrow 0.6 \text{ kg}$$

This work links up with **N2** and **L1** and is an extension of the work in decimal fractions.

Weighing activities using $\frac{1}{100}$ kg, i.e. 10 gram weights may follow, as soon as children understand decimal fractions to two decimal places.

e.g. Children weigh, e.g. 30 grams of peas, beans, chestnuts etc.
50 grams of peas, beans, chestnuts etc.
90 grams of peas, beans, chestnuts etc.

and record 30 g $\longrightarrow$ 0.03 kg
50 g $\longrightarrow$ 0.05 kg
90 g $\longrightarrow$ 0.09 kg

To weigh more accurately, children are introduced to the gram weight, now available in plastic in a variety of shapes and colours. Objects are weighed on the balance scales, children selecting weights which are appropriate (beginning with heaviest and completing the balance with gram weights).

e.g.

Object	Estimated weight	Result by weighing	500g	200g	100g	50g	10g	1g
Cabbage	700g	752g	✓	✓		✓		✓✓
Melon	550g	603g	✓		✓			✓✓
Apple	125g	131g			✓		✓✓	✓
Orange	142g	152g			✓	✓		✓✓

Using a variety of weighing devices
When children have become familiar with weighing by balancing, other types of scales may be introduced:—

e.g. (a)  (b)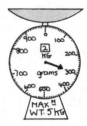

Type (a) is graduated in kilograms and tenths of a kilogram (100g) to weigh a maximum load of 5 kg. The pointer records a weight of 2.5 kg.

Type (b) is graduated in tenths and hundredths of a kilogram to weigh a maximum of 5 kg. The number of kilograms appears in the window, while the pointer indicates the number of grams to the nearest 10g. The weight recorded for (b) is 2.3 kg.

(2) Spring balances

The object to be weighed is attached to the hook with cord. This stretches the spring and moves the metal bar to indicate the weight, 1.2 kg.

This spring balance weighs to the nearest 100 grams.

(3) Home-made devices
(a)

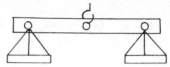

Tin lids are attached by string to a wooden rod suspended by wire from a shelf. If lids do not balance, a small piece of plasticine may be stuck in the bottom of one of them.

The balance may be tested by weighing out, e.g. 200 g of sand. Remove the 200 g weight and transfer sand from one lid to the other until they balance.

Remove the sand from one lid and check the weight with a 100 g weight.

(b) Comparing weights using an elastic band suspended from a pin.

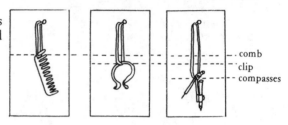

   comb
   clip
   compasses

The greater the weight, the greater the stretch of the elastic band. If two bicycle clips are weighed instead of one, the amount of stretch should be doubled. If weights (5g, 10g, 15g etc) are attached and the position of each marked, a simple spring balance has been made.

W3: WEIGHING A COLLECTION OF COINS

Children discover weight/value relationships as they balance coins on the scales:—

e.g. 2 ½p coins balance 1 1p coin
      2 1p coins balance 1 2p coin
      4 ½p coins balance 1 2p coin
      2 5p coins balance 1 10p coin

The fifty pence coin does not have a weight/value relationship with any other coin.

Questions to be answered by weighing
The coins placed in one pan are shown on the left-hand side of the diagram.

Children select coins from the columns indicated to balance these. The first one is done to illustrate what is required.

½p	1p	2p	5p	10p	½p	1p	2p	5p	10p
6						1	1		
10						?	?		
	4	2			?				
				6				?	
			8						?

W4: AVERAGE WEIGHTS OF CHILDREN IN A CLASS

In **W4** of the P4-P5 section, children used personal scales to find the weights of members of a group. The exercises may be repeated and children asked to find the average weight of a group:—

			kg
e.g.	Ted	weighs	42.3
	Maud	weighs	36.4
	Robert	weighs	38.7
	Angela	weighs	34.6
	Ian	weighs	35.5

The total weight is 187.5 kg

The average weight is $\dfrac{187.5 \text{ kg}}{5} = 37.5$ kg.

Refer to **N6** and **PR4** for practical work related to averages.

W5: WEIGHING 1 LITRE OF WATER

In **C/V 5** children studied relationships between capacity/volume and weight by weighing an empty litre jug and then the same jug filled with water. They discovered that 1 litre of water weighed 1 kg.

The experiment could be repeated using an open cube 10 cm × 10 cm × 10 cm. Children weigh it empty, and record the weight. They pour in one litre of water and weigh again, recording the weight. The difference in the two weights should be 1 kg, i.e. the weight of 1 litre of water. This should also be related to 1000 cm³ (refer to **C/V 5**).

W6: INTRODUCTION OF THE WORD 'MASS'

The distinction between mass and weight is too difficult for most children in the primary school and is best ignored (see **Metrication in the Primary School**, published by the Ministry of Education, Northern Ireland, page 7). The fact

W6: INTRODUCTION OF THE WORD 'MASS' (cont'd)

that weight changes, while mass remains constant has been demonstrated by astronauts when they go into outer space and children's attention may be drawn to this.

'Weighing' is still the correct term for balancing objects or reading dials when they are put on scale pans, so it seems reasonable that 'weight' is the term used rather than 'mass'.

W7: THE METRIC TONNE

As the kilogram is too small to weigh goods in bulk, the megagram (Mg) is useful. It is often called a metre tonne and is equal to 1 000 000 grams. It is only about 16 kilograms lighter than the old Imperial ton.

Children may be asked to complete the following table:—

Weight in grams	Weight in kilograms	Weight in tonnes
1 000 000		
	8 000	
		2
2 500 000		
	10 000	

W8: CALCULATIONS INVOLVING THE FOUR OPERATIONS USING DECIMAL FRACTIONS

e.g.

(1) Parcel A weighs 1.732 kg, parcel B weighs 0.564 kg and parcel C weighs 1.749 kg. Find the total weight in kg. How much less than 10 kg is the total weight?

(2) If 7 bricks weigh 19.6 kg, what is the weight of each brick?

(3) 3 kg of apples cost £1.65. Complete the following table:—

Weight of apples in kg	1	2	3	4	5	6
Cost in £						

(4) A basket full of groceries weighs 5.603 kg. The basket weighs 1.264 kg. What is the weight of the groceries?

(5) A coalman loaded 50 bags of coal each weighing 50 kg. The lorry when empty weighed 5500 kg. What was the total weight of the loaded lorry in tonnes?

(6) 9 jars of jam weigh 5.22 kg. What is the weight of one jar? 7 jars?

312

TIME

T1: THE 24-HOUR CLOCK

As the 24-hour system is now used for boat, rail and air timetables, children need to be familiar with it. Rubber stamps are available and show the clock face as illustrated:—

A movable hand may be attached and children count the hours from 1 to 12, on to 13, 14... to reach 24 hours or midnight.

The relationships between the 12-hour and 24-hour systems are shown on the following diagram:—

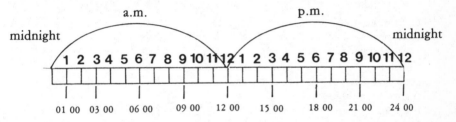

In this system we always use four digits to express the time; the first two for the hours, the last two for the minutes. Children need practice, not only in writing the time but in saying what they have written, e.g.

        1.00 p.m. is 13 00 hours   (thirteen hundred hours)
        1.30 p.m. is 13 30 hours   (thirteen thirty hours)
        midnight is 24 00 hours   (twenty-four hundred hours)
        midday is 12 00 hours   (twelve hundred hours)
                                      etc.

Children may be asked to complete the following tables:—

(a)

12-hour system	24-hour system
1.30 a.m.	
	06 40 hours
12.00 p.m.	
	24 00 hours
10.20 a.m.	

313

(b)

12-hour system	24-hour system
	15 50 hours
12.15 a.m.	
	00 01 hours
11.59 p.m.	
	20 20 hours

T2: STUDY OF TIMETABLES

Children should be given opportunities to study bus, train, boat and air time-tables to extract information. The following is part of a Sealink (Stranraer-Larne) summer time-table.

Train connections from England and Dumfries		(a)		Saturdays (b)	(c)		(d)
London Euston	dep.	09 45			10 45		10 50
Coventry	dep.			10 40			11 24
Birmingham New Street	dep.			11 06			12 05
Crewe	dep.			12 08			13 10
Liverpool Lime Street	dep.			11 17			12 59
Manchester Victoria	dep.			11 45			12 45
Preston	dep.	12 23		12 48	13 16		13 57
Lancaster	dep.	12 43					14 16
Carlisle	arr.	13 49		14 00			
Carlisle	dep.		15 08				15 25
Dumfries	dep.		15 43				
Glasgow Central	arr.				15 45		16 53
Glasgow Central	dep.					18 00	
Stranraer	arr.		18 33				20 45

Questions

(1) What is the length of time taken for the journey from London to Stranraer, travelling by train (a)?

(2) How long is the journey when travelling by train (c)?

(3) What is the difference between these times?

(4) How long does a passenger take to travel from Preston to Stranraer by train (a)? How long does the same journey take travelling by train (b)? Why are these times different?

(5) What is the waiting time at Carlisle for: train (a)?
train (b)?

(6) On which train would a London business man travel if he had an appointment in Preston for 1300 hours?

(7) What is the time taken from London to Carlisle: by train (a)?

by train (d)?

Record the difference in minutes.

(8) Complete the following table:—

Time taken by trains as shown on previous time-table

From	To	a	b	c	d	Difference in mins. between longest and shortest times
		hr. min.	hr. min.	hr. min.	hr. min.	
London	Preston	2 38	—	2 31	3 7	36
Coventry	Crewe					
Preston	Carlisle					
Birmingham	Manchester					
London	Glasgow					
Lancaster	Carlisle					

T3: WIDENING THE CONCEPT OF TIME

At this stage it may be possible to widen the concept of time to introduce the idea of speed. To measure speed we must know two things:—

(a) the distance travelled

(b) the time taken.

Speed is expressed in metres per second or kilometres per hour.

Children may measure the speed of members of their group using a stop watch and a trundle wheel. As a child walks round the playground with the trundle wheel, his partner counts the number of revolutions made in a given time, e.g. 20 seconds. To calculate his speed, it is necessary to find the number of metres walked each second.

e.g. In 20 seconds John walks 25 metres.

In 1 second he walks $\frac{\overset{5}{\cancel{25}}}{\underset{4}{\cancel{20}}}$ metres, i.e. 1.25 metres

His speed is 1.25 metres per second expressed as 1.25 m/s.

315

Children may be asked to complete the following table for members of their group in order to compare their walking speeds. Running speeds may also be measured, recorded and comparisons made.

e.g.

Name	Distance walked in 20 seconds	Distance walked in 1 second	Speed

The speeds of aeroplanes, cars etc. are expressed in kilometres per hour and again we need to know the distance travelled and the time taken.

e.g. In 2 hours a train travels 150 kilometres.
   In 1 hour it travels 75 kilometres.
   Its speed is 75 kilometres per hour, expressed as 75 km/h.

Children will probably be aware that in a motor cycle race, e.g. speeds vary at different sections of the course and for different laps. At the end of the race, the **average** speeds are calculated from the total distances travelled and the total time taken.

e.g. In 2½ hours the distance travelled by rider A was 420 km

   In 1 hour the distance travelled was $(420 \div 2\frac{1}{2})$ km

$$= \frac{(420 \times 2)}{5} \text{ km}$$

$$= 168 \text{ km}$$

The average speed of rider A was 168 km/h.

T4: MOVEMENT OF THE EARTH TO EXPLAIN DAY AND NIGHT ETC.

Children may be interested, at this stage, in the scientific and historical aspects of the measurement of time and should be encouraged to read appropriate books:—

e.g. (1) **Exploring Time** by Henry Printon and Patrick Moore published by Odhams Books Ltd.
   (2) **Time and Timepieces** from the Macdonald Junior Reference Library.
   (3) **Children's Britannica**, Volume 3, pages 21, 22, 23
   Volume 12, pages 98, 99
   Volume 13, pages 96, 97.

It is important to realize that there are three **natural** time-units:—

(a) **The day** is the time taken by the earth to rotate on its axis (24 hours approximately)

(b) **The year** is the time taken by the earth to travel round the sun (365¼ days approximately)

(c) **The lunar month** is the time between two new moons (29½ days approximately).

The movements of the earth relative to the sun may be demonstrated in a practical way as suggested in (1), (3) on page 316, using a tennis ball (orange or ball of wool), knitting needle and torch (or candle). The knitting needle is pushed through the centre of the ball to represent the earth on its axis. The room is darkened and the light placed on a table. As the ball is rotated on its axis (tilted at approximately 66½ degrees and mounted, if possible, on a block of wood) it moves around the 'sun'. The variations of light and shadow may be used to explain day and night, seasons etc. as the following diagrams show.

(a) **Night and Day**

(b) **The Seasons**

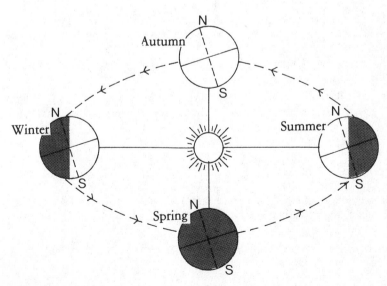

T5: THE HISTORY OF THE CALENDAR

Children should be encouraged to read pages 40-51 of **Exploring Time** and pages 57-59 of **Time and Timepieces**, mentioned in **T4** (or other appropriate account), to help them to realize how difficult was the task of devising a calendar. Early civilizations built their calendars on the natural units of time: the solar day, the lunar month and the solar year, but as there was no simple relationship between any two of these units, the task was formidable.

Children may be interested to study the Julian Calendar and compare it with the Gregorian calendar which is now used throughout the world. Both of these calendars had 365 days and both added an extra day every fourth year, known as 'leap' year. This adjustment was an improvement on previous calendars, but still was not completely accurate. A further alteration was made by Pope Gregory in 1582, which rejected the century years as leap years, unless they were exactly divisible by 400. The error in the Gregorian calendar is only 26 seconds per year and will not amount to a full day until 3 000 years have passed by.

The idea of a 'World Calendar', in which dates are arranged so that they fall on the same day of the week in every year, might be discussed.

T6: THE PENDULUM

Children experiment with home-made pendulums (piece of cord with weight attached) to find how the time of swing can be altered:—

e.g. 1. Count 10 complete swings and time with a stop watch.
2. Change the weight and count again. What did you notice?
3. Try swinging high up. Is the time altered?
4. Shorten the string and swing again. Try with different weights.
5. Make a graph to plot the time taken for 10 swings by pendulums of different lengths (30-100 cm).
6. What is the length of the pendulum that swings backwards and forwards in 1 second?

If children realize that it is the length of the pendulum and not the weight attached that determines the time of swing, then the experiment has been worthwhile.

T7: CALCULATIONS

In **T3 speeds** were calculated from information given about **distance** travelled and **time** taken. It is possible to find any one of the variables, given the other two:—

e.g. If the distance travelled was 100 km and the average speed was 60 km/h, how long did the journey take?

60 km travelled in 1 hour
1 km travelled in 1 minute
100 km travelled in 100 minutes or 1 hr 40 mins.

The following table may be completed.

Average Speed	Distance	Time
100 km/h		2½ hours
	350 km	1¾ hours
90 km/h	120 km	
	390 km	3¼ hours
120 km/h	50 km	

MONEY

M1: HANDLING COINS. TABULATING TOTALS

M1: At all stages of the development of the topic, children need practice in handling coins and counting collections of them. Opportunities for this arise naturally within the classroom, e.g. collecting and counting dinner money and issuing dinner tickets. Results of the operation may be tabulated as illustrated in the diagram below. Children may be asked to fill in the blank spaces in the table which relates to the entire school.

e.g.

	Price of ticket	Serial number of first ticket sold	Serial number of last ticket sold	Number of tickets sold	Total cost
A	25p	0156	0411		
B	12½p	1345			80
C	60p		2770		£18
				Totals	

M2: PROBLEMS

(a) Shop Bills

Supermarket bills may be collected and used to give practice in addition of money. Children should be encouraged to collect information about prices of products which may be used in the preparation of work cards. A visit to the local butcher's provides the information used in the following work card.

Children are asked to complete the table.

Item purchased	Cost per kg	Amount purchased	Total cost
sausages	£1.15	1.5 kg	
boiling beef	£1.20		£6.60
steak pieces	£2.25	3 kg	
lamp chops	£4.00	0.25 kg	
stewing steak	£2.50		£6.25
frying steak	£3.80	1.75	

The above is an example of only one way of using the information to provide computation in money. Other examples dealing with weekly, monthly and yearly expenditure for meat may be devised. Similar calculations for a whole range of products may also be included.

(b) Holidays

This could be tackled as a project involving children in discussion, investigation and finally in calculations about the cost of a holiday for one person or for a family. Links with geography are obvious as brochures are studied and holiday resorts chosen.

The following is a copy of the fares charged on the Liverpool/Belfast P & O Ferries. Obviously the cost of travelling to the chosen resort must be taken into account before bookings are made.

PASSENGER FARES.

Single.	first class.	£11.20
	economy class.	£8.50
Return.	first class (valid 3 months).	£22.40
	economy class (valid 3 months).	£17.00

Daylight single fare (one class).	£9.85

Children (accompanying adult) under 3 years — free, under 14 years — 50% adult fare.

CABIN & BERTH CHARGES.

	First class single journey
Cabin de luxe, one person.	£9.70
Cabin de luxe, two persons.	£11.80
Cabin de luxe, three persons.	£14.00
Single-berth cabin.	£4.50
Berth in two-berth cabin.	£3.10

(Cabin and berth charges on daylight sailings are 50% of above.)

	Economy class single journey
Berth in two/three or four-berth cabin.	£2.80

VEHICLES.

Single journey (at owner's risk) when accompanied by a passenger. Motor cars, motor vans, unladen not over 8ft 0 ins. (2.44m) high excluding commercial movements.

Length not exceeding 11ft 0 ins. (3.35m).	£18.00
Length not exceeding 12ft 6 ins. (3.81m).	21.40
Length not edceeding 14ft 0 ins. (4.27m).	£24.80
Length not exceeding 15ft 6 ins. (4.72m).	£28.20
Length exceeding 15ft 6 ins. (4.72m)—each additional foot (0.3m) or part thereof.	£3.40

CARAVANS & TRAILERS.

	Single journey
Up to 8ft 0 ins. (2.44m) in length and not over 8ft 0 ins. (2.44m) in height.	£12.70
Over 8ft 0 ins. (2.44m) in length—as per car rate.	

MOTOR CYCLES.

	Single journey
Solo motor cycles and scooters.	£4.60
Motor cycle combinations.	£8.00

Dogs, prams, bicycles accompanying passengers. Single—£4.20. Return—£8.40.
Dogs remaining in owner's cars—50% of above rate.

The information may be used to provide many and varied calculations:—

e.g. (1) A family of four (two adults and two children under 14) are travelling from Belfast to Liverpool (economy class) and require a four berth cabin. Work out the cost of the return journey.

(2) Two adults travelling first class from Belfast to Liverpool with a Vauxhall Viva (length 4.4m), require two single-berth cabins. What is the cost of fares for the return journey?

	Single		Return		Cabin		Car		
	1st class	economy class	1st class	economy class	single	two-berth	4.5m	3.3m	Total cost
A			2			1		1 .	
B	1			2		1	1		

Children are asked to find the total amount of travelling expenses for family A and compare it with the amount for family B. (Use information given on page 320).

(4) A family of four (2 adults, a child of 5 and a child of 2) travelling from Liverpool to Belfast, economy class, with a car (length 4.5 metres) and caravan (length 4.7 metres; height 2.3 metres) require a four-berth cabin. Calculate the cost of the single journey.

Prices for accommodation are readily available from travel agents and tourist offices. These can be used to continue the project so that the total cost for various types of holidays may be compared.

M3: MULTIPLICATION BY TWO DIGIT NUMBERS

The same sequence of operations as suggested in **N11** of section 2 may again be followed to demonstrate multiplication of sums of money by two digit numbers.

e.g. (1) **Multiplication by 10**

£4.50 ——→ £45

£3.25 ——→ £32.50

£7.05 ——→ £70.50 etc

(2) **Multiplication by 20**

(a) in two operations (× 10 and then × 2)

$$× 10 \qquad × 2$$

e.g. £4.50 ——→ £45 ——→ £90

£3.25 ——→ £32.50 ——→ £65

(b) in one operation : multiplying by 2 and moving each digit one place to the left, which is in effect multiplying by 10.

e.g. £4.35   £37.05
     × 20   or   × 20
     87.00   741.00

(3) Multiplication by any two digit numbers

        e.g.   £4.50
                × 25

                90.00   20 times
                22.50   5 times

               112.50   25 times

Problem situations to give practice in multiplication by two-digit numbers may arise naturally in the classroom or may be created as the need arises:—

e.g. (a) Find the total cost of providing new clocks for 16 classrooms if each clock costs £12.50.

(b) 34 children go on a trip to Edinburgh. What is the total cost if each child pays £31.15?

(c) Find the cost of purchasing 24 chairs and 6 tables for a classroom, if each table costs £29.75 and each chair costs £8.50.

etc.

Division of Money

As division and multiplication are inverse processes, they may be used as checks for each other. The problems in **M3** may be reconstructed to give practice in division:—

e.g. 3(b) The total cost of a trip to Edinburgh for 15 children is £487.50. What does each child pay?

This may be done as a sharing process or as repeated subtraction (see **N5**).

e.g.   £
             32.50
        15 |487.50
            300.00   £20 each   ⎫
            187.50   ⎪
            150.00   £10 each   ⎪ totalled to give
             37.50   ⎬ £32.50
             30.00   £2 each   ⎪
              7.50   ⎪
              7.50   50p each   ⎭
                 0

M4: PRACTICAL SITUATIONS: PURCHASE, DEPOSIT, INSTALMENT ETC.

Hire purchase, or the practice of paying for an article by weekly or monthly instalments will be familiar to most children. Data may be collected and calculations made comparing cash prices with hire purchase prices. The following table gives examples of these and children are asked to complete it.

Article bought	(a) Cash Price	Hire Purchase Arrangements		(b) Total cost	Difference between (a) and (b)
		Deposit	Payments		
Bicycle	£55	£6	22 weekly instalments of £2.75		
T.V. Set		£30	12 monthly of £18.25		£9
Tape Recorder	£40	£5	14 weekly instalments of £3		
Record Player			30 weekly instalments of £2.15	£71.50	£11.50
Washing Machine	£190	£30		£228	

M5: INVESTIGATION OF TIME-TABLES AND PRICES OF TICKETS

In **T2** time-tables were investigated in relation to the 'time' aspect. Now the investigation links 'time' and 'money' as tickets are purchased for journeys made.

The following information was taken from a British Midland Time-table (Air travel).

Route	Normal Fare Valid 1 year		Excursion Fare Valid 1 month	Advance Purchase Fare	Standby Fare	Senior Citizens Fare	
	Single	Return	Return	Return	Single	Single	Return
BELFAST to							
East Midlands	£30.00	£60.00	£45.00	£37.00	£18.00	£18.00	£36.00
Isle of Man	£16.00	£32.00	£26.00	£26.00	-	£10.00	£20.00
Liverpool	£23.00	£46.00	-	£28.00	£14.00	£14.00	£28.00
London-Gatwick	£30.00	£60.00	£41.00	-	£18.00	£18.00	£36.00

Children should be encouraged to study this and other similar tables in order to extract information about the various fares available and their relative prices.

Questions to help the investigation:—

e.g. (1) Calculate the cost of return fares for 4 adults travelling from Belfast to East Midlands:—

   Normal Fare
   Advance Purchase
   Standby Fare

How much is saved by purchasing tickets in advance?

(2) Calculate the cost of return fares for a party of 10 adults (excursion fare) and 5 senior citizens travelling from Belfast to the Isle of Man. Compare this with the cost of return fares for 15 adults travelling at the normal rate.

(3) Complete the following table:—

Route	Normal return fare	Standby return fare	Difference in price for 1 adult	Difference in price for 25 adults
Belfast to:				
East Midlands				
Isle of Man				
Liverpool				

etc.

M6: PRICES OF MATERIALS ETC.

Practical problems relating to the cost of various household materials, e.g. curtains, carpets etc. provide plenty of scope for computation in length and area as well as money.

(1) Curtain material

Discussion in class as to the length and width of curtains required highlights the following points:—

(a) Decide on the finished length of curtains and add 0.2 metres (approximately) for hems.

(b) Measure the width of the window and allow at least 1½ times this in material to be made into two curtains.

Completing the following table provides practice in a variety of calculations. Hem allowances are included.

Length of material for 1 curtain	Minimum width of 1 curtain	Width of material	Number of widths required for 2 curtains	Total length of material required	Cost of material per metre	Cost of material for 2 curtains
2.5 metres	2.4 metres	1.22 metres			£2.25	
1.5 metres	2 metres	1.38 metres				£6.75
	1.75 metres	1.83 metres		4.5 metres		£18.45
1.75 metres		1.53 metres	2		£1.50	

Further calculations may be made to find the cost of putting tape on the curtains: standard, at 17p per metre or 'regis' at 62p per metre. Linings may also be required and calculations similar to those already made for the curtains, could be repeated (standard width of lining material is 1.22 metres).

(2) **Floor coverings** (Carpets and carpet tiles)
Discussion is needed to make children aware of the variety of widths available and also of the range in quality and price.

Questions
Calculate the cost of covering a floor 4 metres by 3 metres in each of the following ways:—

(a) Carpet tiles, ½ metre square at £8 per square metre.
(b) Grade 5 (00) carpet, 4 metres wide at £12.50 per square metre.
(c) Grade 4 (0) carpet, 3 metres wide at £9.50 per square metre.
(d) Grade 3 (1) carpet, 2 metres wide at £6.00 per square metre.

Fitting charges for (b) and (c) are 65p per square metre; for (d), 50p per square metre.

If children draw a plan of the room (to scale) they can illustrate how the carpets (or tiles) may be placed:—

4 metres

e.g. (a)

3 metres

Scale: 2 cm represent 1 metre.

The plan is marked out in square metres; 4 tiles are required for each. Total number of tiles ——> 48.

Total cost of tiles at £8 per square metre ——> £8 × 12 = £96.

The calculations refer to plain carpets only.

Household bills

(a) Electricity accounts
Discussion may centre on how consumption is measured; current prices of units; fixed charges etc.

Completing the following table gives a variety of calculations relating only to the **cost of consumption.**

Previous meter reading	Present meter reading	Number of units used	Cost of each unit	Total cost
58073	61548		2.9p	
61546	62651		3.1p	
54323	58073			£116.25

(b) Gas bills
Similar calculations relating to gas consumption may also be devised.

e.g.

Present index	Previous index	Units used	Cost per unit	Total cost
3656	3626		35.5p	
3906	3852		35.5p	
	3412	36		£11.07
4231			36p	£18.72

(c) Telephone accounts
Simplified accounts give further practice in computation.

e.g.

Rental for quarter	Meter reading at beginning of quarter	Meter reading at end of quarter	Number of units	Cost at 3p per unit	Operator controlled calls	Total cost
£8.25	000006	001500			£1.47	
£8.25	001500	002010			0.36	
£8.25		003400			0.90	£46

Study of Gross and Net Prices
These may be illustrated by reference to the following:—

(a) **School concert**
    gross takings ——⟶ sale of tickets
    net takings   ——⟶ sale of tickets less expenditure in connection with concert.

(b) **Trading account**
    gross profit ——⟶ difference between buying and selling prices.
    net profit   ——⟶ gross profit less expenses
                        (rent, rates, lighting, heating, salaries etc.)

(c) Gross salary ——⟶ total amount earned.
    net salary   ——⟶ gross salary less deductions (income tax, pension scheme, National Health insurance etc.)

Children may complete the following table which relates to monthly wages:—

Gross earnings	National Health Insurance	Income Tax	Pension Scheme	Net earnings
£406.25	£8.14	£117.25	£24.38	
£422	£8.44		£25.32	£273.84
£465.75	£9.32	£115.10		£313.38
	£22.70	£137.50	£32	£345.30

M7: EXCHANGE VALUES OF SOME FOREIGN COINS

Exchange values of some foreign coins appear in the following table which children are asked to complete.

Country	Exchange value of £1	Exchange value of £100	Exchange value of £500
France	8.46 francs		
Germany	3.69 marks		
Italy	1635 lire		
Spain	138 pesetas		
USA	1.96 dollars		

Country	Standard currency	Value in pence
Canada	dollar	43.15
Holland	guilder	24.68
Switzerland	franc	29.53
Belgium	franc	1.68
Denmark	krone	9.75

Use the information given in the preceding diagram to calculate the cost of the following in our currency:—

(a) A meal in Holland   —   19.5 guilders
(b) A watch in Switzerland   —   110 francs
(c) A visit to a zoo in Denmark   —   11.25 krone
(d) Chocolates in Belgium   —   230 francs
(e) Train fare in Canada   —   123.5 dollars

A calculator may be used to check the work; alternatively children may use it for the laborious calculations.

As the rate of exchange fluctuates, current values should be obtained from the foreign department of a bank.

Bibliography

Association of Teachers of Mathematics
Notes on Mathematics in Primary Schools.
Cambridge University Press, 1969.

Banwell, C. S., Saunders, K. D. and Tahta, D. G.
Starting Points.
Oxford University Press, 1972.

Bell, A., Wigley, A. and Rooke, D.
Journey into Maths.
The South Nottinghamshire Project.
Blackie, 1978.

Bell, D., Hughes, E. R. and Rogers, J.
Area, Weight and Volume.
Nelson for the Schools Council, 1975.

Bell, S. E.
Mathematics in the Making.
Longman, 1968.

Biggs, E.
Mathematics for Older Children
Macmillan for Schools Council, 1972.

Boucher, J.
Hey Mathematics.
Caffrey, Smith, 1974.

Bradshaw, M. F.
Logic Blocks in the Junior School.
E. J. Arnold, 1974.

Brinton, H. and Moore, P.
Exploring Time.
Odhams, 1965.

Briten, P.
Clearway Maths.
Oxford University Press, 1977.

Caine, P. A.
Patterns in Mathematics.
Chatto and Windus, 1969-1972.

Children's Britannica.
Encyclopaedia Britannica London, 1971.

Churchill, E.
Counting and Measuring.
Routledge & Kegan Paul, 1966.

Clarke, J.
The Magic Square.
E. J. Arnold, 1969.

Cooke, C. and Anderson, I.
The Mathematics Curriculum.

Blackie for the Schools
Council, 1978.

Deboys, M.
Place Value.
Number Patterns.

The Queen's University of
Belfast Teachers' Centre,
1976.

Dienes, Z. P. and Holt, M.
Let's Play Maths.

Penguin, 1973.

Dienes, Z. P. and Golding, E. W.
Exploration of Space and Practical
Measurement.
Learning Logic and Logical
Games.
Sets, Numbers and Powers.

E.S.A. and University of
London, 1972.
E.S.A., 1970.

E.S.A., 1969.

Dienes, Z. P.
Relations and Functions
(edited by Seaborne, P. L.)

Hodder & Stoughton, 1974.

Evans, D.
Mathematics : Friend or Foe?

George Allen & Unwin,
1977.

Elffers, J.
Tangram (translated by Hollingdale, R. J.)

Penguin, 1976.

Fletcher, H.
Mathematics for Schools.

Addison-Wesley, 1971.

**Gardner, K., Glenn, J. A. and
Renton, A. I. G.**
Children using Mathematics.

Oxford University Press,
1973.

Glenn, J. A. and Sturgess, D. A.
Towards Mathematics.

Schofield & Sims,
1977.

Goddard, T. R. and Grattidge, A. W.
Alpha Mathematics.

Schofield & Sims,
1970.

Beta Mathematics.

Schofield & Sims,
1969.

Goutard, M.
Talks for Primary School Teachers.

Educational Explorers, 1963.

Griffiths, A. L.
Basic Mathematics.
Key Mathematics.

Oliver & Boyd, 1972.
Oliver & Boyd, 1977.

Hunter, J. and Cundy, M.
The Mathematics Curriculum.
Number.

Blackie for the Schools
Council, 1973-1977.

Lackie, L.
New Mathematics.
Understanding Shapes and Solids.

Nelson, 1970.

MacDonald Junior Reference Library
Time and Timepieces.

Macdonald Educational,
1970.

McIntosh, A. J.
Notes for T.V. Programmes:—
'It's Maths'.

Tonbridge Printers for
School Broadcasting
Council, 1977.

Number Work in the Infant School.

Leicestershire Education
Committee, 1970.

Marsh, L. G.
Let's Discover Mathematics.
Children Explore Mathematics.
Alongside the Child in the Primary School.
Approach to Mathematics.

A. & C. Black, 1975.
A. & C. Black, 1969.
A. & C. Black, 1970.
A. & C. Black, 1970.

Martin, G.
Primary Aim Mathematics.

The Educational Company,
1975.

**Mathematics Department of Manchester
College of Education.**
Notes on Guidelines in School Mathematics.

Rupert Hart-Davis, 1970.

Matthews, G.
Mathematics through School.

John Murray, 1972.

Metrication Board.
How to Write Metric.

H.M.S.O., 1977.

Moore, N. and Williams, A.
Mathematics for Life.

Oxford University Press,
1976.

Nuffield/Cedo Handbook.
Mathematics: the First Three Years

Chambers/Murray/Wiley,
1970.

Nuffield/British Council Handbook.
Mathematics: the Later Primary Years.

Chambers/Murray/Wiley,
1972.

Nuffield Foundation.
Computers and Young Children.

Chambers/Murray/Wiley,
1972.

Hollands, R.
  Mathematical Games and Activities for   Chatto & Windus, 1971.
    First Schools.
  Mathematical Games and Activities.   Hart-Davis, 1977.

Nuffield Mathematics Project.
  Logic.   Chambers/Murray/Wiley,
                                            1972.

Rodda, G. W.
  New Mathematics.   Nelson, 1969.
  Understanding Number.   Nelson, 1970.
Schools Council.
  Curriculum Bulletin No. 1.   H.M.S.O., 1966.
Scopes, P. G.
  Mathematics for Primary Teachers.   Longman, 1976.
Scottish Primary Mathematics Group.
  Primary Mathematics.   Heinemann, 1975-1978.
Smeltzer, D.
  Man and Number.   A. & C. Black, 1970.
Stanfield, J.
  Maths Adventure.   Evans, 1971.
The Schools Mathematics Project.   Cambridge University Press,
                                            1970.

Williams, E. M. and Shuard, H.
  Primary Mathematics Today.   Longman, 1976.